Mawzy's Hope Chest

Jackie,
Never lose hope!
MuₐA

Myra Alley Kingsbury

Myra Alley Kingsbury

The cardinal in the trees on the front cover is drawn
by David Alley, my brother and the Birdman of
Bills Creek. Legend has it when a cardinal,
the West Virginia state bird, appears it's a
gentle reminder of a loved one that has passed.

*To my brother, David, who knows
the back stories of this book
better than anyone else on earth,
who patiently listened to every word of the story,
sometimes more than once,
and who helped fill in many of the gaps.
Thanks for being with me on this ride of life.*

Foreword:
Dr. Kendra S. Boggess,
President, Concord University

As a small liberal arts college tucked away in the mountains of southern West Virginia, Concord University has been educating students for nearly 150 years. Our student population is small, less than 2,000, and is made up of primarily West Virginia residents. Forty percent are first-generation college students and nearly half are eligible for federal need-based funding. Many are non-traditional students, attending classes while working a full-time job and managing a family.

The unmet need is tremendous, and we often find some students who contemplate quitting because they their financial need is so great. In a scholarship application, one of our students wrote, "I come from a big family that can't afford to help me with college and I don't want to be a financial burden to them. The only way I can afford college is through some of the scholarships that I earned and student loans."

To say we rely heavily on our alumni and other donors for their financial support of our students would be a gross understatement. I am overwhelmed by the generosity of all our donors. Most recently Concord alumnae Myra Alley Kingsbury '75 funded The Hope Chest Scholarship at the Concord University Foundation. Both Myra's grandmother, Grace Walker Campbell; and mother, Gloria Campbell Bridges, graduated from Concord in 1949 and 1956 respectively.

Inspired after exploring her grandmother's hope chest, Myra wrote and published *Mawzy's Hope Chest*. Proceeds from the sale of this book will also be used to further fund The Hope Chest Scholarship in honor of Myra's mother and grandmother.

This scholarship will benefit future women from southern West Virginia pursuing degrees in business and education. Myra's contribution and commitment to funding a scholarship will continue to give our students the resources they need and opens doors for the next generation. She is truly helping further Concord's mission of improving the lives of our students.

I feel a deep sense of gratitude to her for investing in future alumni.

Sincerely,
Kendra S. Boggess, Ph.D.
Concord University

Hope is the Thing with Feathers

Hope is the thing with feathers
That perches in the soul,
And sings the tune without the
words
And never stops at all.
And sweetest in the Gale is heard;
And sore must be the storm,
That could abash the little Bird
That kept so many warm.
I've heard it in the chilliest land
And on the strangest Sea;
Yet never in Extremity,
It asked a crumb of me.

Emily Dickinson

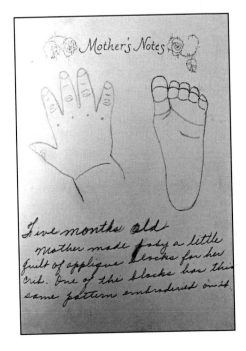

Prologue:
Tuesday's Child

You never know what you'll find when you open the lid of a cedar chest that's almost 100 years old – Mawzy's hope chest that traveled from her home place in Springdale, West Virginia to Gentry Holler then back to Springdale when she purchased her own home. This is the house where Mom, Dad, brother David and I lived on and off over the years. It's the only place in West Virginia I've ever called home.

I always thought the chest was just storage for a bunch of old pictures like my and David's baby albums. When Mom started to struggle with her memory, a friend suggested I go through the family photo albums with her. So, on my next trip back home from Nebraska to Springdale I took Mom to the back bedroom where the hope chest rested under a window.

We sat on the bed and paged through several albums but the activity was fruitless as Mom couldn't identify many of the people in the photos.

I decided to dig deeper into the chest and found layer upon layer of the richness of a life gone by - that of my maternal grandmother Grace, more affectionately known as Mawzy. The harder I dug the more I realized Mawzy had discovered the eye of the needle and threaded her life through it one stitch at a time. I found the intricacies of her tenacity and discipline, her passion for knowledge, her love of teaching, her sense of humor and the struggles, sorrows and tragedies of her life.

I had never thought about writing a book, but the first seed was planted when I unearthed a ledger from the hope chest which itemized Mawzy's expenses when she was a senior at Woodrow Wilson High School in Beckley in the late 1920s. I fantasized about her life back then as I saw purchases such as bloomers, penpoints, Marcels and a circus ticket. It was too far to commute from her Springdale home place so she worked and lived with a family in Beckley for room and board.

I started combing through all the pictures with a sharper eye for Mawzy's life story. Then I started digging beyond the chest.

Tears came to my eyes many times as a new discovery was made. One of the most heartfelt was finding the baby quilt Mawzy made for my mom in 1934. In Mom's baby book Mawzy wrote about a quilt of appliqued blocks she made for Gloria June's crib when she was five months old. Outlines of Mom's little hand and foot were embroidered on one of the blocks and were replicated in her baby book. Mawzy also embroidered Gloria June's name above the outline of a camel in the center block on the bottom row of the quilt. I thought the camel was a bit odd until I later found Mom's birth certificate. Her last name was misspelled Camel instead of Campbell. It was Mawzy's sense of humor shining through. The quilt also radiated love and sacrifice.

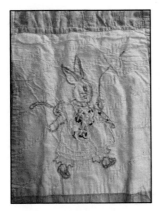

I found an old jewelry box filled with a lot of the costume broaches, necklaces and earrings Mawzy wore. She was a professional woman, principal of Springdale Elementary, and dressed the part. She liked pretty things. Pictures of her broaches are featured at the beginning of each chapter.

I uncovered cancelled checks dating back as far back as 1954. They gave great insight into her frugal lifestyle, sense of discipline and a charitable attitude.

It felt like I was trying to work a 1000-piece puzzle with only 500 pieces at my disposal, but as I kept digging additional pieces materialized. Mawzy led me on a scavenger hunt that did not disappoint. When I couldn't find a puzzle piece, assumptions were made. Right or wrong hopefully they are realistic in helping move the story along.

Many examples of synchronicity cropped up as I wrote the story. One is the fact that Mawzy was born on a Tuesday so was "Tuesday's child full of grace", also her God given name.

This is how Mawzy got her nickname. In 1955, when Mom was pushing to complete her college degree, Mawzy encouraged her to go to summer school and offered to take care of David and me while she was away. Being a schoolteacher, Mawzy had that summer off. David was three years old and I was 16 months. Since birth, we had lived with Mawzy and depended on her in so many ways.

One Friday on Mom's return home from school she walked through the front door and overheard David calling out, "Can I have a cookie, Mom?"

"Mother, we can't have the kids calling you Mom," she noted as she approached Mawzy. "It'll be confusing for them."

"Yes, I agree," Mawzy responded. "Maybe they could call me Mawzy. Kids, how 'bout you call me Mawzy from now on?"

"Mawzy. Mawzy," David and I called out as we jumped around her. The name stuck and was so endearing a lot of the community started calling her by that name as well.

"I guess that means you can call me Pawzy," was my Dad's response. It was one of those rare occasions when he happened to be around.

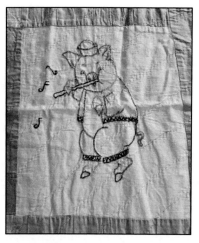

I'm a hillbilly from West (by God) Virginia, with roots that meander deep into the woods and the coal seams. I am a coal miner's daughter. I am a coal miner's granddaughter on both sides.

I moved away from the state in 1978 to explore what the country had to offer. But each time I fly back home for my hillbilly refresher course, my heart swells as I descend toward the runway of Charleston airport. I look out the airplane window at the top of one rolling hill after another. In the spring and summer, I see a lush green, as most of the trees are deciduous. The mountain laurel and

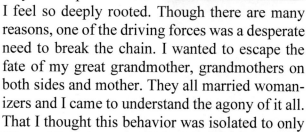

rhododendrons add a bit of brilliance with their large flowering blooms. The fall brings a color wheel display of foliage in yellows, oranges and burgundies that stand second to none. Then there's a drabness in winter when all leaves are gone. Yet during this season shadows made by hill vs ravine provide a beauty of their own. I can't help but sing The Hills of West Virginia, "Oh the hills, beautiful hills…" under my breath.

You may wonder why I left a place where I feel so deeply rooted. Though there are many reasons, one of the driving forces was a desperate need to break the chain. I wanted to escape the fate of my great grandmother, grandmothers on both sides and mother. They all married womanizers and I came to understand the agony of it all. That I thought this behavior was isolated to only West Virginia, I'll chalk up to the naivete of youth.

Throughout her life and even in death, Mawzy has always been my rock and my guiding light. Writing this book has solidified the feeling a hundredfold. I hope it would have made her proud. Appalachians are story tellers and this is my story.

Table of Contents

Mawzy always shielded her children and grandchildren, like David and Myra, under her protective wings.

Early Memories of Living at Mawzy's House

 I can't recall my first memory here on earth, but it must have been at my grandmother Mawzy's house in Springdale. The house sat on a hilltop embraced by heavily forested peaks. It was a peaceful setting, nature at its finest. It's where Mawzy raised her three children, Eleanor, Billy, and Mom, as well as helping with my brother David and me. As I dwelled on the surrounding land and the rooms of Mawzy's house, memory after memory emerged.

Going to and from the house, we walked between an elevated porch and a row of six trees. When Mawzy bought the house in the last 1930s, her dad, Poppy Walker, helped her transplant four white pines from his

Gloria June by new pine trees.

nearby farm. She added several maple seedlings which grew together to form two gnarly tree trunks. By the time I came along, these trees had grown to a height of 20 feet or more, dwarfing the small house. The pine branches were droopy, so it was like walking through a tunnel, protected from the elements. The smell of the pines was pungent - musty yet fresh. A plethora of birds made their homes in these trees, so chirps, squawks,

One of our blue jays in the pines, Myra in her play-pen, hanging out with neighbor kids, Shelia and Bur, Uncle Jack's painting.

songs, and sightings were a part of our daily life. A gate was installed at the end of the porch to keep us kids from falling down the steps when we were little.

A small two-foot gap between the steps and the house made a perfect refuge for toads. If I was on a toad hunt this was the first place I looked. The risk of a

wart infestation was worth it to be able to hug up on my newest found pet. When I was a little tyke my playpen was placed on the east side of the house near the toad resort. At this location Mawzy and Mom could easily see me out the dining room window.

At the far end of the porch was a wooden swing. Many a time I swung alone with a book in hand or with my brother,

4

David, or with Mawzy. Uncle Billy's boys liked to pile in the swing with David, me and Mawzy when they came to visit. Mawzy always held the youngest in her arms to make more room for the rest of us. Because of the trees, it was shaded and felt safe.

The living room was plainly decorated. However, an original piece of art hung on the west wall - a color pastel of a lake cottage painted by Uncle Jack, Aunt Eleanor's husband. It was one of his Concord College art assignments. When Mawzy saw it, she fell in love with it, so Jack gave it to her.

A picture window, which Mawzy added when she was having other work done on the house, was parallel to the entry. I broke it once throwing a jar of paste at David. My temper got me in trouble on more than one occasion.

Mom attempted to begin our "birds and bees" instruction in the living room. With her question-and-answer book in hand, she proceeded to ask if David or I had any questions. I squirmed around for a few minutes and came up with my first question, "When is George Washington's birthday?" Mom just shook her head and put the book away, deciding she had jumped the gun on our sex education.

Early one rainy morning I sauntered into the kitchen where Mawzy was making crust for a blackberry pie.

"Mawzy, its icky out," I whined. "I wanted to play outside today."

"Go find David and see what he is doing," she suggested. "Maybe he'll play a game with you."

"David, where are you?" I yelled.

"In here," he answered. "What ya want?"

I found him in the middle bedroom lounging on the bed with a Superman comic book in his face. "Will you play a game with me?" I begged.

"OK. I guess, but the game has to be armies."

Though not one of my favorites, I was desperate for some action. We dragged Lincoln logs, grey plastic Confederate soldiers and blue plastic Yankee soldiers out of the dining room closet and dumped them on the living room floor.

"Here's your share of the Lincoln logs," said David. "You build your fort over there by the chair and I'll build mine over here next to the couch. Then set up your grey armies for battle like I'm doing with my blue armies."

"Charge!!!" David yelled once we were lined up and ready for battle.

We began firing at each other's men with toy cannons and finger bombs. After a few minutes, my grey boys were getting the best of David's blue ones.

"Stop! He shouted. "I have to win the battle."

"Why? You always win. I want to win this time."

"No! The Confederates lost in real life so you can't win with the grey army."

"Ok," I countered. "Then let me take charge of the blue army."

"No, I'm always in charge of the blue army," he said.

"Mawzy, make him let me win," I insisted as I hopped up from the floor and ran into the kitchen in a huff.

"Why don't you let her win this time?" she said to David as she walked into the battlefield. He refused. I started crying. He started yelling.

"Restrain every nerve," Mawzy began repeating over and over in a stern voice with her hands on her hips, stomping from one foot to the other. There was always a pause between each word for emphasis. It was a routine we saw many times when we were going at each other, so we knew she wouldn't stop until we did. If all else failed for me, she said, "Last word or die." It was her sure fired way to get me to put a lid on it.

"I don't want to lead army guys who were for slavery," David explained.

"Why do ya think I'd want to either?" I countered as I sulked out of the living room to seek the comfort of my dolls.

When Uncle Billy's family came to Mawzy's house, Billy roughhoused with Billy Boy, Stevie, David, and me. After he got tired of chasing us around, he plopped down and stretched out on the couch in the living room. We giggled nonstop as we kept running past him, just out of his reach. He threatened to put us in the crack if he caught us. Experiencing "the crack" was like being on a roller coaster at the state fair – fear and thrill all rolled into one.

Billy and Billy Boy near the crack.

I got put in the crack once and never tempted that fate again. He caught me by the arm, pulled me onto his chest then stuffed me between his body and the back of the couch. I was laughing and crying at the same time as he tickled me.

To Mother

with my love

I thought that I was going to suffocate. When he sensed my fear, he let me go. What a relief. Somebody else's turn. When he nabbed one of us, the rest knew we were safe for a bit and got a kick out of watching the one in the crack squirm.

Mom's bedroom was off the living room in the southwest corner of the house. It's also where I slept when Dad wasn't there. The room had just enough space for a double bed and dresser. Opposite the dresser, Mawzy created a closet with wall shelving covered by sheer curtains. Behind the curtains was one of my favorite hiding places. There was an old shotgun propped up against the side of the dresser. It had a broken pin so was not functional but Mawzy hoped pointing it at an intruder would be enough to scare them away. In earlier times, when the gun was operable, Uncle Billy took a shot at a gypsy who had ventured onto the property. The gypsy jumped the fence with a butt full of buckshot, never to be seen again.

The window of Mom's bedroom faced the porch and was often left open at night to cool the house with fresh mountain air. One night there was a terrible crash outside. My Dad, after tying one on, fell over the gate Mawzy latched in an attempt to catch him in the act. She heard him fall, saw him fumble to get up and caught him in a lie. "I was out playing cards and was almost home when someone hit me over the head and took all my winnings," was his story. She knew he had lost his paycheck to gambling and booze and wouldn't be able to contribute to the household expenses that week. When Dad was out late, Mom and Mawzy started locking the front door so he couldn't get in. After that he slept off his binges at his friend, James' house. Mawzy nor Mom made very good choices for their mates. The repercussions spilled over into all our lives for years to come.

Mom liked to sleep in on Saturdays. David and I were always up before her, watching cartoons. Mawzy was an early riser so we could count on her to take care of our needs. We used to laugh at Mom and mock her because she moaned instead of snoring. Sometimes it was a loud moan but more often was a softer, lengthy one.

"Come in here," Mawzy called to David and me. "I have something fun for you to do." As we approached, we saw a mixture of art supplies laid out on the dining room table. "While your Mother's at the grocery store, I thought you two might like to make Mother's Day cards for her."

"That sounds like fun," I responded at once. "Look at all the construction paper and crayon colors. There's even glitter!"

"Let's see who can make the best one," David challenged.

We worked with diligence as we didn't have much time before Mom got back home. Once completed, Mawzy helped us hide the cards until the appointed day.

"Hey, what do you think about fixing breakfast for Mom and taking it to her in bed?" David asked on Mother's Day morning.

"Good idea." I said as I headed toward the pantry. "Let's see what we can find. Oh boy. Sugar Pops. See if there's any milk in the fridge."

"Yeah, there's milk. Come in here. Let's see what else there is."

What a spread we ended up with on the tray, which included Sugar Pops and milk, radishes, pickles, a cheese sandwich, a leftover piece of pie and anything else we could pull from the refrigerator that we thought Mom might like. Quantity over quality was the focus.

Uncle Billy, his wife Annie and their boys, Billy, Steve, and Randy; hanging out with the cousins, and Mawzy with David, Myra, and Billy's family.

"Remember that World's Greatest Mom trophy I won from the claw machine?" David asked. "I'm goin' a put that on the tray. We'll put one of my yellow cat's eye marbles with it. It can be from you, so we both have a gift for her."

"Happy Mother's Day!" we shouted in unison as we ran into Mom's bedroom, shook her awake and handed her our homemade cards. David ran back to the kitchen for the tray of food. What a surprise to wake up to! After our presentation we sat on the bed anxiously waiting for Mom to dive into her special meal. Poor Mom. Hope she didn't get indigestion that day.

A fun memory of Billy's old bedroom was when Uncle Billy, his wife Annie and their boys came home to see us. The two older cousins, Billy Boy and Stevie, and David and I slept in this room. We took the mattress off the box springs and placed it on the floor so that two of us slept on one piece of the bed and two on the other. The room was so small the floor space was completely covered. Once situated a jumping fest always followed with no worries about falling off the bed.

David and I also used this bedroom as a playroom and it's where we liked to play spaceship. We gathered everything necessary for our long journey into space. David was the Captain and I was his assistant.

On one of our space trips, I decided I wanted to have a baby while on the ship. I put my Betsy Wetsy doll under my shirt and went into the kitchen to ask Mom how babies were born. After a bit of explanation, I decided to skip that part and bring my already born baby with me. Mom probably decided it was time to bring out the question-and-answer book again.

In the dining room we made a fort by draping Mawzy's quilts over the table and chairs. I got stung by a bee one day as I was crawling around under the quilt wrapped table. I kicked and screamed at the top of my lungs. Everyone thought I was just having a "bull fit." My character was redeemed after the truth was known.

Mawzy's dining room housed a small wooden telephone stand. The telephone was an old black rotary style and we were on a party line. Our number was 438-7906 and the ring was "two longs and a short". Several teenage boys were on our line and liked to call each other after school. One day I decided to eavesdrop. Mawzy had forbidden this in our household, but I couldn't help myself. The two boys on the other end of the line thought one of their friends was listening in and did I ever get an earful, "Bruce, is that you? You'd better hang up now or else!" I was lucky not to have been caught by Mawzy or the boys in this shenanigan. They were the same boys who wouldn't let me cross the bridge over the creek when I was walking home from school. Eavesdropping was my way playing a trick on them.

My school dresses hung in the dining room closet. I was picky about what I wore. One morning Mom selected a dress for me that I refused to put on, so she told me to pick my own dress. I pulled out an old ugly thing with a rip under the arm and slipped it over my head. I knew she wouldn't allow me to go to school with that awful dress on, but she surprised me and told me to suit myself. Being too stubborn to take it off, I headed to school without changing. My classmate Mikey's really cute cousin came to school with him that day. I was miserable as I couldn't play softball at recess for fear of revealing my torn dress. It was quite the effort to hold my arm down by my side for the whole day.

David and I occasionally climbed up the ladder on the right-hand side of the closet to explore the attic. We heard the same "Don't step off the rafters" warning as the previous generation. It's where I discovered my Easter basket and decided there really was not an Easter bunny after all.

The most dramatic event in the dining room was a telephone call in the middle of the night to inform Mawzy of Uncle Billy's death. I was in Mawzy's bed at the time and heard her wail all night long while sitting at the dining room table. I eventually figured out what happened. I never cried but shook uncontrollably most of the night. The next morning, I did not let on that I knew about Uncle Billy when they told me. I had never been around death before nor experienced grief at that level. I was thankful when Mom decided to ship me off to Aunt Eleanor's in-laws until the service and burial were over. When David got up that morning Mawzy hugged him so hard it scared him. "You're the only boy I have left now," she said through her sobbing.

Mawzy's snoring is the first thing that comes to mind when I think of her bedroom. I slept with her sometimes and remember praying I would fall asleep before she did to escape the fear of her snoring, which literally rocked the window above her bed. I know now that she had sleep apnea, as she snored like a freight train. Then there was dead silence for what seemed like an hour. Then she sucked in her breath resulting in something that sounded closely akin to a huge porcine barnyard snort.

Her favorite magazines, *Reader's Digest* and *True Story*, were kept in the headboard of her bed. *True Story* was launched in 1919 but had many revisions over the years. By the 1950s the focus was on teenage girls whose stories revealed poor life choices. Because of Mawzy's personal heartbreak she could relate to their stories, so she ended up reliving her own plight over and over again. It's said that "misery loves company" and so I'm sure she found many a friend between the magazine covers.

The only picture in her bedroom was of Jesus. It hung on the wall above her hope chest and was a symbol of her strong faith. When David got the mumps, he was ordered to get in Mawzy's bed, put on a pair of sunglasses and stay quiet. His condition was taken seriously to protect his fertility. I didn't understand why it was such a big deal. He didn't seem all that sick to me. He soon got bored of laying around and without leaving the bed started shooting his newly acquired rubber band gun at Jesus' picture. There was no malicious intent, as he aspired to be a preacher for a while. Even preached a funeral. It came about when cousins Billy Boy and Stevie were visiting.

We were playing in the back yard and ran upon a dead yellow finch at the edge of the rhubarb patch. He was beautiful. We were saddened and decided to give him a proper burial. I ran into the house to find a casket for him. Mawzy gave me a large match box and one of her old hankies to wrap him in. It was perfect for the little bird's size. Billy Boy got one of Mawzy's garden tools from the garage and dug his grave. David volunteered to be the preacher for his funeral. After a few words and a prayer, I thought a song would be appropriate. Stevie started singing his own rendition of *Bird Dog* by the Everly Brothers - "Johnny is a joker, (he's a bird), A very funny joker (he's just a dead bird.)" That brought some levity to the table and off we went on another adventure.

You wouldn't think there would be many memories of a bathroom but three come to mind for me. The first was when I was around four years old. Mom put me in the bathtub and left me there to play for a bit. I decided to lay flat until only my nose and mouth were above water. Mom came in to check on me and thought I had drowned. It was weird as I felt her fear and was ashamed I had caused it.

The second memory was discovering my Dad's bloody clothes in the bathroom closet when I was five. They were cut off him after he got caught in a coal mine conveyor belt. It was eerie. I remember going to see him in the hospital. I was crying on the way and saying," My Daddy's too pretty to be in the hospital." The staff wheeled him into the main floor hallway so David and I could see him, as kids were not allowed in the rooms. Coal dust was ground into the side of his face and stayed with him for life like a tattoo.

My temper popped up again in another bathroom memory. Being upset for getting scolded prompted me to lock myself in the bathroom and tear chunks of wallpaper off the wall. After I had calmed down enough to realize I was going to be in big trouble again, I escaped out the window over the bathtub. Once the error of my ways was discovered, Mawzy stuffed me back through the window so I could unlock the door to make the bathroom accessible again. Restrain every nerve.

The house was heated by coal which was relatively inexpensive and easily accessible. Floor registers of various sizes were scattered throughout the house, with the largest being in the living room. On a cold winter day, it was wonderful to stand on the living room register in my nightgown and absorb the heat.

The furnace was buried in a hole in the ground and could only be reached from an outside entry, down a set of concrete stairs. The rusty colored dirt wall made for a damp, dark, dusty smelling place. It was scary yet held some curiosity. Wooden shelving was built into the earth to the right of the furnace and is where Mawzy stored her home canned fruits and vegetables. Going down in the hole was doable, but I didn't have the guts to go all the way around the furnace. I was

John, Mitzi, Myra, and David in Mawzy's back yard.

sure this is where the trolls lived or if not, a wad of snakes would be hanging there. It was the perfect hide and seek spot though.

Mawzy's brown and white bulldog, Mitzi, made the furnace hole her reprieve when she wasn't wandering around the property. Her food and water bowl were kept there, as she wasn't allowed in the house. Mitzi lived to be around 20 years old. She was old by the time I came along so wasn't very playful, but I enjoyed having her around. She was one of those dogs who was so ugly she was cute in a comical sort of way. When she died David and a family friend put her in a box and buried her up Dallow Holler.

Burning coal made a sooty deposit all over the house, so the walls were dingy and had to be frequently washed and repainted to be revived. The coal heat was dry, so I had to get out of bed in the winter to "water my nose." Though fearing I would get in trouble, the discomfort outweighed the risk. I went to the kitchen sink and put my finger under the faucet to get it wet. Then I stuck my finger up my nose to moisten it. It did help for a bit and I never got in trouble for watering my nose.

Mawzy didn't drive until she was almost 50. Her first car was a 1956 two tone blue Chevy. Finally, she had a car to park in her old, detached garage. She loved that car and the freedom it gave her to go places. Her favorite Sunday drive was over the Loops Road, an open country roller coaster type route. While driving, a favorite activity was observing cumulus clouds. She saw beyond the cotton ball shapes to find all sorts of animals. I still search for animals in the clouds and always think of Mawzy looking down on me from heaven.

Many of our trips included a stop at the Dairy Queen in Rainelle. When we were younger and knew we were headed to the DQ, David and I started singing,

12

"We want one of those whirly things, whirly things, whirly things," over and over as we banged our heads against the back seat of the car. We were begging for a whirligig with a candy filled clear stem. If victorious, on the way home we alternated between eating the multicolored candy pellets and sticking the whirligig out the car window to watch it flap around.

David and Myra behind Mawzy's first car.

On one of Uncle Billy's visits, Mawzy drove David, Billy Boy, Stevie and me to the DQ. We ate our Dilly bars on the way home. As Mawzy pulled into the driveway the boys decided it would be macho to crawl through the back car window instead of going out the door. Being last, I decided if they could do it, so could I. As I proceeded to climb out, one of them shut the door with my finger wrapped around the edge. My tomboyish nature cost me a mashed finger and some of the worst pain I can ever remember. I ran screaming into the house and found Mawzy to make it better. Before long I was back out with the boys making pea shooters under Uncle Billy's tutelage. We found hollow elderberry stems for the shooters and used their unripened berries for our peas. Though warned not to run with the shooters in our mouths, Stevie didn't listen so when he tripped and fell, his shooter rammed into the roof of his mouth. He was a sobbing, bloody mess for a while. We were all worried he was badly hurt. Lesson learned.

In the beginning, driving wasn't easy for Mawzy to grasp. After returning home from an excursion, she pulled into the driveway and got out of the car without putting it in park. David and I were in the back seat. Because of the driveway's elevation, the car started to roll backwards. We were headed toward a big tree with the creek looming behind it. We didn't know what to do. We kept looking behind us then at Mawzy who had utter fear in her eyes. She tried to grab the side view mirror to stop the backward motion. The car won out and threw her onto the ground. Our panic shifted toward whether Mawzy was hurt. The car bumped into the tree but was going slow enough for us nor the car to be harmed. The tree was a blessing as it stopped us from going into the creek. Mawzy got by with just a scrape or two.

Mawzy became a movie buff in her youth and loved taking us in her car to the drive-in movie theatre in Charmco, near Rainelle. She always made a big bag of popcorn, cookies, and lemonade to take along as she refused to pay the prices at the theatre food stand. The movies I remember the most are *The 10*

Commandments, *Old Yeller* and *King Kong vs Godzilla*. Cousins Billy Boy and Stevie were with us for the King Kong movie. We all got a kick out of the fact that Mawzy was a King Kong fan and couldn't stand Godzilla. I cried my eyes out at the end of *Old Yeller*. It had an impact on me for several days as I pondered the finality of death.

A small chateau style filling station caught Mawzy's eye on one of our road trips, so she pulled over. She thought it would make an adorable playhouse for David and me. It appeared to have been closed for some time. We kids started exploring the interior and immediately fantasized about who got which room and how we would make it our own. David envisioned a laboratory. I was planning a nursery for my doll babies. Mawzy had a neighbor look it over. Because it had a dirt floor, he said it would likely collapse if a move was attempted.

In lieu of the filling station, Mawzy helped David and me convert the attic above the back half of the garage into our playhouse. Mom later told me the garage attic had been a hiding place for her as a child when she wanted to be alone. There were no steps, so we entered from the outside by climbing on a tar barrel and then a cinder block. Once on the block, we could shinny ourselves up into our play area. David's most cherished item in the playhouse was a chemistry set. A family friend, Enoch Cox, built him a case for all his bottles. The tar in the barrel was used to repair leaks in the roof. Even after being warned, David curiosity got the best of him and as he pried opened the barrel, he inadvertently smeared himself with a goodly amount of tar. Boy, was Mawzy mad. "I'm going to get that tar off you even if I have to take the skin off with it," she warned. Into the bathtub he went for a scrubbing the likes of which he'd never felt before. Restrain every nerve.

Initially there was a detached wash house where the laundry was done throughout the year. Mawzy loved hanging clothes on the back-yard line in freezing weather, as she said they dried softer than in warmer temperatures. An addition was added to the back of the house, so a modern washer and dryer could be installed. This was prompted by the discovery of a copperhead snake den in the old wash house. To eliminate the snakes, gasoline was poured in the den and lit on fire.

Mawzy planted a big garden every summer. When I was just a little thing, I pulled green onions and used the tops as a straw for my milk. When the milk was gone, I ate the onion top. It always amazed Mom and Mawzy that I could eat onions that way. Behind the garden, in the north corner of Mawzy's property, sat Uncle Billy's 4-H bee-hive box. David and I were warned to keep away from it to avoid getting stung. Mawzy kept it going as she couldn't bear to get rid of it. It was a piece of Billy's life she still clung to.

One of the most anticipated events of the year was the West Virginia State Fair in Lewisburg as entertainment options in the area were limited. Eleanor, Billy, and Mom exhibited their 4-H projects there.

Views from Mawzy's home.

When I asked Mom what her biggest thrill was as a kid she answered without hesitation, "The state fair. I liked the rides, the animals and the grandstand shows." Her answer remained true for us kids as well.

As an adult, Mom loved to play bingo. One year it rained so much the fairgrounds became a huge mud hole. Mom drove us there, about 30 miles from home, took one look at the quagmire then turned around and headed back home. Though David and I understood, it was a huge let down.

Murphy's was a five and dime store in Rainelle, about seven miles away. They stocked a variety of household goods, school and office supplies, clothing, and magazines. It initially became popular in the area as it provided an alternative for the coal mine company stores.

"You two kids want to go to Murphy's with me today?" Mawzy hollered. "I need to pick up a few things."

"Yes!" David and I responded in unison.

We loved going there to see what toys and new comic books were available. David liked the action figure comics like *Superman* and *Batman*. My favorites were *Richie Rich* and *Archie and Friends*. There was a sign posted above the comic book rack that read," Nice to look at. Nice to hold. Once they're opened, then they're sold!"

As we headed out the door, I ran back into Mawzy's bedroom, opened her top dresser drawer, and grabbed my money stash. It was burning a hole in my pocket. I was so excited as I had decided I was going to buy a new doll. When we got to Murphy's the three of us went our separate ways. I ventured back to the doll section and proceeded to agonize over which doll I wanted and if it was in my price range. I narrowed my choice to either a two-foot walking doll or a bride doll with a case, accessories, and another outfit. Finally, I decided on the walking doll. One of my neighbor friends, Judy, had one and I figured we could take our dolls on walks together.

"Do you want me to put it in a bag for you?" the clerk asked as she rang the doll up for me.

"Yes," I said as I felt it would help hide my purchase from Mawzy. The clerk left the doll with me and ventured off to find a large bag.

"Are you buying that?" David asked as he wondered by and saw the doll. When I nodded yes, he said, "I'm goin' a go tell Mawzy." At that point I started to question my decision. I waited for what seemed like hours for the clerk's return. She didn't show up before I saw Mawzy coming down the aisle toward me.

"What are you doing?" Mawzy chided. "You can't buy that doll."

"But I already paid for it."

"That doesn't matter. The clerk can ring it up as a return and refund your money."

I was dreadfully embarrassed and in tears while the unusually long transaction took place. I rode home in silence. Once home, Mawzy explained to Mom what

Gloria June, David, and Myra playing with Sputnik.

had happened. Mom's comment was, "Mother, why didn't you let her keep it?" The tears started to roll again.

Around Easter Murphy's stocked baby chicks and ducks whose feathers were died in festive colors. They bounced around on an end cap in a low edged crate, cheeping nonstop.

I don't know how we managed it, but David and I talked Mawzy into letting us bring home a baby duck. I had the same love of animals as Mawzy. We were so excited with our new pet and decided to name him Sputnik after the Russian satellite. The cuteness wore off as Sputnik grew up and turned mean. Every time he saw our car pull into the driveway he ran toward us. As we headed for the house, he chased us and nipped at our heels. It scared me to death, as he could run faster than I. He came to a bad end. David found him dead by the creek near the house with his feet chewed off. A neighbor boy said a stray dog killed him. David was so upset he laid plans to kill the dog with his toy knife but was unsuccessful. Many years later, he discovered the neighbor boys drowned Sputnik.

Oh, the West Virginia hills! How majestic and how grand,
With their summits bathed in glory, like the Prince Immanuel's Land!
Is it any wonder then, that my heart with rapture thrills,
As I stand once more with loved ones on those West Virginia hills?
Oh, the hills, beautiful hills, how I love those West Virginia hills!
If o'er sea o'er land I roam, still I'll think of happy home,
And my friends among the West Virginia hills.

Official State Song of West Virginia (First Verse and Chorus)
Ellen King

David and Myra on Mawzy's quilt.

A Kid's Playground

As a kid growing up in the hills of West Virginia, summer days seemed to last forever. There weren't a lot of distractions, so creativity became a necessity. My day usually started with a jaunt out the front door of Mawzy's house. I was on a mission to get the *Beckley Post-Herald* from the orange box just outside the white picket fence. Right there on the spot, I unfolded the newspaper and looked in the upper right-hand corner for one of three symbols – a radiant sun, a wad of clouds or a cloud burst. I was ecstatic if the radiant sun was displayed, as it meant a whole day in the great of outdoors! On the sunny days, I bound back

19

into the house and grabbed one of Mawzy's old quilts. Her quilts made me feel like she was with me as they were pieced together with left-over scraps of house dresses she made. Having lived through the hard times of the Great Depression, "waste not, want not" was a lesson she learned and passed on.

Once I had the quilt spread out on the west side of the house, I went about the task of setting

up two stations – one for housekeeping and one for work.

On the upper half were my dolls and their accessories which included clothes, bottles, a bathtub, and beds made from moss lined cockleburs. I had a set of kid sized kitchen appliances for meal prep and a small tub and washboard for doing laundry. All ingredients for meals

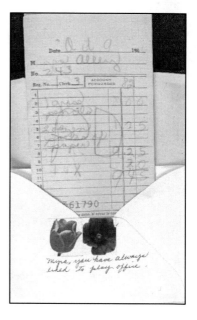

Cockleburs for doll beds, Betsy Wetsy and Myra, receipts Gloria June saved for Myra, inside of milkweed pod for doll food.

came from the wild. My favorite was "fish" taken from a milkweed pod, because it looked so real and was just the right size for my dolls. I served the dolls' food on my own child's dish set. Mawzy bought it for me for my second birthday via mail order. I recently found the $1.50 cancelled check made out to The Branchell Company with the set identified in the memo. My laundry theme song was "All I Have to Do is Dream" by the Everly Brothers. It gave me the rhythm to get those clothes extra clean. The sweetheart of my household was my Betsy Wetsy doll. She had moving joints and "sleep" eyes that closed when I laid her down for a nap.

On the lower half of the quilt was my office. I was a record keeper. When we went to Murphy's five and dime store, I would sometimes bypass the toy isle and go to the office section where I settled on a receipt book and a ledger. I called myself Boss Jones and had imaginary employees. I often wonder if this is where I got my start as a financial advisor.

David was usually off doing his own thing but on occasion we teamed up for an adventure together. There was a small creek across the dirt road from Mawzy's house. It was a great place to go exploring.

Tree branches draped over the sides, providing welcomed shade. The water was usually shallow, slow moving and crystal clear, but cold and very rocky which made for treacherous maneuvering. We loved to catch crawdads and put them in a galvanized tub. One day after we caught a ton of crawdads, David took off to play with his friends. I decided to tear the heads off all the little fellers to see if there were any "pearls" inside. It was a gutsy move for me. I was successful in collecting a handful of the crawdad stones, which they create in an effort to retain calcium for their exoskeletons. Was I ever in trouble with David when he came back to a tub of headless crawdads. Wanting to be in charge got me in trouble more than once. Karma always bites and this is how it got me. I put the "pearls" on top of my Mom's boyfriend's car, which was parked in the church lot next door, and got distracted as kids will do. By the time

I remembered them, his car was gone and my precious "pearls" were lost forever, embedded along the dirt road.

"Hey Myra. I'm bored," David said one day as he walked over to my quilted play area. "Richard and Billy went home to do chores. What ya say we go for a hike up in the woods?"

"Sure. Why not. I'm kinda bored too," I said as I got up off the quilt and put my shoes on.

The first part of our trek was through the pasture behind Mawzy's house, which didn't appear to be a big deal, but the distance to the woods was longer than it seemed and it wasn't like walking through the yard. The hay and weeds were often knee high and camouflaged the gopher holes we kept tripping over.

"I'm tired," I complained when we finally got to the wood's edge.

"I didn't think it would take so long to get here. I don't wanna to go any further."

"Aw, come on. We might be able to find Uncle Billy's cabin. I don't think it's very far from here." Billy was Mawzy's middle child and only son.

"Well, that might be fun, if you promise it's not too far."

Now we were on a mission. The woods were magic. The forest was thick with deciduous trees in all their summer glory, so the canopy made me feel as if I were stepping into a huge, cavernous house. The ground was soft with dead bark and fallen leaves. Patches of moss were so big and lush I was tempted to lay down on them for a nap. Ferns, wildflowers, and mushrooms added another layer to the forest floor. As we walked along, we foraged for pungent teaberry leaves to gnaw on.

"Hey, look up ahead," David yelled after we had been traipsing through the woods for a half hour or so. "I think it's the cabin."

We took off running and sure enough, there before our very eyes was Uncle Billy's cabin. It was about twenty feet square, and the logs had been stacked four layers high by Billy and a couple of his friends.

"Wow, can you believe it's still here?" I marveled as I walked all the way around it.

"Hey, look over here. Uncle Billy carved his initials in the wood," David pointed out with pride in his discovery.

22

Next, we decided to go in search of grapevines to swing on. Success was ours again.

"David, look at that bunch of grapevines hangin' off the trees," I exclaimed as we crested the hill. I was proud I had made the discovery before him.

"I see them. I'll test a couple," he said as he grabbed a vine and pulled down on it with all his weight to be assured it was firmly attached to the tree. "I think this is a good one," he concluded feeling confident he had found a worthy vine. With a firm grip he backed up as far as the vine would allow, then took a flying leap over the side of the hill. As he was dangling in mid-air the vine broke loose and he came crashing down, like a monkey sliding from a tree.

"Oh no! Are you OK?" I hollered, afraid he was badly hurt. He was scraped and bruised but thankfully did not have any broken bones. "I think we should start for home."

"Me too. Let's head down to the ravine. It's probably the closest way out of here."

Up ahead we spotted a fence. As we approached and started to climb it, we heard a rattling sound. Sure enough, on the other side of the fence was a rattle snake coiled and ready to strike.

"What we goin' a do now?" I whispered.

"We'll have to find another way. We shouldn't try to walk around him," David whispered back.

Never taking our eyes off our foe, we slowly climbed down the fence and qui-etly backtracked, shaking in our boots. Somewhere along the way we took a wrong turn and became lost. David's plan was to walk the ravine in the hope it would eventually lead us to familiar ground, so that's what we did.

"Look up there," I said as I pointed to the right. "There's a fence at the top of the hill. Let's go see what we can see."

"OK, fine. You lead the way."

Pleased to be in charge, I took off up the hill. Once we reached the top, panic began to subside as I recognized our location. I think it irritated David that I found our way home.

"Give me your shoe," he demanded. Though an odd request, I obliged and he immediately threw it to the bottom of the hill.

"What'd ya do that for?" I barked, as mad as could be. I was pooped and wanted to get home. I stomped down the hill, grabbed my shoe and as I was climbing back up, stepped right smack dab on a hornet's nest. It was very traumatic as I got stung several times. It startled David, so he decided to save the day.

"Here, let me help," he said as he pulled his toy knife from his pants pocket. "I'll cut each sting with a crisscross and suck the poison out." Thank goodness the knife blade was dull and the first aid effort was aborted.

We were dragging by then and ready for our adventure to be over. As we headed down into the pasture, we could hear Mom and Mawzy yelling for us. We didn't have a clue how long we'd been gone. They were worried sick and we got a good scolding as our welcome home. No whoppin' though as they knew nature's punishment was enough. Mawzy went to her medicine cabinet, grabbed the Merthiolate and patched up our wounds. For a while, we were the orange polka dotted kids.

On another occasion we decided to pull David's wagon up the hill behind Mawzy's house. A neighbor friend, Kay, was with us. The mission was to get to the top of the hill and ride the wagon back down. The hill was steepest on the east side, so would provide the most thrilling ride. The issue with this plan was the cattle pond at the bottom of the hill. David was convinced he could maneuver the wagon around the pond. Because of my cynical nature, I questioned the wisdom of trying to take the narrow path between the pond and the spillway. David was confident he could steer the wagon through the passage, so I insisted he go first.

 He hopped in the wagon, gave himself a push with his foot and down the hill he went, right into the cattle pond. He was soaking wet and concerned that he would be in trouble once we got home. Though embarrassed, he stripped down to his undies and draped his shorts and shirt over some bushes to dry. After exploring the area for a bit, we decided his clothes were so wet they would never dry before dark. The excursion was terminated, we headed home, and it was David's turn to get in trouble.

Wild strawberries grew in several spots near the house. I loved to pick and eat them. Finding the berries was a challenge as they were small and the plants were nestled among taller weeds. On one of my picking expeditions, I thought I had found the largest wild strawberry ever. As I reached closer to pick it, I was alarmed to see the red section of a snake. Its head nor tail were visible so I imagined it was huge. Like a bolt of lightning, I tucked tail and beelined for the house. I had that snake's colors burned into my brain, but I never found a picture of it in our World Book Encyclopedia. I decided it was quite venomous so this experience intensified my repulson of snakes. After the incident, I started having a recurring

24

nightmare. In the dream I was in Mawzy's back yard playing when I saw a snake in the grass. As I ran from it, I spotted one snake after another until the entire back yard slithered with snakes of all kinds and sizes. I had a hard time finding a place to plant my feet as I bolted toward the house to escape getting bit. I always woke up with a fright at this point because I could never quite make it to the back door.

As fall approached, we took off down Mawzy's road in search of Touch-Me-Nots or Jewelweed with ripened seed pods. The flowers were orange and the pods

green. They were so abundant, it became a game to see how many pods we could pop. When fully ripened, the half inch long pods were fat and once touched they exploded like a Jack-in-the-box into a wad of curly green vines. No matter how many pods we touched, it was always startling when they sprang open.

Even in the winter we spent a lot of time outdoors. Sled riding was always a hit in the neighborhood. One Saturday, bundled up with sleds in tow, nine of us girls and boys went up to the Sims house to sleigh ride down their driveway. I was the youngest. The snow had started to thaw so about one fourth of the way down the drive was a bare spot. I questioned the ability of the sled to get past that area. The boys told me it was muddy and would be about as slick as the snow. They encouraged me to go first. I trusted them, so took off with a starter run to help build up my speed.

When I hit the dirt, my sled stopped in its tracks but I kept going, face first into the mud. Everybody laughed at me. I was so mad at those boys. I was crying as I stomped home with my nose, mouth, and ears full of mud.

Time for Mawzy's TLC. I vowed then and there to never listen to anything those boys ever told me again. I, like David with the wagon, had exhibited poor judgment about my control over nature. Perhaps it was karma again.

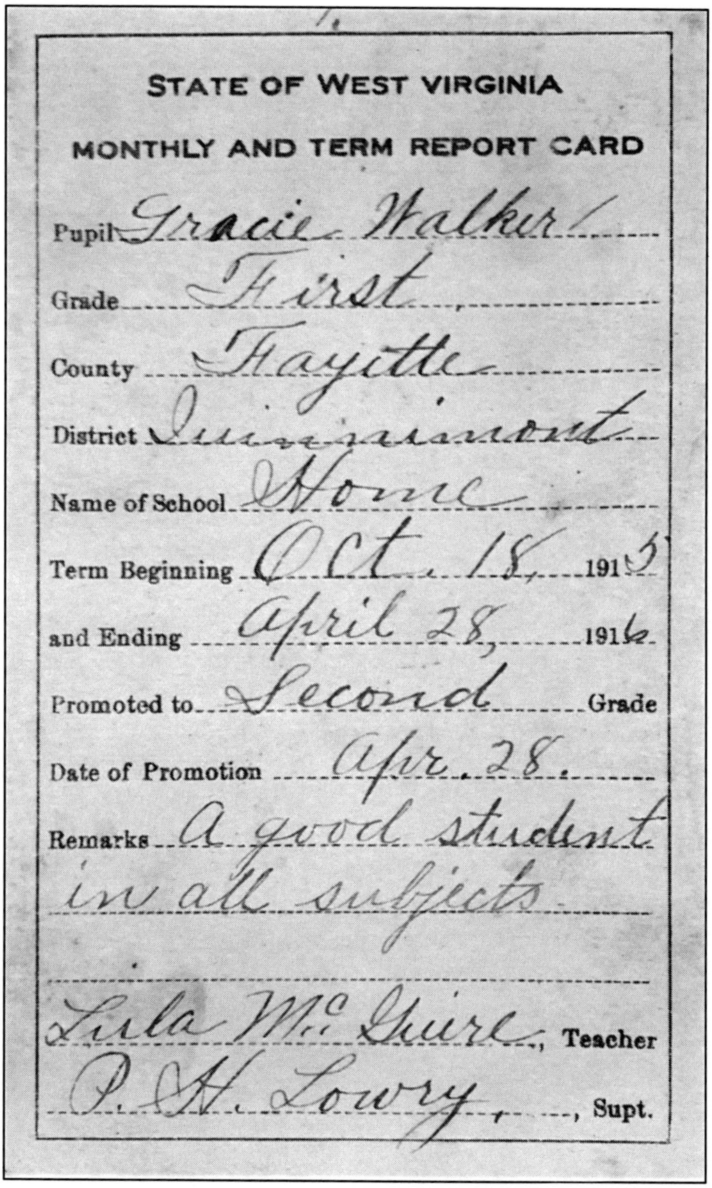

STATE OF WEST VIRGINIA

MONTHLY AND TERM REPORT CARD

Pupil _Gracie Walker_

Grade _First_

County _Fayette_

District _Nuttallburg_

Name of School _Home_

Term Beginning _Oct. 18,_ 1915

and Ending _April 28,_ 1916

Promoted to _Second_ Grade

Date of Promotion _Apr. 28._

Remarks _A good student in all subjects_

Lula McGuire, Teacher

P. H. Lowry, Supt.

Mawzy's first grade report card was the oldest item found in her hope chest.

STUDIES	Months									Written Tests			Term Av.
	1	2	3	4	5	6	7	8	9	1st	2nd	3rd	Av.
Reading or Literature	89	90	92	94	96	98							93
Writing	85	87	88	90	94	96							90
Spelling	80	83	85	90	93	94							88
Arithmetic	82	84	87	90	92	94							88
Geography													
Language or Grammar													
U. S. and W. Va. History													
Physiology & Hygiene													
Civil Government													
Nature Study or Agriculture													
Drawing													
Music													
Days Present	20	16½	13½	1	5	20							13
Times Tardy	0	0	0	0	0	0							
Deportment	100	100	100	100	100	100							100
Average													

NOTE: 100 is perfect; 90 very good; 80 good; 70 unsatisfactory; below 70 very poor.

OUTLINE OF STUDIES BY GRADES

FIRST GRADE. Reading, writing, spelling, arithmetic, nature study, physiology and hygiene, drawing, music.

SECOND GRADE. Reading, writing, spelling, nature study, arithmetic, history, physiology and hygiene, drawing, music.

THIRD GRADE. Reading, writing, spelling, arithmetic, nature study, history, physiology and hygiene, drawing, music.

FOURTH GRADE. Reading, language, writing, spelling, arithmetic, geography, history, nature study, physiology and hygiene, drawing, music.

FIFTH GRADE. Reading, language, writing, spelling, arithmetic, nature study, history, geography, physiology and hygiene, drawing, music.

SIXTH GRADE. Reading, language, writing, spelling, arithmetic, nature study, geography, United States history, physiology and hygiene, drawing, music.

SEVENTH GRADE. Reading, language, writing, spelling, arithmetic, agriculture, United States history, drawing, music.

EIGHTH GRADE. Reading, language, writing, spelling, arithmetic, agriculture, United States and West Virginia history, civil government, physiology and hygiene, drawing, music.

Mothers Always Do

I made mama an apron, I tried to sew it true;
And I'm sure she'll think it's lovely – mothers always do.
I crocheted papa's slippers, they look so fine and new;
Of course my mother helped me – mothers always do.
I knit a ball for baby, of soft yarn, red and blue;
My mother showed me how 'twas done - mothers always do.
I want a ring for Christmas and another dolly too;
Mother said she'd write to Santa – mothers always do.

A.B. Canfield
(found in Mawzy's hope chest)

Education Devotion

Seven was the typical age to start school in the early 1900s, but Mommy Walker wanted Mawzy at home that year as she needed help with a two-year-old and a four-year-old and was five months pregnant. Mawzy, the first-born child, enjoyed caring for her siblings but she was anxious to see what school was all about. The next fall, in the year 1915, Mommy and Poppy gave Mawzy their blessing to head down the road to knowledge.

Mommy was nervous as she sent Mawzy out the door with her lunch pail and school supplies to make the two-mile trek to the Springdale Home School. She was relieved Mawzy would be able to catch up with a few neighboring kids along the way.

Mawzy soaked up every bit of information her teacher, Miss McGuire, sent her way. Her grades improved as the year progressed. By the last month she was scoring in the mid to high 90s in reading, writing, spelling, and arithmetic. Every month her score in deportment was 100. Poppy always signed her report card as "W.C. Walker." Back then school lasted about six months, as children were needed at home to care for siblings and to help with farming during the spring, summer, and early fall.

As the school year neared its end, Miss McGuire gave the students an assignment to write a letter to a family member or friend. Mawzy decided to write to her grandma Walker. Poppy's parents lived in Valley Heights along the Greenbrier River, between Buggar Lick Creek and Buggy Branch and four miles north of Pence Springs. It's where Poppy grew up. They didn't get a chance to see each other very often. Grandma Walker responded to Mawzy's letter in a post card dated March 25, 1916.

Dear Gracie, I will answer your card. We are all first tolerable well. Hope you all are well. You all come up this summer and see us. I will close. Love to all from grandma

Mawzy cherished the post card and kept track of it until it eventually made its way into her hope chest.

World War I was raging in Europe and had everyone on edge. The Selective Service Act was passed when the war came to a head in May 2017, so Poppy was required to register for the draft. There wasn't much concern of his getting drafted though, as he had a dependent spouse and children and was at the top of the age bracket.

I had a little bird,
Its name was Enza,
I opened the window
and in-flu-enza

A children's song during the Spanish flu pandemic of 1918-19

The spring of 1918, at the end of Mawzy's third grade year, the Spanish Influenza swept the nation. Schools closed that fall as the flu made its way through the state, peaking by late October. Church attendance and social gatherings were also prohibited. It hit

Chester and Earl, "cupid awake, cupid asleep." Below, Mawzy, Pansie, and Lawrence on right.

youth the hardest. Most reported deaths were between the ages of 5 and 39. In December, *The Raleigh Register*, a major source of news for the area, reported:

The big building boom that is sure to prevail in Beckley in the next year or two gives promise of continued prosperity for this section, if we can ever get rid of the "flu." While the plague continues it hampers every activity that moral man engages in.

Public service ads were common and promoted the use of a handkerchief.

Sisters Evie and Pansie were born back-to-back in 1917 and 1918 so Mommy Walker was glad to have Mawzy at home during the day to help with their care. Mawzy was their "little Mom." The older kids, Glenna, Lawrence, and Thelma always begged her to play school with them. She gladly obliged, as it kept her mind on her studies.

Around this time, West Virginia was booming as it was a natural resource mecca. The lumber business was strong but was slowing down. Coal had become king. In 1918, West Virginia was the second largest coal producer in the United States, with 81 million tons being extracted from the hills.

During this time in Mawzy's young life women were gaining political power. The suffrage movement was often a point of discussion. She'd overheard Mommy and Poppy Walker argue about it. One night at the dining room table, they made their feelings known.

"What's the point in you gettin to vote, Elsie?" Poppy asked as he stuffed a big bite of chicken and dumplings in his mouth. "I'm the provider for the family and I can vote for the family."

"Yes, but I contribute a good plenty to this family too," Mommy answered. "You couldn't do without me. Who does all the cookin' and cannin' and cleanin' and carin' for the children and workin' the garden and feedin' the chickens, horses and cows? Why shouldn't I have some say in how our government's bein' handled? Besides what about the families where the woman's a widow? Heaven only knows that happens a lot 'round here with all the coal minin' accidents and explosions."

Mawzy, Earl, Thelma, Chester, Pansie, and Jewell.

Glenna, Mawzy, Lawrence, Thelma, and Evie.

"Shut up, woman. I don't wanta hear no more 'bout it," Poppy responded as he scratched his head, pounded his fist on the table, stomped off and left his plate for some-one else to handle. He knew, but didn't want to admit, she had a point.

By the time Mawzy started the fifth grade, she was 13 years old and the 19th amend-ment had finally been ratified. Women could vote.

She saved her fifth-grade report card in her hope chest. Her grades were in the mid-80s to high 90s and her top subject was spelling. Her teacher, Ida Neff, also gave her the highest marks in de-portment.

Three years later, at the start of her eighth-grade year, Mawzy's mind was moving to-ward the next step. Her appetite for learning was insatiable. She didn't want school to end but could go no further than eighth grade in Springdale or anywhere nearby. One day after school, she approached her teacher.

"Miss Neff may I talk to you?" Mawzy asked.

"Of course, Gracie. Come on over here."

"I've been wondering about going on to high school. I thought you might have some ideas for me."

"You're a smart young woman and I'm pleased you're interested in furthering your education. It's too bad there's not a high school close by. If you could find a place to board, you might want to consider Beckley High School. You could catch the motor car from Springdale to Beckley, which should be relatively close to the school. I can get enrollment information for you if you would like."

"That would be wonderful. I appreciate your help."

Mawzy liked this idea because she would not have to depend on Poppy Walker for her transport. The motor car, also known as a "doodlebug," was a single unit

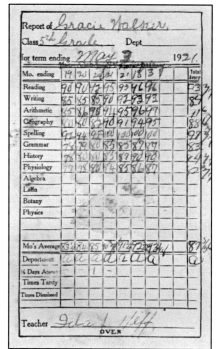

Mawzy's good grades; a "doodlebug." Photo provided by Patty Burwell, from C&O Archives.

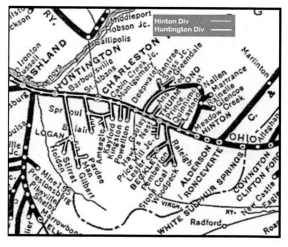

passenger railroad car which was powered by gasoline. There was a C&O connection station in Springdale, recently established for the transport of lumber. This was also the motor car track. In those days, the motor car was often the most efficient way to travel. The unpaved roads were rough and in inclement weather, could quickly turn into impassable mud holes.

That night during supper Mawzy worked up the nerve to broach the subject with Poppy and Mommy, as this was often the only time the family was together.

"I talked with Miss Neff today about going on to high school in the fall. It's something I would really like to do. What do ya' think?" Mawzy asked.

"What the hell ya wanta do that for?" Poppy boomed out. "It's a waste of time. You'll just end up gettin' married anyway and then what's that education gonna do for ya?"

"Poppy, why don't ya hear her out?" Mommy interjected to stop his tirade.

"Next thing ya know, she'll want a be votin'. A woman's place is in the home. We need her here."

That silenced Mawzy but she was determined. She found Mommy in the kitchen later that night after Poppy had gone to bed and revisited her desire.

"Momma, I have my heart set on going to high school. I've been thinking a lot about becoming a teacher someday."

"Gracie, I know you've got the ability to continue your schooling. And yes, I could use your help but I know ya' won't stay here forever. Let me see what I can do to soften Poppy up."

Mommy went to bat for her. She contacted Poppy's sister, Alice, who lived in Mabscott and she and her husband agreed to let Mawzy live with them while she went to high school.

On May 1, 1924, at age 16, Mawzy graduated from the eighth grade. It marked the first of many diplomas she ultimately received and stored in her hope chest. Around that time Poppy finally caved. Mawzy was headed to high school. She was ecstatic and immediately began planning for her first move away from home come that fall.

Mawzy was starting to have suitors approach her at community events and church. Occasionally one showed up at the home place. Ruffner, a red-head with a rough reputation, stopped by one Sunday for a visit and Poppy answered the door.

"Get out of here and go hang out with some of your own damn equals," Poppy yelled as he slammed the door in Ruffner's face. He then proceeded to lecture Mawzy about not to spending time with the likes of him in the future.

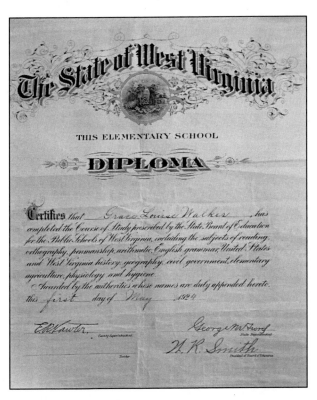

Mawzy wanted to visit Beckley High School ahead of time, so that summer she took the motor car to deliver the enrollment forms Miss Neff procured for her. The day of the trip she was nervous and excited at the same time. Mommy reminded her there would be people along the route who would help her know when and where to transfer so she could stay on the right track. She was instructed to look for a cab once she got to the Beckley train depot.

When she climbed on the motor car in Springdale, she saw a few familiar faces which helped put her mind at ease. All transfers were seamless and a cab was easily hailed, as Mommy had promised.

Meadow River Lumber Company

As Mawzy walked into the school, her heart fluttered with joy. She knew this was the path she wanted to take. The school secretary greeted her with compassion, reviewed her completed forms and gave her a tour of the school.

When she got home that afternoon, Mommy was relieved.

"Momma, I'm so excited. The school is huge compared to our little Springdale School. You should see the library. More books than I've ever seen in all my life!"

"Let's go shoppin' for supplies in the next week or so," Mommy offered. "We can go to the Rainelle Department Store to buy items you'll need for school. You can pick out some material and I'll make you a couple of dresses over the summer."

"Momma, thank you. That would be wonderful."

Though it was less than nine miles to Rainelle, the unpaved road was rough. About three miles from town, travelers had to stop to open gates at two points.

Dozens of horses were kept in a pasture between the gates and were used by the Meadow River Lumber Company in Rainelle to haul lumber from the woods to the mill. So again, the motor car was the most efficient way to go. It left Springdale and headed over Wallow Hole Mountain then along Sewell Creek into Rainelle.

Rainelle was a bustling town, as the Meadow River Lumber Company was located on its outskirts and was the largest hardwood lumber mill in the world. Many workers were hired not only to fell timber but to haul it, process it and to build the railroads necessary for its transport. They made a decent living, but the owners became the wealthy ones on the shoulders of the locals.

The Rainelle Department Store was a two-story building with an attic on the third floor and was the preferred place to shop, as it stocked goods to accommodate most needs. When Mommy Walker and Mawzy arrived in town, they walked to the department store, went in, picked up a basket and began selecting toiletries and school supplies. School items included an Eversharp mechanical pencil and lead, a good fountain pen, ink, an ink well, a wooden handled ink blotter and composition notebooks.

"Now I think we're ready to head to the piece goods section," Mommy noted.

As they reached that part of the store, Mawzy's jaw dropped in awe of all the bolts of fabric.

"Oh Mamma, look at all the material to choose from. How will I ever be able to make up my mind?"

"The first thing we need to do is find two or three patterns you like. Then we'll look at material that don't cost more than $1.00 per yard. That should make your selection easier."

Mawzy chose three patterns that reflected current fashion trends she had seen in the newspaper. One was a loose fit, another a dropped waist and the third featured a V neck designed to be accessorized with a scarf or tie. Patterns in hand, they headed back to the bolts of fabric. Mawzy decided on a purple, white and burgundy plaid gingham which cost only $0.16 per yard. Her next choice was a peach floral dress voile at $0.25 per yard. She was trying to be conservative as she knew money was tight.

"How 'bout this crepe silk and cotton blend?" Mommy suggested. She could sense that Mawzy was being very cautious with the cost of her choices.

"I don't know Mamma, don't you think it's too expensive?"

"Your other two pieces aren't too bad so I think we'll be ok with one piece that's a little fancier. The silk bein' blended with cotton helps keep the cost down to $0.99 per yard. I've been savin' back a bit of my egg money, so we'll be ok."

"Well, I do like the palmetto green with the white dots."

"Me too. I think it'll look nice with your ivory complexion. Grab it up and let's get someone to measure for us, then we must be on our way. It's gettin' close to supper time. Besides, I don't feel too good. Gotta tooth botherin' me."

By the next morning Mommy was in terrible pain. Her tooth had started to abscess. She used a home remedy to rectify the problem. She put lye on the tooth to kill the nerve. That created so much pain she went running out of the house screaming. It scared everybody half to death, but eventually it worked and she moved on about her business.

Add Campbell

Helen and Buddy Trump

Over the remainder of the summer Mommy worked on Mawzy's dresses as she had time. Mawzy helped with pattern layout and some of the simpler sections of sewing. All three dresses were completed by fall and both were happy with the results.

That summer Mawzy met Add Campbell at a church revival. He came on strong. Mawzy was shy so he had his work cut out for him. She did find him quite charming. They started dating. He was three years older than Mawzy and was a coal miner grabbing a job wherever he could.

In late August Mawzy loaded up a trunk with her belongings, hopped on the motor car and headed for high school. In the beginning she was lonely for her family but was glad to be staying with Aunt Alice. She thrived on her studies and completed her freshman year without a hitch. Add came to Beckley to see her as often as he could.

He began writing her letters when she headed back to school for her sophomore year. He missed her terribly. Right after she departed for Beckley, he wrote, *...we've been together so much in the last year it doesn't seem as if we should be apart.*

Mawzy appreciated staying with Aunt Alice but had a desire to earn her own way. That fall she saw a help wanted ad that caught her eye. The Trump family was offering room and board as well as a wage for assistance with cooking, housework and caring for Buddy and Helen, their two young children.

Mr. Trump was one of Beckley's up and coming businessmen who had recently started dealings in real estate, a movie theatre, and a restaurant. He was also a deputy sheriff for the town district and occasionally entered the political scene. Mrs. Trump dabbled in interior decorating and was sometimes called away to consult with a client.

Williams Street became Mawzy's home away from home for the rest of the 1925 school year. It was a good fit for all. The house was close to the school so made for an easy walk. The Trumps liked Mawzy's conscientious, take-charge attitude. Mawzy loved the kids and the feeling was mutual because of her attention and genuine interest in their activities. This was evident from saved Trump family newspaper clippings and photographs Mawzy kept in her hope chest. Among the photos was a picture of "Buddy" seated in a small wooden wagon being pulled by a goat and one of Helen hugging up on her cat.

Shortly after her move to the Trump house, Add wrote, *How do you like your new home by now. Fine I hope. Just so you don't work too hard and you know there is no use in you doing that. It is just like I've always tried to tell you. That I would see you safely through but you won't listen to me for some reason.*

Two significant letters Mawzy saved in her hope chest were written during her second year of high school. She received a letter dated September 16, 1925 from her close friend, Blanche, offering words of encouragement.

Dear Gracie:

Haven't heard from you for some time. Was not sure you were home but suppose this will reach you.

Suppose you are going to school. This is about as good a thing as you can do. I don't think you will ever regret having spent these years for that purpose. Your school days are your happiest and most care-free of all your life. You may not think so now but later you will realize....

Mommy Walker wrote to Mawzy as often as she could, but her time was limited with seven kids at home and farm chores to manage. Mawzy received the following letter, dated March 29, 1926, which was written less than a month before Mommy's ninth child, Jewell, was born.

Dear Gracie,

I am sending you $10.00 this morning for you to buy your school supplies with. Do the best you can with it. Money is getting scarce again. Your papa and Lawrence went to Layland yesterday and paid the note. Papa (my) cut $50.00 on the interest. Guess that will help to get a start again. He has only got $95 in the bank now. I will send your hat to you tomorrow. Haven't had time to fix it up this morn and it is just some times that Sis will do anything. I don't know how silk sells over there but I saw several pieces in National that would make a nice dress that you *can get for 98 ct and 1.25 per yard. I would think that would be plenty good to larn to sew on.*

We will write you again when we find out about the examinations. Guess this is all for this time. So you can spend the money to the best advantage you can.

From Mamma

Mommy Walker

The National was a popular mail order company. The fabric Mommy was describing was from a National Bellas Hess catalog, which was one of five thriving general merchandise catalog companies.

By the summer of 1926, after completing two years of high school, Mawzy started to think more seriously about becoming a teacher. One of her high school friends told her that single women who were eighth grade graduates could teach school without having finished high school or college. Intrigued, she wrote a letter to the Fayette County superintendent regarding certification and the reply indicated she could enroll for an exam which, if passed, would entitle her to a one-year teaching contract. The exam schedule was provided with the next exam slated for early July.

As soon as Mawzy got home from school for the summer, she broached the subject with Mommy Walker.

"Momma, can I talk to you for a minute?" Mawzy asked just as Mommy was headed out the back door with a bucket on her arm to fetch chicken eggs from the coop.

"Ok but make it a quick minute. I'm runnin' behind on my chores. Preacher went longer than usual today."

"Yes ma'am, I'll walk with you and help gather eggs. You told me yesterday you and Poppy wanted me to stay home from high school this fall to help out with my brothers and sisters, especially baby Jewell. I found out I can teach with an eighth-grade diploma if I pass a test. It sure would be helpful to earn some money for my expenses when I go back to high school. I promise I would come home on weekends and holidays to help out."

Mawzy with baby Jewell.

"I'm proud of you, Gracie, and I like your ambition. Why don't ya' plan to sit for the exam. I'll discuss it with Poppy. I know he won't be excited about it, but hopefully he'll come around. Then we'll see what happens from there. Besides your sister, Glenna is old enough to start helping more than she is now. She still has a bit of a lazy streak."

Early morning on the day of the exam, Mawzy and Poppy hopped in the old Ford truck and headed toward Fayetteville. Because the mountainous dirt road conditions weren't the greatest, it took two hours each way. Poppy decided he could take advantage of the trip to pick up some supplies and feed for home. The test lasted all day.

A few weeks later, a much-anticipated letter arrived.

"Gracie, there's a letter for you came in the mail today. That brother of yours, Lawrence, just got back from the post office," Mommy Walker yelled from the kitchen.

Mawzy came running into the kitchen. The letter was from the Fayette County superintendent. She nervously opened the envelope and unfolded the letter. She passed the exam.

When testing in Fayetteville, Mawzy inquired about available positions in the area. The closest was teaching in a one room schoolhouse up on Backus

Rules Of Conduct For A Teacher Included:

- Not being married, nor keeping company with men
- No smoking
- No dresses shorter than two inches above the ankle and no bright colors
- No dyed hair
- No dancing in public

The job description included:
- Starting and maintaining the fire, if needed
- Cleaning the school building
- Sanitation, including a system for washing the students' hands
- Testing children for nearsightedness
- Fund raising for schoolbooks and supplies
- Being present with children on the playground
- Maintaining playground equipment

Mountain, about 18 miles from Springdale. She made application and was summoned for an interview the end of July.

The interview was more involved than she expected. Questions about her moral and spiritual character were asked. If offered the job, she would be expected to board with a family in the community.

It was overwhelming but Mawzy felt she could handle it, at least for one year. She was offered the job and accepted it. So, at 18 years of age she taught her first year of school in the Backus one room schoolhouse. She found room and board on the mountain with an elderly woman who had recently lost her husband. It worked well for them both. Mawzy had a quiet evening environment to literally "burn the midnight oil" for lesson planning and Margaret had company and someone to help with the chores.

By the time spring rolled around Mawzy knew, without a doubt, teaching was her calling. Her relationship with her beau, Add, was tumultuous. He wrote often and she welcomed his letters but was often unsettled after reading them. She had a hard time getting him to understand they needed to be discreet while she was teaching. Marriage was on his mind, but she knew that would end her career before it ever got started.

Add frequently made weekend visits to Poppy and Mommy's house. He had worked his charm on the Walker family and had a standing invitation for Sunday dinner. He sometimes went even if Mawzy wasn't there. Spent the night on occasion.

During one of his visits, the dinner table conversation turned to the making, transport, and ill effects of moonshine. It was during the Prohibition era, so it was always popping up in the news and in local conversations.

"I see they're still tryin' to sneak that Kentucky "burst head" across the border to West Virginia," Poppy reported. "A couple from Catlettsburg was caught at the Beckley train depot with 60 pints of tanglefoot in the woman's suitcase. Boy, I'd like to have a nip of that batch. Bet it'd curl your toes."

"W.C., you need to leave that stuff alone," Mommy countered. "It's dangerous. There was this feller who drank some wood alcohol moonshine. He ended up in the hospital with a bad case of the cotton eye. Can't see. Can't walk."

"A buddy of mine at the mines, originally from up around Fairmount, was talking about the booze room up there in the basement of the courthouse where they store confiscated liquor," Add chimed in. "He said he's heard there's at least 1,000 gallons of the stuff there right now. They're supposed to have a pourin' day before long. That's the day they dump it all down the sewer drain. What a waste."

"Wait. This is the best one yet," Poppy barged on. "They caught seven men posing as pallbearers and a minister. The coffin was plumb full of white lightnin'. Can you imagine how heavy that son of a bitch was?" Poppy chortled with the older kids in unison.

"Enough about this nonsense," Mommy said as she began clearing the dishes from the table. That the kids were all ears did not escape Mommy's attention.

As Mawzy arose from the table, Add pulled her aside.

"Let's go talk outside," he whispered to her as they headed out of the dining room and onto the back porch.

"What you want to talk about? Hopefully, it doesn't concern that nasty hooch."

"No, it's not about that. I told you I was layin' off that rotgut stuff. I miss you and I want to get married. I'm frustrated waiting on you to make up your mind."

"Add, we've been over this a hundred times. I can't marry you now and continue teaching on Backus Mountain."

"Then quit that stupid teaching job. I told you I could take care of you!"

"I've made a commitment to the school that I will not renege on," Mawzy said as she planted her feet and placed her hands on her hips. She looked out over the hills and saw the clouds swallowing them up. A storm was coming.

"Alright. Suit yourself," Add snorted as he jammed his hat on his head and stomped down the porch steps in route to his car. He stopped and turned around just long enough to get the last word in. "But I won't wait forever. There's lots of women out there who would jump at the chance to marry me. Think it over and give me your idea of a deadline before it's too late."

…...Well darling it will soon be work time. Only wish I could see those deep thinking eyes that I loved from the first time that I ever felt the life pulse of you in my arms and wonder if you loved me the same as I did you…

Yours only,
WA Campbell

Excerpt from letter written to Mawzy on 10/18/28

66 Love Letters

In Mawzy's hope chest, buried under layers of photo albums, memorabilia, and local newspapers with significant headlines, like the start of World War II, I found an old dark brown wooden box.

The hinged lid was cracked and had a picture of a hunting dog on it. The box was about five inches deep and large enough to hold a business sized envelope. Inside, laying on the top, was the marriage certificate of Mawzy and Add, bound in tan leather and tied with a baby blue tasseled cord.

Below the certificate were four years of carefully stacked love letters from Add, dated from the fall of 1925 through the spring of 1929. Though still in their envelopes, it was obvious they had been folded, unfolded, and reread several times. This part of Mawzy's life was contained in a sacred spot of its own.

Add spiffed up for a date with Mawzy.

Add was a handsome fellow. In pictures of him as a young man, he had an impish smile, hair as dark as the coal he mined and the swagger of a lady's man. It was easy to see why Mawzy was smitten.

One of Mawzy's favorite courting stories was of Add laying a Kewpie doll next to her on her church pew, then quietly slipping away. She cherished the doll and displayed it on the bed she and sister Glenna shared. Pansie, one of the younger sisters, sneaked into their bedroom one day and started playing with the doll. When Mawzy caught her in the act, Pansie ran with the doll toward the kitchen and tripped on a rug. As she fell, the porcelain doll flew out of her arms and shattered. She started wailing like a banshee and repeating, "Oh, I broke Sasie's doll." She called Mawzy Sasie instead of Gracie as she couldn't talk plainly. Mawzy was quite upset but quickly forgave Pansie as she knew it was an accident.

It was evident from Add's letters they spent quite a bit of time together in Springdale the summer of 1925. During their long-distance courtship Mawzy completed her second and third years of high school in Beckley, taught school for two years in two different locations, took coursework two summers at two different schools and then headed back to Beckley to finish high school. Add's letters were mailed from nine different locations as he migrated from one job to another, mostly in various coal mines.

Add's romantic side surfaced in many of his letters. Shortly after Mawzy moved to Beckley for her second year of high school, he wrote, *... I'm so lonesome I can't hardly stay still a moment. Seems as if you have been gone a year...*

In another letter he proudly noted, *...Got your picture back yesterday. Sure was a nice one. Anytime I want to look at you all I have to do is look at that picture. Just looks as if it is going to say something to me... Everybody that has seen it says that you look awful pleasing looking. Of course I know you do myself...*

One night he pined away, *...I'm about half a notion writing a book tonight as I am in that mood and they are playing that record "I am drifting back to dreamland" and of course it changes a fellows feelings a little. I can almost see you standing in front of me when I hear that song played. Just you with a half way grinning smile...*

Add had Mawzy's younger siblings wrapped around his little finger in no time. He often took them places in his car. In one letter he talked of this, *...Pansie and Chester loaded in the front seat but Pansie had to sit by me. They sure are some kids. One so afraid that I think more of the one that they don't know what to do. But they are not much worse than you are ha ha...* Pansie was nine and Chester was five at the time.

Add attempted to make Mawzy jealous by writing about women he was with in her absence. In one of his earliest letters he rambled, *...Didn't like the Red Headed girl at all... Went up to church one night and she called me in to sit down beside her. I said something she didn't approve of and she undertook to call me but I wouldn't stand for that so I told her to go straight to you know where. You know dearie I couldn't give the snap of my finger for her...*

In another letter he wrote, *...Well you know what that girl said about wanting to make a date. Saw her last Wednesday and she wanted me to take her to Cliff Top today. She has been having a quarrel with her fellow over there and wanted*

Add with a few of his "girlfriends."

me to take her to spite him. Said she knew that you wouldn't care if I went but I put up all kind of excuses and the best one was that I was leaving which I did...

It seemed to never end, ...*You know the girl I was telling you about over here. She said the other day there was two things I had to stop and that was writing or seeing you and working at night if I went with her. I told her I wouldn't do either and as far as going with her I didn't want to...*

When he was living at home, he teased, ...*I don't know much to write as I told it all yesterday except today is a pretty day and am not expecting any of the family back before in the morning. Am going out and see if I can get me a hired girl to stay with me. Ha. Ha. ...*

Add wanted Mawzy to know he was being a good boy by attending church, but he still pointed out his appeal to the opposite sex and that he was the life of the party. During a week-long revival he reported, ...*Have been going to Meadow Bridge every night. Sure do wish you were here to go. They have been coming on believe me. Didn't have the feet washing last Sunday night. Put it off till this Friday. Suppose I shall have to take Sister that night. They are going to close Sunday night or at least that is what the old woman said. Tuesday night she asked for all*

the liars to hold up their hand and I was the only one that held up my hand and the old woman said, "Thank God for one honest liar." Talk about a laugh...

At the time, foot washing for some denominations was a fairly common practice in the area.

While Mawzy was away, Add and Mawzy's sister, Glenna, became close. Everyone called her

Add with girls at schoolhouse; below, Add with Glenna.

Sister. He mentioned being with her in several of his letters, including the one above.

He also wrote, *...Glenna and I went to Meadow Bridge Sunday night and talk about a rain but we sure did have one.* Then the next day, *See Glenna about every day. Sure do have a lot of fun out there. Haven't been down to your home since Sunday night. That's the longest I have stayed away from down there for a long time...* Then, *...Glenna and Pansie and I went to the show at Meadow Bridge last night... I knew you wouldn't say anything if you knew I was with your sister...*

Sister was uninhibited, so she and Add may have shared a nip or two. It was a double-edged sword for Sister as it appears she enjoyed Add's company yet felt, perhaps out of guilt, the need to keep Mawzy apprised of his meandering. This comes through in one of Add's letters.

...No Sister is mistaken about Eloise ... I talk a lot to her when I see her but I'm never with her and have never been. I expect you think

47

sometimes that I am always running around with some woman but I never do that...

When Mawzy questioned Add's relationship with Sister, he responded,....*So sister was wondering what I wanted to see her for. Well what have I always wanted to see her for but you. Know I never think of her in the same way I do you. She is more like one of my sisters to me. You are just dreaming your head away aren't you...*

Add's propensity for alcohol was another of Mawzy's concerns. After he had been to visit her in Beckley, she worried over his drinking and driving and pointed this out to him. His response was, *...No made it fine. You know I wouldn't until I got back to Springdale. Well they arrested ... and his wife today. Understand they got a whole lot of whiskey and his still. So you know what that means. Don't let Aunt Alice see this letter or she will be talking to me about whiskey again...*

Alice was quite feisty, had an opinion about everything and was especially vocal about her approval of prohibition. Being quite fond of Mawzy, who lived with her at the time, Alice always looked out for her best interests. One of Alice's expressions the family always got a kick out of was, "I like peanut butter but it's too hard to get in and too hard to get out."

That Alice didn't care much for Add came through in another letter. *...Tell Aunt Alice that I said I wasn't wanting to claim kin to anyone that didn't want me to. I hope some day she will see that we are satisfied together and not froze apart...*

Add always had excuses for his drinking behavior. On more than one occasion he insinuated that Mawzy's connections with other men have driven him to drink. In one letter he ranted, *...Some of them tried to tell me you and "Red Head" was going to get married in about three weeks. Can't explain...how I came to hear it but will see you in a few days and then will tell you all. I told the party that told me...that I knew it couldn't be so and that if it was that you had told a lie to me and that I would much rather the other fellow would have a liar for a wife than I... All that gossip made me feel blue and I got on a high spree Sat night and Sunday just to drive away the blues, but its all over with now and couldn't be helped and I know you will forgive me won't you...*

Add tried with all his might to make amends after being a bad boy again. The strain of their relationship became apparent to Mawzy's family. Poppy and Mommy Walker were concerned about Add's behavior and encouraged Mawzy to look elsewhere for a suitable relationship. He graveled in the following letter.

Dear Grace,
...Am worried mad and God knows what else. There is a thousand thoughts running through my mind... Dearie, I won't give you any advice this time... I may

be wrong ... because you have always been willing to believe what I tell you... I can change, join church and be a preacher if that could help but it wouldn't... I say about listening to your parents its all right some times but that's what I did and lost a good chance and perhaps it is the cause of me being wild today because I did things that I would have never done if they hadn't aggravated the life out of me... Just to be plain about things I'd turn the world down for you and all that is in it because I trust you but what you will do am unable to say.

Suppose that set over there is bound to pick for you. Wonder what kind of a saint he would be. I guess too nice for the sun to shine on but I stake my life he'd never be any better or truer to you than I have already been. And so far as me going out there to see those girls that's a lie. I wasn't outside of the store to speak to either one of them.... Now I am going to say one thing if you can't stand your treatment you don't half to because we will remedy that some way or the other and I believe it would only be worse if we had to stay away from each other. Am not going to try and write the rest but will reason it out with you if we are ever alone... Will come to see you again and decide upon something.

Write me soon and be a good girl.

Yours in trouble,

Add "the condemned"

P.S. Was the ever a perfect person that no one did not condemn?

After Mawzy completed her first year of teaching on Backus Mountain, she was offered a job at Springdale Elementary for the 1927-28 school year, contingent upon renewing her provisional teaching certificate. She discovered she could

Mawzy (far right) with classmates in Montgomery.

49

go to summer school at New River State College in Montgomery and take course-work to renew her certificate while also procuring additional high school credits. Being able to catch the motor car from Springdale to Meadow Creek, then join the main railroad line to Montgomery meant her transport was not an issue. So off to summer school she went.

Add was trying to change his ways again, … *Suppose I'd better write to you this morning although I expect I've got you mad and you won't appreciate my letter. I'm about half way in good humor this morning. My work aggravates me sometimes and then everything else just seems to go wrong and since I don't drink any seems like I just blow up for a day or two…*

He headed for Tennessee to work on a steel job and wrote back to let Mawzy know, …*haven't had anything to drink or any woman to hug since I left W Va…*

Being on the wagon didn't last. In a letter he sent while Mawzy was teaching school at Springdale he said, …*Never mind staying away from you until I come to see you and then come back and it seems like for a week or so that I am not satisfied at all just blue because I don't have you with me and if I go to studying why I sometimes get about half that is what makes me write like I do…*

When Add thought Mawzy was drifting away from the relationship, he played the tit for tat game, …*Well I've stayed away a long time and expect I could stay away longer but am realizing the outcome of it. I don't blame you in the least for wanting a date with someone. Its been so long since I was to see you but I can't see why that fellow had to pick the same time that I had thought I might come myself… I'll give the other fellow a chance and you one too. But I am going to make you a proposition. If I don't come and let the other fellow come then I won't get mad if you will let me go see a girl of mine…*

When I was in Virginia I met a girl down in East Radford. Didn't talk much to her but it seems as if I left some impression on her… Was over there today and they said that she had told them to tell me to come down to see her. Grace she is almost the very image of you. Blue eyes and brown hair. I guess that is one reason I took a liking to her. Now if you want to see that fellow guess I can go back to East Radford to see Bessie. Of course I'd rather not because it might develop into something that would put a wall between us and you know what that means… Or else perhaps I'll be your brother-in-law. Ha. Ha…Be a good baby and when in someone else's arms remember there has been another…

Add chased the buck as he shifted from one job to the next to prove himself a worthy breadwinner. He talked about working in several different coal mines where he sometimes lived with his parents and other times was in a boarding house. There were periods where he talked about loafing around, then he headed south for short-term carpentry and steel jobs. Some of the jobs only lasted a week, like one with Otis Elevator Company.

Small coal mining companies dotted the map everywhere in the area. As railroads expanded, boomtowns cropped up all over the place. Mining was hard, dangerous work. At that time there were no unions, no overtime, and no right to work laws. Add never knew what his hours would be or when he would be called into the mines to run coal. This necessitated the need to move from location to location to try to obtain steady hours.

Miners were paid by the ton for the coal they loaded in cars that were pulled out of the mine. If Add couldn't get work loading, he accepted a job cutting coal. This entailed working the night shift where he used a large saw-like machine to cut across the bottom of a wall of coal. The next step was to drill holes in the top of the wall where dynamite was detonated. This broke up the coal so it could be loaded by the miners on the morning shift. The hourly wage for coal cutting was a pittance.

Add was discouraged with cutting coal, ...*They are starting to work me another week. I guess the boss came around just before dinner and said I had better sleep this evening as I would have to work tonight. That means I'll have to work seventeen hours before I get any sleep but I don't mind that. Will just keep me from getting into any meanness because all I get done then is to work and sleep*...

And in another letter, ...*Am going to stop working at night the first of June. Its too hard for the money I get and then I can run as good as any of the rest of them and they promised the machine...so am going to work at day until then*...

Mawzy remained extremely focused on her education and teaching mission. She had steady hours, respectability, and a guaranteed income. This was hard on Add's ego because of his nomadic life. He had an overriding sense he may lose her to her career. Mawzy was getting pulled in two directions – education and teaching vs domestic life. This became apparent in Add's letters when she was a student and a teacher.

...*Not going to let you work if I can help myself. You have enough to do to go to school. Course it wouldn't be so bad if you would work like a person aught to but I know you. You won't do that*...

...*Grace you are always talking about me working hard sometimes but I'll have to tell you not to try to do so much. I know there is lots to do at home but don't try to teach school and do that work too cause I always want you to look pretty and if you work and break yourself down you can't. Of course I'd love you anyway*...

When Mawzy went to live with and work for the Trump family while in high school in Beckley, Add again let his feelings be known. ...*I don't much like the idea of you changing places for I know what you want to do is get some place*

51

where you can work and you'll just be like you always are. Want to work yourself to death...

During one of his coal mining stints he stressed his need to be the breadwinner, *...thought I'd better write to you tonight before I went for I never know when I'll get out when I go to work. Went in at six o'clock yesterday morning and got out at seven today... I can make good money if they run even if I do have to work a little hard and that was what men were made for. Women wasn't made for to work like men. They are more for beauty than anything else. That is why I don't want you to over work. I always want you to look pretty like you do now and it doesn't hurt me the way it would you...*

Add liked to tout his domestic skills. In one letter he noted, *...Suppose I shall have to close as I have to iron my shirt. Just bet you will laugh about that but I can iron and press my clothes as good as any woman. I really don't never need a woman anyway all I want one for is to have someone to love all time. Ha. Ha. ...*

In another he said, *...Suppose I might as well write you a line or so this morning as I have about run out of anything to do. Since I've got breakfast, washed the dishes. Swept the house and made up the bed and Lord knows what else...*

On many occasions he laid a guilt trip on Mawzy for not writing more often, *...I am tired and worried haven't got but one little letter from you this week and you said you were going to write to me again and I am still looking for that letter. Suppose you are getting too busy to write me...*

When hopping from coal mine to coal mine, in Nallen he agonized, *...I am wondering what happened. Haven't heard from you for a whole week. Sure would appreciate a line or two just to know what is wrong. Everything is wrong with me. Got the blues and everything else. Am leaving here today for good. Am going home for a day or so and might work awhile over there. If I just knew you would let me come I'd be over one day while I was off but you won't write me. Won't you please write and tell me what has gone wrong... So if you are offended in any way to be honest and square with me you will tell me. Now please darling write and tell me something. Would just love to see you. Write me if you will at Pittman. Will be there for five days...*

Three days later he continued to complain about no letter and then shortly after got two letters from Mawzy and realized it was the slow mail delivery service. All was forgiven until the next episode. Add's most scathing letter was written while Mawzy was going to summer school in Montgomery:

...Suppose I'd better write you a line although I'm all out of humor and expect I ought not write for I've just been thinking and my thoughts I expect would make you mad. Didn't hear from you until today. Suppose you think I aught to write my

fool head off to you and then you could write just when it suited you but I'm not going to. You have often told me you wouldn't write until you had a letter to answer so I'm going to do the same. It doesn't take all day to write and if things are like they used to be down there you don't have to go to the office so your excuse is too weak or in other words you have none...

Yet when the shoe was on the other foot, it was no big deal, *...Suppose I had better write to you before you declare it has been a year since I wrote you. The way I am working now makes it hard for me to write and get the letter out the same day. Go in about two o'clock at day and get out about eleven at night and then then the lights are off... Seems I'm always in a hurry...*

Mawzy and Add were engaged by the summer of 1927, which was apparent in one of his letters, *...You said something about your ring. Well if anything would happen which I don't see any chance for, you could keep it because I'll never get any girl another one...*

Ironically, in the same letter he still talked about other girls:

...You was talking about me going home with the girls from the dances. Are you ever going to get over the idea that I won't because I used to isn't saying I will again. How many have you saw me with or even heard of me being with in the last year... I've got more will power and respect for you than to start doing the things I once did. Now will that satisfy you. Am I going to have to say I am going to stop dancing. I would rather do that than to have you fretting...

By summer's end Mawzy had passed the certification exam. At age 19 she was ready to begin her second teaching job at her alma mater in the old two room schoolhouse that sat up on a hill two miles from the home place.

Add was madder than a hornet when Mawzy broke the news to him that she had accepted the Springdale teaching job. It was the same battle they had fought for the last two years. He wanted to get married sooner than later. Now they would have to wait yet another eight months before tying the knot, as Mawzy wouldn't be allowed to teach if married. His ego was bruised again. He wanted in the worst way to wear the pants in the family. After all that's how it was supposed to be. Add had an overriding sense he may lose Mawzy to her career. He wrote:

...I've been thinking about what you said about me waiting. Do you think you could wait as long as I have and still feel the same way? I've never felt but one way and that was I loved you and you only. Of course the first year I went with you I didn't give things any deep thought cause I was "care free happy go lucky" then and I've often wondered if that hasn't been a great hold back with you. You know I'm not now what I was then... I changed and now I'd love you only for a lifetime...

Though Mawzy loved him with all her heart, she had come too far to turn back now. She was driven and sometimes felt Add was holding her back from her dreams. Yet she was torn by the prevailing norm that her place was in the home, being married and raising a family. She struggled to figure out a way to make their relationship work.

Around that time Add was putting in quite a few hours in the coal mine where his dad worked. He reported:

…Have just got in and it is about ten. Talk about some one being tired but I am. I went the limit today. Made twelve dollars and was inside about thirteen hours. Had good luck or I would of still been in. Dad he's just raving. Said I was trying to over do things but I don't guess I am…

A few months later he indicated, *…I expect I shall be pretty busy as they are going to run five days this week and the boss said he wanted me to work night and day a little so that means nothing but work eat and sleep…*

Then a bit later, *…I haven't any buddie today. Sterlie went home yesterday morning and of course I wouldn't lay off. Have to work every day or at least I think I do. I about halfway suspect this week will be my last on this job. The boss and I can't agree and you know how I am. All fire when I am mad…*

Add finally resolved himself to the fact that marriage would be postponed again. Shortly before Mawzy's Springdale teaching job began, he wrote:

Dearest Grace,
Received your letter and was awful glad to hear from you. Was a little surprised to think that you dreaded writing to me. Dearie I am not going to talk harsh to you. Of course, sometimes you do things I don't like for you to do but I don't care this time. Whatever you do satisfies me. I like for you to go to school but darling if you want to teach school all right I'm am going to let you please yourself and I myself will do as you want me to. Now is that what you want me to say. I hope so. Am glad you are going to keep your promise. I was just afraid that if you went home to teach something would happen to discourage you. But as far as teaching for the money you needn't do that cause I figure I can make that myself if I do have to work hard that is if we take care of it which I think we will. Well baby hope you are satisfied with this letter…

Mawzy walked to Springdale school every day - rain, snow, or sunshine, hot or cold. She taught 25 students in grades one through four. A co-worker, Ellen Fleshman, taught grades five through eight.

Her siblings, Evie, Pansie and Earl had Mawzy as their teacher as did her future sister-in-law, Lucille. Two older siblings, Thelma and Lawrence, were under Ms. Fleshman's tutelage. Having Mawzy escort her brothers and sisters to school

Evie, Lawrence with Rover, and Thelma.

every day was a huge relief for Mommy Walker. All the family was happy to have her home once again, including Poppy.

Aunt Lucille said Mawzy was a strong disciplinarian. Students were not allowed up from their desks during class time. Lucille vividly remembered the time she got up to throw a piece of paper in the garbage can and was called out by Mawzy.

Plans for married life started to surface. One night that winter Add wrote from Lawton, near the Greenwood Coal Company where he was working:

... Think they are going to start up and run a little better. I hope so anyway. Got to work four days this week. I don't mind it so much as long as they do that well. I told them the other day I wished they would start up and run steady. Mr. Lawton said he guesses I would want him to build me a house. I told him yes. Said he would build me a four-room house in the spring over in Gentry Holler. Mr. Gwinn was asking me where you were. I told him. Wanted to know why we didn't get married. Said he didn't believe I could get you...

Mr. Lawton was an owner of the Greenwood Coal Company and Mr. Green was the company store manager.

Add made Mawzy's hope chest and wrote about the finishing touches, *...After so long a time I got that corner block for your cedar chest. Suppose you can glue it on can't you or are you good for anything except just to look at. Ha. Ha. ...*

He talked about a slow spell in the mines again, *...Working on the pickup here now. We only got to work 6 days last half. Bad for the month of March. That isn't much work but I did pretty well. Made $122.60. That isn't any money for me. Might be alright if I was married but single it takes money...*

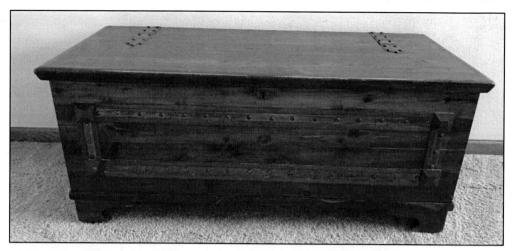

Add made the hope chest Mawzy treasured for decades.

Two weeks later he was very discouraged, ...*Will not get to work before Wednesday night or at least that is what kind of a notice has been posted that makes me a little sick and blue sometimes and then I just try and make the best of it but am not going to try this way of work very long...*

Mommy Walker was pregnant with twins and went into labor early. Eugene and Jennings were born prematurely on January 29, 1928 and both died that same day. On that day, Sister met her future husband, Dr. J. C. Jett, as he was the attending physician who pronounced the twins deceased. The family was terribly upset. Mawzy was glad she had been there to hold and care for both the little boys during their short life. The tears flowed as she sewed their tiny little burial gowns.

Add was sympathetic and loving in a letter written less than a week after the twins died. He expounded on religion and his potential baptism as he knew the importance the church held for Mawzy.

Received your letter yesterday which I was more than anxious to get... Sure was sorry that the babies died but you know things like that must happen. Often think of my little brother that died when he was a baby but it is always for some cause. One can never tell what God's plan is. We often have to think of that...

They said they are expecting a steady run here. Are running today for the first time for a week. I hope they will run steady for I would like to go to housekeeping sometime this summer... I suppose you are still thinking the same as you were. I hope so anyway for you know Grace I love you and you only or I wouldn't tell you ever thing like I do. Though I expect sometimes you think I don't care whether you are happy or not I do and I'm like you. Wouldn't be satisfied if I never get the chance and if we are not happy I'll be one of the worst beat men that ever walked.

I haven't heard from home for quite a while. I don't know what is wrong with them. They are always asking about you and mother said she would like to see you awfully well.

There is a revival meeting going on here. Has gone on for three weeks. Have gone myself what nights I didn't work and decided that I would change my ways... I've took a stand on the opposite to what I have been and only hope that I'll never turn back. That will seem strange to you but I'm in earnest this time. I thought if Stanley held his meeting out at Springdale if he baptizes anyone I'll just let him duck me under the water too. But you will have to stay at home so you can't laugh if it worked on me as deep as my confession did. I expect I'd shout as they said I did here...

...You never said anything about your mother. I suppose she is all right or at least I hope so. Give them all my love and kiss Jewell once for me...

With some of her teaching money, Mawzy bought a Kodak camera. In her hope chest was an old photo album chalked full of pictures she had taken of Add, friends, family, and the Springdale school students. Several photos were taken at the closing of the school year. A sense of pride was written on all faces – students, parents, and teachers alike.

Add knew taking school pictures was important to Mawzy and enjoyed being a part of it. Prior to the end of the school year he wrote, *...Grace got you 3 rolls of films at Meadow Creek today... Was afraid you wouldn't get yours and even if you do guess we can take more pictures some other time if there ever is another...*

The camera had such meaning for Mawzy she kept it in her hope chest long after it ceased to function, nestled among her other treasures.

By the time Mawzy finished teaching at Springdale for the year, Add had become more settled working for the Greenwood Coal Company. He wrote:

...I like my new boarding house fine. I like to stay in the bottom. It is so much handier to the store and office. But I'd much rather have you and a home of my own... Would be happier and am sure you would to... I'd love to hold you in my arms a few minutes before I went under the hills again.

He continued to discuss a timeline for marriage, *...Whatever you want to call me you can cause I don't think anyone would ever love you any better than I do. I believe we had better get married about the first of Sept anyway or before don't you...They are not going to say anything or even if they do it won't do them any good as for myself I rather be married than to be single.*

Mawzy's Springdale school class. Below, Mawzy at the end of the school year.

Just a few days later marriage was still heavy on his mind:

...Am deprived of the only thing I love and that is a beautiful pure and true woman or at least I think so and hope you never trust anyone but me with your love... I would just love to see you this evening. I'd never want you to slip from my arms... Darling when I am lonesome and blue you would be heaven to me. I've always heard that the best gold lays at the end of the hardest trails so our married life aught to be happy as much trouble as we have gone through in order that we may sometime be as one and that can't be many more months off...

"Yet, taught by time my heart has learned to glow,
For others' good and melt at other's woe."

Mawzy's senior motto, placed next to her picture
in the 1929 Echo yearbook.
The quote by Homer was apropos of her spirit

Woodrow Wilson High School

Woodrow Wilson High

Mawzy could have used a break from teaching and her studies, but she warmed to the idea of going to summer school again. Doing this would allow her to obtain the credits needed to enter high school as a senior that fall.

Add provided encouragement and indicated he might even pursue some training for himself. He wrote, *...I'd believe if I were you I'd go to school but if you would rather have a rest do that but schooling won't never hurt you but darling don't try to take up only just what subjects you can get along with easy. I'd love awful well to see you through school. I may take three months in mining management myself if I can only make papers this summer and I'm putting in about all of my spare time in it. I shall be happy then. There will come another day when I shall be a lot happier and that is when we are married...*

Add followed through on his training. Mawzy received a letter the summer of 1928 from Holley Hotel in Charleston, West Virginia. *...I sure have had a time today believe me the exam wasn't very long but as usual some little and fool questions a person never would of thought of I answered wrong. So chances are about ten to one against me I expect but if they are I'm not going to stop trying my luck. My examiner this morning was Mr. Foster and he knew dad. Just looked me over and said kid where did you blow from... He helped me out and told me to answer all my questions short and brief as that was best... Then had the oral test which I was afraid of but as luck would have it was only asked four questions which I knew... Just have an air map for tomorrow which is the most important and am*

61

told it is on the plan of a shaft... Have changed hotels as this one is a little closer to the place and some of the fellows here I got half acquainted with... The other hotel wasn't lively enough for me. Ha. Ha. Guess I will go back with some of the boys from Layland in the car tomorrow evening... Hope I'll get to come over on Sunday.

In her early high school years Mawzy attended Beckley High. During the two years she taught on Backus Mountain and in Springdale, a new Beckley school was built and renamed Woodrow Wilson High School. Mawzy followed its progress in *The Raleigh Register*, from bond issue news to site selection and through subsequent construction to renaming. She wanted to take her summer coursework here. She found employment with a family for room and board at 123 Granville Avenue. It was a three mile walk to and from school. She had set aside money while teaching, but additional employment gave her the comfort needed to see her through graduation.

After summer school began Add wrote, ... *Don't study to hard at school and take life a little easy cause too much isn't good for you and I wouldn't want to see you sick or looking bad for anything in the world...* And two weeks later, ... *Received your letter and sure was glad to hear from you and glad you are getting along good at school. Of course you always make good or at least it seemed that way...*

When summer school was over, Mawzy headed back to Poppy and Mommy's place for a short break. Meadow Bridge, only four miles from the home place, built a high school in 1926 but it burned down a year later. Whether it would reopen by the fall of 1928 was uncertain. Since Mawzy had lived and gone to school in Beckley in the past, this was where she wanted to finish her high school education. Being a larger school, she felt it had more to offer. The family on Granville Avenue appreciated her dedication and was glad to see her return that fall. Finally, at almost 22 years of age, Mawzy entered the new school as a senior.

Because of the Meadow Bridge High School fire, Sister decided, with Mommy and Poppy's blessing, to head to Woodrow Wilson High as well. She also boarded at the Granville Avenue home where she and Mawzy shared a room. With Sister being the wild child, Mommy knew Mawzy would keep watch over her and be a good influence. Sister enrolled as a junior.

When Add found out Sister was going to Beckley his comment was, ...*I'll bet it will tickle Sis to get to come over there to school but she might have a harder time than she would at home...*

Later he wrote, ...*When will you have to start to school? Before long though I suppose you will be better satisfied this winter than you have been by Sister going and I'm not going to be so far away. Am going to Sprague or Raleigh about the 15th or first of October then I'll see you real often too often for your good perhaps. Ha. Ha. ...*

It was the roaring '20s and Beckley was a bustling town. It was southern West Virginia's main retail hub as coal mining became more prominent in the area.

Mawzy was caught up in the excitement of her senior year as she headed down the halls of Woodrow Wilson High that fall. A class ring was ordered, senior pictures scheduled, a personal senior motto pondered, and club selections made.

The very first item I uncovered in Mawzy's hope chest that piqued my curiosity was a 5 x 7 ledger. On the front cover it read *Personal Account Book*, Grace Walker, Woodrow Wilson High School. It was a Home Economics class assignment to journal her expenses and provided an incredible amount of insight into her life that year.

One of the ledger entries was for club dues, which totaled $0.90. In the *Echo* yearbook Mawzy was pictured with members of the two clubs she joined - The Home Economics Club and The Social Service Club.

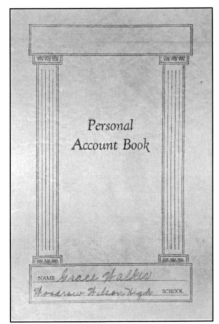

The Home Economics club goals, as outlined in the yearbook, were: *To form a connecting link between home and school. To train young women to be active and efficient useful members and leaders in home and community life.* Meetings were held weekly. As Mawzy entered the room for the first club meeting she heard someone calling her name. It was Helen Trump, the little girl she had taken care of in her earlier school years. Mawzy gave her a big hug and once again pulled Helen, now a freshman, under her wing. They worked together on three projects that year - the planning and preparation for a food sale and bazaar; studying noted artists and their works and exploring famous women connected with Home Economics.

The Social Service Club was considered one

Above, Mawzy's ledger; left, Home Economics Club pic in Echo *yearbook. Mawzy is in the second row, second from left.*

63

Social Service Club photograph from the Echo *yearbook. Mawzy is in the third row, far right.*

of the most outstanding clubs of the high school. In affiliation with the Associated Charities, a local organization, club members helped with Thanksgiving and Christmas relief work.

Mawzy's giving nature was strengthened by the club and was reflected in her ledger where she documented donations to the Puerto Rico Disaster fund for hurricane victims, Red Cross Christmas Seals, and church. Several Christmas gifts were purchased in December. The most expensive purchase, a billfold and socks for Add, totaled $5.85. She also bought Valentines, cards, and a birthday present for sister Jewell.

Expenses attributed to being a senior were itemized in Mawzy's ledger throughout the year.

$6.50	class ring
2.50	annual picture
0.50	annual
2.20	cap and gown
6.40	graduation announcements and calling cards

Mawzy's senior picture

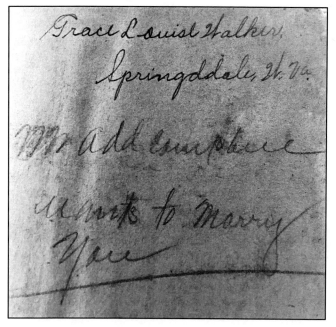

Book purchases were entered as well. I found three of the high school books she saved – *Ideas and Forms in English and American Literature, History of the United States of America,* and *Early European Civilization.*

Inside the front cover of the third book Mawzy wrote, Grace Louise Walker, Springdale, WV. Below that Add had written *Wm. Add Campbell wants to marry you.*

Jean Porter, Mawzy's English teacher, was outstanding. The Beckley *Images of America* book noted: *Those who were fortunate enough to have Jean Porter for English were definitely among the high achievers. She taught her students to use their own minds and think for themselves. Educators of decades past were not bound by federal regulations...* Jean was a role model for Mawzy, who emulated Jean's creativity and enthusiasm for education for the rest of her life.

Mawzy covered all her expenses for the year. Her food was not a big-ticket item as the family with whom she boarded allowed her to pack lunches from their food supply. She prepared the evening meals and ate with the family. So, food expenditures were for incidentals like candy and fruit.

Transportation was not a big expense either as she walked almost everywhere she went. She only took the train three times, to get to school initially and on a round trip home over the Christmas holiday. Each train fare was $1.50. On two occasions, she took a taxi – one fare was $0.25 an the other $0.85. She likely hailed a cab due to inclement weather or after a shopping trip if her purchases were too cumbersome for the walk back to her boarding house.

Clothing was one of Mawzy's major expenses, totaling $90.36 for the school year. Not only was she buying for her senior picture and graduation but also for her wedding. For all three events, salon visits were made to get a Marcell, a popular hair styling technique used to make wavy curls.

"Quality only stings once" was an adage Mawzy learned in grade school. A candy company promoted various prizes for students who sold a certain quantity of their product. Mawzy worked hard at her sales as she was eyeing a fancy, shiny pair of shoes for her prize. After achieving her goal, she anxiously awaited their arrival and was excited as she opened her package. The shoes were beautiful. She put them on the next morning for school. Before the day was over, they crumbled as the soles were made of cardboard.

Her most expensive clothing item was a coat for $34.95 which was purchased the beginning of November. The weather had turned dreadfully cold around Halloween. Because of her long walk to and from school she considered a good, warm coat a necessity. Add was complaining about the weather in a letter he wrote around that time, …*It sure is cold over here. The ground was white with frost this morning. When we came in from work I had on all kind of clothes and then like to froze to tender. Ha. Ha.*

Overall, Mawzy was frugal. On four separate occasions she recorded shoe repair costs at under $1.00 each. All that walking took its toll. She was a patron of the Service Shoe Repair Company on Neville Street, below the Lyric Theatre, as they did their work while she waited. Private waiting booths were offered so she took her shoes there after school and did homework in a booth while repairs were completed.

The shoe shop was near Klaus Office Equipment Company which stocked school supplies. Sometimes she picked up supplies while her shoes were getting soled. Many purchases were recorded in her ledger for tablets, paper, ink, and pen points.

It was a Presidential election year and in Add's letters it became apparent their political viewpoints were at odds. After Herbert Hoover was elected, Add wrote, …*Suppose your president takes his seat today but he'll never be mine...*" Though she was becoming more politically savvy, Mawzy was still influenced by Poppy Walker, a staunch Republican.

One of her journal entries was the purchase of a lyceum ticket for $0.50 on October 31. Lyceums were forums where lecturers could expound their wisdom to those in attendance. The Beckley lyceum was likely held in the Woodrow Wilson High auditorium as the *Echo* yearbook indicated juniors and seniors sold tickets. It may have been a political debate as the election was less than two weeks away. Al Smith, a Democrat and New York governor at the time, was running for President and may have been one of the speakers. Members of the Southern Women's National Democratic Organization orchestrated campaign stops for Al, as he was making an appeal to women voters. West Virginia was included in their circuit. Shortly after the event, Al placed a full-page ad in *The Raleigh Register* newspaper, which targeted

	General Account							General Account								
		INCOME				EXPENDITURES										
DATE	ITEMIZATION	Earnings	Gifts and Allowance	Total	Savings	Food	Clothes	Education	Pleasure	Gifts and Donations	Car Fare	Misc.	Total	Cash on Hand
	Balance Forward														
Dec. 1	Marcelle, Blade											.85	.85	
Dec. 3	Ribbon & Book, towel					.10				.55			.65	
Dec. 5	Red Cross Xmas seals									.10			.10	
Dec. 6	Tablet					.10							.10	
Dec. 7	Beads											.25	.25	
Dec. 8	Candy											.10	.10	
Dec. 10	Pictures .75, Brassiere & apples					.10 .05	.85					3.75	4.65	
Dec. 11	Bill Glass 5.20, socks .65									5.85			5.85	
Dec. 12	Hkf, Handkerchief & Party funds									.30			.30	
Dec. 13	Stamps, egg & sandwich mat									.33	.20		.53	
Dec. 14	Club, gluent thread									.20			.35	
Dec. 15	Dress, pumps, hose & gloves					.15	21.79						21.79	
Dec. 17	Sugar, chocolate & grapes					1.11							1.11	
Dec. 18	Book, brassiere & ball					.17	.35			.60			.95	
Dec. 19	Rain coat & lunch										1.44		1.71	
Totals Forward			1.68	22.99	.20					2.18	1.44	5.79	39.28	XXXX

women voters. The main headline read, *WOMEN! You Who Think for Yourselves, Vote for Yourselves, Elect Alfred E. Smith.*

That fall Add broached the subject of eloping over Mawzy's Christmas break. He didn't want to wait until the school year was over. He felt he had waited long enough. In a melancholy letter two months before the break he wrote, ...*Its been a few years of rough and tumble for me and when I think of you sometimes I wonder whether I'm right by you or not on the account of my life. Of course you are the only one that knows about my inside life which I have lived wrong and high and if it had of not been for you perhaps I would have been in a worse state of condition and rambling this wide world over but you have always been the turning of me. And again I'm just past my romantic days of life. Started young and now I've seen enough of romance. I've often thought that probably marriage would bring back more real happiness than anything else while my money is the only thing to give me any happiness now and it's a curse to me more than moral joy... But don't think of me Grace. Ask yourself this one question and be honest. Could I be satisfied with him and if you can I'm going to because you are a woman and no trash like the most of the rest and one I would be proud of...*

Mawzy finally agreed so they laid their plan to travel to Catlettsburg, Kentucky on December 26, 1928 to wed. On December 15, Mawzy went shopping for her wedding ensemble - a dress, pumps, hose, a brassier, bloomers and gloves totaling $23.69. On December 19 she took the train back to the home place for her semester break.

Certificate of Person Performing Marriage Ceremony
TO BE DELIVERED TO PARTIES MARRIED

No. 105

I, W.C. Pierce, pastor
of the Catlettsburg Baptist Church, or religious order of that name,
do certify that on the 26ᵗʰ day of Dec 192⁵
at Catlettsburg Kentucky, under authority of a
license issued by J. Jacreti, Clerk of County Court of Boyd
County (or City), State of Kentucky, dated the 26ᵗʰ day of Dec 192⁵ united
William A. Campbell and Grace Louise Walker
Husband and his Wife, in the presence of Herbert McGuire
and Opal McGuire
Given under my hand, this 26ᵗʰ day of Dec 192⁵

W.C. Pierce
Person Performing Ceremony, Sign Here

Pastor 1st Baptist Ch
Title of Office

Newlyweds

Christmas with the family was important to Mawzy so holidays were celebrated as usual. Neither of their families were made aware of wedding plans. Add feared Poppy and Mommy Walker would attempt to derail his scheme.

Early the morning of December 26, Add drove to Springdale, Mawzy slipped out of the house and off they went for the 150-mile trek across the West Virginia boarder to Catlettsburg. Mawzy was adamant about being married by a minister so W.C. Pierce, pastor of the Catlettsburg Baptist Church, conducted the ceremony. They had a short honeymoon in Kentucky.

Sister spilled the beans on Mawzy's disappearance, though no one was surprised. When they returned from Catlettsburg, Add dropped Mawzy off at the home place. He didn't go in and used the excuse that he didn't feel well and had to get back to Lawton for work the next day.

Mawzy quietly entered the house so as not to draw attention, but Poppy saw Add drop her off and waited for her by the front door.

"What the hell have you gone and done now?" Poppy mouthed off. "I'll swear. I dress ya up like a butterfly and the first thing ya do is go and land on a horse turd."

Mommy walked into living room just as Poppy stomped out. She could see the tears ready to spill so she took Mawzy into her arms.

"Pay him no mind," she whispered. "Ya know how he can be. I'm happy for ya."

Before Mawzy agreed to elope, she made it crystal clear she would finish her schooling. On January 1 she took the train back to Beckley to begin the second semester of her senior year. Both she and Add caught a cold on their honeymoon. Add wrote about his lingering sickness. In Mawzy's journal were entries for the purchase of cough syrup, salve, pills, and Vaseline.

Add's letters after marriage were fewer and further between and less poignant, but the dynamics of the relationship had not changed. Mawzy was still not under his thumb. On January 2, he wrote:

Dear Grace,

Am wondering what you are doing this old snowy day. Have just gotten up and eat my breakfast. Guess you have gotten started back to school. Hope you are satisfied. I miss you a whole lot but I guess that is better owing to conditions isn't it darling.

I would liked to have heard what they had to say to you at home when you went back.

Have you ever decided whether you are married yet. I can't notice no whole lot of difference yet but maybe it will take effect in a couple of years. Ha. Ha....
Your loving husband,
Add

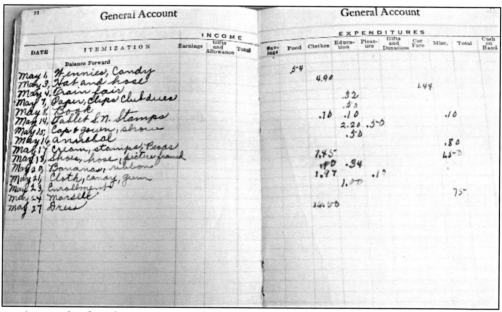

A month after they were married, in frustration, Add was back to his old ways. Though getting his way about their marriage, he wasn't happy they were still apart. From Lawton where he continued mining for the Greenwood Coal Company he wrote, ...*My dearest loving wife, isn't that some sign to start a letter with. Well anyhow I wanted to just see how such words would look on white paper... I got in last night at 9:30. There wasn't but seven men out and I don't think any of them wanted to work. Well I came home and changed clothes and went to the bottom to see part of the dance.*

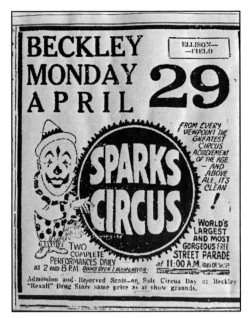

I expect you will kill me for that but I didn't do anything that would hurt you any. I overheard some girl telling another one that I didn't seem myself. The other one said oh he's married and believe me she looked me over and then said to the other one that it was a shame for a darn good man running himself to the dogs over some one woman. I just almost laughed myself to death over that cause darling I know I have one of the sweetest of all women. Don't scold me too much for going to that dance...

The last letter he wrote, on March 6, 1929, reflected his being anxious to move forward with their life together. They were still waiting for the Greenwood Coal Company to build their house. He said, *...Don't think they have started our house yet but the weather is too bad now but they say they are going to build it right away. I hope so anyway before you take a fit. Ha. Ha. ...*

By spring, the new talking picture shows were all the rage. Sister always tried to get Mawzy to lighten up and take life a little less seriously.

"Come on ol' married woman," Sister persuaded. "Put those books down and let's go see us a show. I've heard the new talkie shows are somethin' else. It's only a fifteen-minute walk to the Lyric Theatre down on Neville Street."

"Well, I suppose I could," Mawzy replied. "I'm caught up with my homework for tomorrow. How 'bout you?"

Mawzy grabbed *The Raleigh Register* and found the Lyric ad. It read - *Warner Brothers Vitaphone Talking Pictures, The First All Talking Picture Ever Shown in Beckley. SEE AND HEAR. Warner Bros. present "ON TRIAL" Admission Prices - Adults 50 cents.* There was even a separate article in the paper about "talkies" making their way to Beckley. She was so enlivened with the experience, she and Add went to a "talkie" a few weeks later.

Mawzy was having fun. Even bought a ticket for $1.25 to the Sparks Circus on April 29. On the promotional flyers it was touted as *FROM EVERY VIEWPOINT THE GREATEST CIRCUS ACHIEVEMENT OF THE AGE – AND ABOVE ALL, IT'S CLEAN!* Mawzy was on the cusp of accomplishing her dream of a high school education and beginning a life together with her husband. It was time to celebrate.

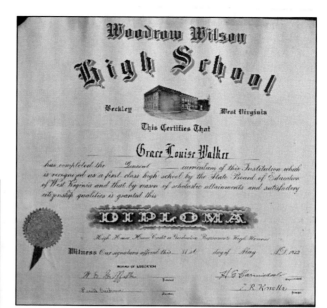

Mawzy in her graduation finery, along with mementoes from the big day she cherished for years.

Finally, the big day arrived. Mawzy was graduating with High Honor from Woodrow Wilson High School. The exercises were held at 8:00 p.m. on Friday, May 31, 1929.

The Honor System was explained in the program.

> *Honors are based upon four standards:*
> 1.   *Scholarship*
> 2.   *Attendance*
> 3.   *Student Activities*
> 4.   *General School Citizenship*
>
> *For High Honor the student must be in the upper fourth of class scholastically, have no unexcused absence or tardies, and must have earned 18 points for student activities and General School Citizenship*

There were 98 students who graduated that day. Mawzy was one of the top 18 students in her class.

She stored her graduation announcement, calling card, and the graduation program in her hope chest, as they commemorated another milestone.

Add attended graduation. After the ceremony was over, he picked Mawzy up and gave her a big hug, as she clutched her diploma, rolled up and tied like a scroll.

"Finally, we'll be starting our life together in Gentry Holler," he said, grinning from ear to ear. "Let's get on home."

The past two years of Mawzy's life had been mostly sunny. They may have been the best two years of her life - teaching at her alma mater; graduating from high school; getting married; enjoying the fruits of her labor; feeling the exuberance of the times. As she headed toward her new life, little did she know heavy clouds were starting to roll in. By the end of the year, the Great Depression was upon the country.

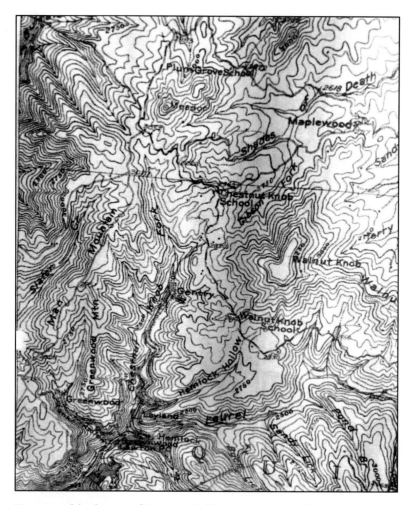

**Topographical map of Gentry Holler and surroundings by I.C.
White, state geologist.**

The lot of the miner,
At best is quite hard,
We work for good money,
Get paid with a card;
We scarcely can live,
And not a cent more,
Since we're paid off in [scrip]
On the company store.

Those great coal monopolies
Are growing apace,
They are making their millions
By grinding our face;
Unto their high prices
The people pay toll,
While they pay fifty cents
For mining their coal…

**Taken from The Company Store, *a poem by Isaac Hanna, published in the*
United Mine Worker's Journal, *May 23, 1895***

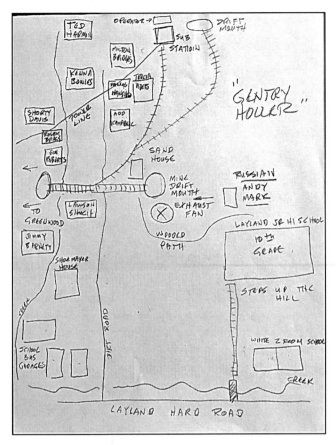

Map of Gentry Holler drawn by Dale Bridges.

Gentry Holler

The house Gentry Holler mine owner, Joe Lawton, promised to build for Add and Mawzy was not ready. They began their married life together with Add's sister and family - Mary, Dallas and baby Dorothy and his father, W.L. Quarters were tight in the tiny, three room, L-shaped company owned house.

Though surrounded by the coal industry all her life, Mawzy had never lived in a coal mining camp. Although Poppy started in mining, logging and farming became his main livelihoods.

Timber was the first natural resource extracted from Gentry Holler, followed by coal. Poppy Walker probably worked there as Mawzy's birth certificate shows she was born in Gentry. In 1915 Gentry was renamed Layland when the New River and Pocahontas Coal Company took over the area. The remains of the old Gentry sawmill sat up on the hill above the Campbell household by the time Mawzy moved there. The sawdust pile became a playground for many a kid.

Ironically, my mother's third husband, Dale Bridges, not only grew up in Gentry Holler, but later lived in that same three-room house when he was a child.

With crowded living conditions, it was fortunate Mawzy and her sister-in-law, Mary, got along so famously. Mawzy was no stranger to hard work and Mary appreciated her help and the company of another woman. Mawzy grew fond of baby Dorothy and began longing for a child of her own.

Greenwood Coal Company operated two mines in the area – Greenwood and Gentry Holler and was near several other mining companies. The rich New River Coal Field, at its peak, had at least 82 coal mining towns within a 50-mile radius. There was a four-foot coal seam just below the surface all along Laurel Creek.

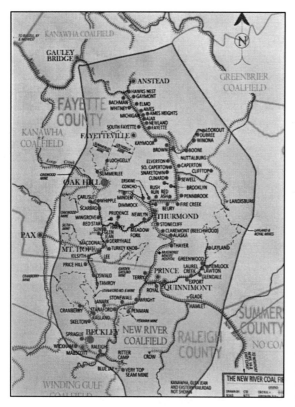

New River Coal Field map; below, abandoned coal mine manager's home in Layland.

The Greenwood coal camp housed around 50 miners and sat on the C & O Railway line. Two miles from there and up a dirt road sandwiched in one of many crevices between Backus and Greenwood mountains was Gentry Holler. It was a camp of less than 20 miners. Two small creeks running through the community were usually more like swamps than flowing water.

Mr. Lawton lived near the Greenwood mines as did the mine superintendent, Mr. A.C. Prince. The towns of Lawton and Prince are named after their families. Their homes were large with all the modern conveniences of the time and were well appointed. Mr. Prince even had a tennis court in his back yard. They weren't always present at the Gentry Holler mines, so they depended on Edgar Archer, Gentry's fire boss, to run a tight ship. The company store for both camps was near the Greenwood mine and was where the company doctor, Dr. Egbert Crank, had his office. Goods for the company store were brought in by train and dropped off at the Brownwood Depot. Fresh fruit and vegetables or milk were seldom among the deliveries.

Electricity was wired in the company houses

76

Former machine shed and bath house in Layland.

for lighting only and consisted of a dimly illuminated bulb hanging from a cord in the ceiling of each room. When needed, heat filtered in from two fireplaces fueled by coal - one for the kitchen/living area and one for the sleeping area. The cook stove was also heated by coal. The miners labored hard to remove coal from the ground, yet the coal company still charged for its use in their homes.

The houses had no running water. Water for drinking, bathing, cooking, and washing clothes was hauled from a natural spring about 75 yards up the hill by the substation. Mawzy made many a trip up that hill to fill buckets with water. When Add came home from the mines, Mawzy heated water on the stove for his bath which he took in a tub behind the cook stove for privacy. Some of the larger mining camps had a bath house, but not Gentry Holler.

Extra buckets of water were carried on Sunday so clothes could be washed on Monday. Laundry day required the use of a washboard and Colgate's brown Octagon soap cakes.

Each family had their own outhouse, placed about 25 feet from the main house. A deep hole was dug in the ground and the outhouse was placed over the top of it. About every two years, when the hole was full, a black man called a honey dipper was hired to dig another hole beside the outhouse and transfer the sewage there.

Coal mining companies controlled the miners and their lives. Home ownership was not an option. Rent was charged. Each company had its own currency, called scrip, which was seldom interchangeable. The company name was imprinted on hole punched coins. The hole was uniquely shaped to make the scrip more distinguishable.

Greenwood Coal Company had a horseshoe-shaped hole in their scrip coins.

Mawzy helped Mary expand her garden plot. With Add's blessing she also bought a few chickens, a pig, and a dairy cow. The more self-sufficient the miner's family was, the less dependent they were on the company store's inflated prices. Cows were always roaming free in Gentry Holler. They liked to go into the drift mouth of the mine where it was cooler and bug free in the summer and warmer in the winter. Originally the job of mules, small electric motor cars were used to pull coal out of the mines. One day miner John Russell accidentally killed a few cows and injured others in the drift mouth as he was motoring out.

Squirrel hunting was big in the hills. Add reminded Mawzy he could supplement their meat supply with a squirrel or two. He read to her from Beckley's September 25, 1932 *Raleigh Register* newspaper:

Squirrel hunters of West Virginia have ample cause for rejoicing and are to be excused for their unusual display of enthusiasm in making preparations for the opening day of this favorite sport for according to Edward Cooper, Jr., chairman of the game, fish and forestry commission, squirrels are more plentiful this year than they have been for many years... Statements from game protectors show that as many as 15 squirrels have been counted in single trees, while other reports show some 300 of the little animals were seen in a day.

J. F. Gwinn was the company store manager and played a large role in budgeting the family's income. An accounting system was developed for each miner. Add's pay and the coal company's charges for a two-week period were likely similar to the 1934 Raleigh County Lillybrook Coal Company itemizations below.

Earnings	
$43.01	112 tons coal @$0.38 per ton
2.48	5 hours @ $0.495 per hour
4.13	59 hours @ $0.07 per hour
$49.62	

Tonnage was tracked for each miner via a brass coin stamped with the miner's number. Wire was strung through a hole in the top of the coin so it could be hooked to each coal car the miner loaded. Once at the tipple, the coal was weighed and registered to the miner's number. Miners always headed to work with a pocket full of these coins, called checks.

Hourly wages were likely paid for removing rock which obscured a coal seam. There were other jobs paying an hourly rate, such as cutting coal which Add wrote about in his letters to Mawzy. This pay reflects less than a full two-week work schedule.

Charges	
$22.00	scrip
4.00	rent
0.21	lights
2.00	coal
0.75	doctor
0.50	hospital
0.90	insurance
0.72	lamps
2.00	transfers
0.56	docks
$33.64	

The scrip charge was the balance due the coal company from credit at the company store. After deductions, any remaining income was paid in scrip to be used exclusively at the mine's company store. It was a monopoly, so prices of goods were usually higher than if purchased elsewhere. Even if other shopping options were available, the miner and his family were expected to shop at the company store. Because of the credit line, there was often no leftover income, thus owing one's "soul to the company store."

A fee was assessed each pay period for Dr. Crank and the miner's hospital. McKendree Hospital, the closest for the families in Gentry Holler, was originally called the Miner's Hospital No. 2. Aunt Sister worked as a nurse at McKendree for a time.

Being a small camp, Gentry Holler was a tight knit community with no shortage of characters.

John Baransky was the Polish cobbler who not only repaired shoes but also made belts and brushes. He had gold teeth and drove a rumble seat car. His company house and shop were near the main road that intersected with the dirt road to Gentry Holler. The school sat on the hill above his place. Some of the kids, on their way home from school, started throwing rocks at his house. First, he put up a mesh net to deter window breakage and other damage. When that didn't help, he got his gun out and started shooting. No one messed with John after that.

The errant kids found something else to occupy their spare time. Fist fights were common. The ringleader hired out his bullying services.

"He charged 5 cents for a callin'," Dale Bridges remembered. "For this fee he would verbally abuse the designated target. For 10 cents he would beat the shit out of some other kid right there on the ground. He called that a whoopin'."

Andy Mark was a Russian who lived alone in a shanty between the drift mouth and the exhaust fan for the mines. He had a huge, fluffy white cat to keep him company and maintained an impeccable terraced garden. He paid the boys in the community to go pick blackberries for him so he could make wine. He drank the wine with his buddy, played his fiddle and sang off key in Russian. He was a track man. He built underground railroad tracks to aid in the transport of coal. About every 50 feet off the main track, each miner worked in their own space, so they needed a track for the movement of their loaded coal cars. The miner's coal car would then connect with a string of other cars on their way to the tipple where they were dumped into main railroad cars for transport.

Dale's dad, Milton Bridges, was a bookie on the side for the numbers racket. Winning numbers were tied to the volume of trading on three national stock market exchanges. The market report in the following day's newspaper would be used to determine the winners for the previous day. The numbers selected coordinated with the seventh digit of the number of shares traded. Bets were taken for any day of the week markets were open. To place a bet, three numbers between 1 and 9 were selected. For a penny bet, the winners would get $5.00. On weekends, Milton would send his sons to colored town to collect the bets.

Dale was one of the collectors. He recalled his dad getting 20% of the take. The "Teaser" ran the money from the Layland area to the "Clown" in Beckley. From there no one was exactly sure where it went. Miners took the numbers racket seriously. If you could win $5 with a penny then $1 could get you $500. That the odds were not in their favor didn't matter. It gave them hope. Getting out from under the company store was paramount. Most families had access to *Aunt Sally's Policy Players Dream Book,* originally published in 1889. The book was designed to help gamblers determine their lucky numbers. Numbers would be given for certain dreams. The book gave a "true interpretation of dreams" as an extra bonus. Other methods of selecting lucky numbers were outlined.

Edgar, the fire boss, didn't load coal. His house was a little nicer and larger than the miners' homes. Water was piped in and the family had a flush toilet which dumped into the creek. They also had central electric heating. Edgar was seldom seen without a chew of tobacco in his jaw or a big cigar hanging out of his mouth. He drove a big car with side panels. He was obviously higher up in the pecking order. "His boys were meaner than stripped ass snakes," Dale recalled. "Always in trouble. I'm almost positive they shot my dog and word had it they killed the shoemaker's cow."

At the beginning of Mawzy's marriage, the three men of the Campbell household had steady work. Dallas and Add headed into the mines at all hours of the day and night, depending on their shift. Add's father manned the electrical substation, a stone building which housed the power for the mines. This was a relatively easy job, so was often given to older miners.

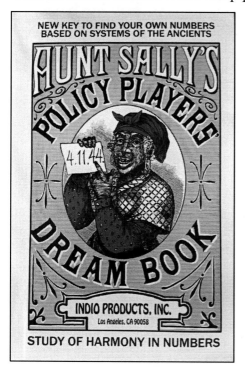

NEW KEY TO FIND YOUR OWN NUMBERS
BASED ON SYSTEMS OF THE ANCIENTS

AUNT SALLY'S
POLICY PLAYERS

4.11.44

DREAM BOOK

INDIO PRODUCTS, INC.
Los Angeles, CA 90058

STUDY OF HARMONY IN NUMBERS

But by late October 1929 the Dow Jones industrial stock market index had fallen by 35% and marked the beginning of the Great Depression. Any sense of stability quickly faded. Prior to that point coal production had been at its highest level. As demand dropped so did prices. The Depression's effect on the coal mining industry was felt almost immediately. It was a tough era for miners as the fight for unions was overlaid on the shoulders of the Depression. They were struggling before the Depression so some would say they didn't have as far to fall.

Though taking her role as a new wife seriously, teaching was still on Mawzy's mind. She decided to sit for the teacher's certification exam in July. Her plea to Add was that she would have the certification in her hip pocket if a teaching opportunity presented itself. But deep down inside she sensed a change coming.

The Gentry Holler mines started shutting down for a few days here and there. Add never knew what his schedule or pay would be. Two families living under one roof helped with the expenses and Mawzy had a bit of money left from her previous teaching job which was used in a pinch.

Add came in from his shift one day in the late spring of 1930 with a wide grin on his face. He gave Mawzy a hug and told her their house was finally ready and that Mr. Lawton had given permission for them to move. Mawzy was so excited she danced a little jig around the room. She told him the extra space was going to be needed as she was pregnant and due with their first child in six months. It was Add's turn to dance a jig. Finally, they could have a home of their own with room for the family's expansion.

Unlike most of the other company houses, their new house was square and had four rooms. Mawzy pulled all the embroidered towels and pillowcases, crocheted doilies, and dishware from her hope chest. The quilt and bed linens had already been used. Both their families gave them a few pieces of furniture to get them started. A few remaining pieces were purchased from the company store. The hope chest became their bedroom trunk.

Not long after Mawzy and Add moved into their new house, word traveled fast that a new supply of pure 180 proof moonshine had been hauled up from Virginia in souped up cars with extra springs to hold the weight. Add didn't think it would do any harm to get a pint or two. He came home intoxicated and an argument ensued. Mine management patrolled the property periodically and just happened to overhear the conflict. Mawzy was reprimanded the next day and was told her job was to keep peace in the family. Add was also told to watch his drinking.

The next six years of Mawzy's life were a whirlwind. She continued to pursue her education. She was listed as a college Freshman in the 1930 New River State College yearbook. Teacher's certification requirements were likely piggybacked with college course work. She kept four English essays in her hope chest dated the fall of 1929 through the early winter of 1930. *(See Appendix)*

Eleanor was born at the McKendree Hospital two days before Thanksgiving in 1930. Dr. Crank was on holiday leave so home delivery was not an option. By the time Eleanor was ready to be placed in the hospital nursery, the last bassinet had just been filled by a little black baby boy. The staff quickly improvised and converted a dynamite box into a bassinet. The family joked that this beginning was "what made Eleanor so feisty."

Once back home in Gentry Holler, Mawzy's energy shifted to the never-ending task of being a new mother while still keeping the household running.

As Add's work became more and more sporadic, finances became tighter. Local news reported that coal production had dropped by 26% since the beginning of the Depression. Mr. Lawton knew of Mawzy's teaching background. He approached her the summer of 1931 about teaching in the one room schoolhouse in the Laurel Smokeless Coal mining camp located in Kathryn. This mine was also owned by the Lawton family.

Mawzy and Add talked it over. Mawzy was torn in two directions. Add was not keen on the idea as he had concerns about Eleanor's care and felt Mawzy working would tarnish his role as the family's breadwinner. Mawzy reminded him Eleanor was another mouth to feed and that his drinking, gambling, and Aunt Sally's dream book were not filling the family coffers.

Trecia Ayers and her family were next door neighbors. She and Mawzy became best of friends. Trecia and her husband Beury often invited Add and Mawzy over to listen to their battery-operated radio. Sundays in the summer they also went on outings to coal camp baseball games, which were in their heyday. The Gentry Holler camp was too small for its own team, but they walked up through the woods to watch Layland's coal camp team play. Leagues were well-established and good baseball players were known to get better mining jobs. A few of the miners even went on to play major league baseball.

Mawzy and Trecia went to church together. Services were held in the school building, as the church had recently burned down. Trecia was Mawzy's confidant so one day after church Mawzy talked with her about her teaching dilemma. Trecia offered to watch Eleanor while Mawzy worked. Four of her five kids were school age so with only one at home during the day adding another was

Mawzy at home in Gentry Holler.

manageable. Finances were tight for Trecia's family too and they had a lot of mouths to feed. A deal was made with cash and barter for milk and eggs.

Early every morning Mawzy bundled Eleanor up in the yellow and green baby quilt she had made, dropped her off at Trecia's house and walked two miles up the road past Greenwood mines to teach the kids in the Kathryn coal camp. She

Glenna holding Billy

was in her element again. About two months after school started Mawzy discovered she was pregnant with their second child, Billy. Being pregnant, teaching and caring for her family was challenging, but Mawzy was grateful she was able to finish the school year before Billy was born in June. They named him William after Add and Gene after Eugene, a twin brother of Mawzy's who died in infancy.

Without Mawzy's teaching income that summer, crisis hit the Campbell household. Add was not getting enough work in the Gentry Holler mines to make ends meet. It was not that he didn't try; he was a hard worker. It was just a sign of the times. A couple of his buddies got work at the mine in Duo which had recently been opened by the Raine Lumber and Coal Company. They told Add the mine was looking for additional workers. Add approached Mr. Lawton about the possibility of getting more work and was told two days a week was tops. He got Mr. Lawton's blessing to seek additional work elsewhere. With the pressure of taking care of his family, Add took the mining job in Duo for three days per week. He stayed at the Duo boarding house which was called the club house.

Shortly after this development, Mawzy was approached about another teaching job, this time in a one-room country school in the town of Chestnut Knob. Trecia came to the rescue again and kept both Eleanor and Billy during the school year. It was a tough two-mile walk up Layland hill to school every day.

Cracks were starting to become more evident in the marriage. Unbeknown to Mawzy, Add had found what he was looking for in the arms of another woman. She was working at the Duo mine boarding house and found Add quite charming. Add had time on his hands. Her family made moonshine, so he often got liquored up and loose around her. He knew he had started digging his hole when she turned up pregnant.

Mawzy was always wondering where Add's money went. Bad habits and having a second family to care for didn't leave much for his first family. Add complained about her being so worn out from working and caring for the kids. After many an argument, he convinced her to give up the teaching job at Chestnut Knob for the following school year. After all, he had steady work again. Mawzy agreed and was happy to be able to spend more time at home with Eleanor and Billy.

With President Roosevelt's New Deal, unions were finally becoming more established in southern West Virginia. Wages improved and work hours became more consistent. Financial pressures for the Campbell family eased a bit. The Christmas of 1933 was a sweet spot for them. Add took a few days off, was kind and loving to Mawzy and enjoyed spending time with Eleanor and Billy. Mawzy became pregnant with my Mom, Gloria June.

Shortly before Gloria June was born, Mawzy took Eleanor and Billy over to Trecia's house to play with her youngest. As soon as Mawzy entered the house she knew something was wrong. Trecia was distressed. She was trying to decide whether to share her news. After much hemming and hawing around she finally told Mawzy about Add and the other woman. She didn't want to be the bearer of bad news but felt Mawzy should know the truth. Trecia said her trusted source had seen them together in Duo on many occasions with a small child. Mawzy was in disbelief. She burst into tears and couldn't be consoled. Trecia came over to her, put her hands on Mawzy's shoulders and whispered a prayer.

Mawzy decided not to panic until she and Add could have a heart to heart when he got home from Duo. She was waiting for him at the door when he pulled in, wringing her hands, and holding back the tears. She hit him with the question before he could even speak.

Mawzy gave him an ultimatum. Leave the other woman, quit the Duo job and work from home or she, bearing his third child, and Eleanor and Billy would start anew. The other stipulation was no more drinking. She felt it had been his ruination. Prohibition being recently lifted had not helped the situation. Add was speechless. He tucked tail and headed back to Duo. He had to let the other woman know the cat was out of the bag.

Mawzy stayed in Gentry Holler for a time, hoping Add would see the error of his ways. Gloria June was delivered at home by Dr. Crank the fall of 1934. I was fascinated to find my Mom's baby book in Mawzy's hope chest. Mawzy kept good records of her children's progress, but Gloria's was the only baby book located. In the book Mawzy had recorded visitors from both sides of the family that came to welcome Gloria June to the world. Dallas, Mary, and Dorothy Hanshew and Trecia stopped by right away. Mrs. Edgar Archer, the mine fire boss' wife, paid respects as well. The Campbell grandparents visited as did several of Add's brothers. Glenna was Mawzy's only sister to show up though others gave baby gifts such as jackets, caps, dolls, dresses, and rattlers. Poppy Walker was even recorded as making an appearance. Eleanor was excited to have a "baby doll" sister to hold and help care for. Billy was jealous of all the attention she was getting from Mawzy and Eleanor.

Mawzy made an entry in the baby book about naming Gloria. For some reason she always referred to herself not as I, but as mother. She wrote: *Baby was named Gloria June, the day she was born. Mother had this name in mind for her second baby but it happened to be a boy, so his daddy named him William Gene and mother just saved the name two years and three months longer. Then another little girl came and was called Gloria June.*

Gloria's weight was recorded for the first 10 months. She liked to sleep with her rear end up in the air, while sucking her thumb. The first outings were noted when Gloria was a month old. They visited Poppy and Mommy Walker and a week later went to see the Campbell grandparents. Given the overriding circumstances, the baby was a positive distraction for Mawzy.

Add was still working two days in the Gentry Holler mine. Eleanor was particularly fond of her dad and was not happy he kept going away. She was too young to understand what was going on. She came up with a scheme to keep Add at home. While he was packing some of his things, she and a couple of the holler boys crammed his car's gas tank full of cicadas' larva cases. Cicadas are a type of locust which emerges from the soil every 17 years to molt and mate. Their clicking and hissing noises were deafening at times. There were millions of them in the holler and their sound was contained by hills on all sides. Because they were so plentiful it made stuffing the gas tank quite easy. Once their deed was done, Eleanor and the boys hid and watched the car leave. Add didn't make it off the Gentry Holler dirt road before the car sputtered to a halt. He was boiling mad. He blamed Mawzy. The car had to be towed. The engine was ruined. The boys got in trouble, but Eleanor never came clean about her involvement. Unfortunately, the stunt didn't stop him from leaving. He got a buddy to take him to his Duo nest. Serendipitously, at the time of this writing, cicadas in the area had hit their 17-year cycle again.

Mawzy's two oldest at play in Gentry Holler. From top left Billy, Eleanor, Billy, and Eleanor pulling Billy in wagon.

One Friday after Add's shift in the Duo

mine, he hopped in his car to head back to Gentry Holler. He claimed just as he was pulling away the other woman, who was hid in the back seat, told him to stop the car. Said she pointed a gun to his head and gave him two choices. Stay with her or get a bullet in his head. His decision was made. His marriage to Mawzy was over.

Add met with Mr. Lawton, gave his resignation and moved to Duo. Shortly after that, Mawzy and the kids were asked to leave their company house as it was needed for a miner's family. She had not let Poppy and Mommy Walker know what was happening as she knew they would say "I told you so." She wasn't ready for that confrontation yet. Add's parents were aware of the situation and his mother invited Mawzy and the kids to come live with them at Cliff Top until she could get things figured out. They had a great respect for her and how she picked up the pieces and moved on. Their son's behavior was not something they were proud of. Add's mother was a Cherokee and ruled the roost. It's been said she wouldn't let the kids from Add's second wife in her house.

The Campbell grandparents gave Mawzy's kids a black and white kitten to distract them from all the turmoil. They tied a bell around its neck for ease of location and named it Jingles. Gloria June took it over as her own. She was always following it around. *She liked feeling the soft fur against her face w*as Mawzy's entry in the "first pet" section of Gloria's baby book. "Kitty" was also recorded as one of Gloria's first words.

Mawzy's filed for a divorce. She was certain it would not be a problem as two of the five reasons for granting a divorce fit her case - adultery and habitual intemperance. Her marriage was officially over on October 15, 1935. Add didn't show up for the court hearing. The divorce decree gave Mawzy custody of the three children and Add was ordered to pay a permanent alimony of $35 per month, which he neglected. Because divorce was uncommon in those days, Mawzy knew she would be wearing the "scarlet letter" once back in Springdale.

Add came around a few times after that to see the kids. He eventually told Mawzy he had made a mistake. He even asked her to consider taking him back.

"I'd never do to your present wife what she did to me," was Mawzy's answer.

Gloria June was a little over a year old when they parted ways. When her dad showed up for a visit, she ran and hid. She didn't know who he was and was scared to death of him. "I don't want you around my Mommy," was her comment on one of those visits. On another visit when she was a little older, her daddy told her to put on her shoes and socks. "Under what circumstances?" she replied as she put her hands on her hips.

The other woman's sister worked in a furniture store not far from Mawzy's house in Springdale. Mawzy refused to go in the store as it was too upsetting for her to be reminded of her failed marriage.

Add's brothers and sisters stayed in touch with Mawzy over the years. Mawzy kept pictures and newspaper clippings about their lives and deaths in her hope chest. She also kept clippings about Add's second family.

Eleanor and Gloria June on Add's car.

Years later when Add died, Mawzy approached the funeral home to arrange a private visitation. They obliged. She wanted to see him one last time without being intrusive to his other family. Eleanor came home for the funeral. Mawzy said she wasn't going but changed her mind. "I wasn't surprised because I know she has always cared for him," was Gloria June's observation. After the funeral, Mawzy commented, "Well, I guess I'm a widow now."

Gentry Holler also faded away. It remains as only a memory. Coal was extracted until the last piece was stripped away in the early 1950s. After that houses rotted to the ground and nature reclaimed the land once again. The ruins of the school are the only glimmer of a life gone by.

Eleanor holding Gloria June

I wish, how I wish I had a little house,
With a mat for the cat and a hole for the mouse.
And a clock going "tock" in a corner of the room
And a kettle and a cupboard and a big birch broom.

**Excerpt from The Shiny Little House *by Nancy M. Hughes, one of*
*Mawzy coursework poems.***

Eleanor, Gloria June, and Billy

A Second Chance

"Root hog or die," was one of Mawzy's favorite expressions which originated from an early colonial practice of turning pigs loose to fend for themselves. It was the theme of many songs over the years including American Revolutionary and Civil War songs and was an expression used by David Crockett in the mid-1800s. The saying truly reflected Mawzy's attitude toward life. She could relate to the June Carter Cash "Root Hog or Die" lyrics depicting the heartache of a woman who met a no-good traveling salesman and married him.

After Poppy Walker became aware of Mawzy's marital problems he offered to help her move back home to Springdale, with one caveat. "This is the last time I'll ever help you, if you go back to that son of a bitch," he warned.

On a gorgeous Sunday morning the fall of 1935, Poppy drove to Cliff Top where Mawzy was staying with her in-laws. He loaded Mawzy, her three children, Eleanor, Billy and my mother, Gloria June, and all their belongings in his old pick-up truck and tied their cow, Bossy, to the side. Gloria sat between Poppy and Mawzy and held tight to her cat, Jingles. Eleanor and Billy rode in the back of the truck to keep an eye on all their stuff. They took narrow roads through the woods up Glade Creek and then crossed the Loops Road to a ridge above Bellwood. From there they came into Springdale via Gilkerson Road. It was a slow, but successful ten-mile trip for all, Bossy and Jingles included.

Mawzy was quiet as she stared out the truck window. She admired the brilliant colors of the fall foliage in the distant landscape as she reflected on her life.

"I tell ya, my nose is runnin' like a sugar tree," Poppy said as he sniffed and pulled Mawzy back to the present.

"Poppy, I sure do thank you for helping me get resettled. I know there's other things you could be doing today."

"You know, this reminds me of the trips me and Elsie used 'ta take 'ta Fire Creek come spring and fall," Poppy reminisced, instead of addressing Mawzy's problems. "Hitched a horse to a covered wagon. Took us most of the day to get there. Stocked up on stuff like flour, sugar, salt, and coffee. Your mother liked to pick up some cloth to sew."

"I remember Mommy talkin' 'bout trips to Fire Creek," Mawzy said. "She told me you spent the night in the wagon to guard your goods, then headed home the next morning."

"We sure had some times," Poppy continued. "I remember once when it was rainin' like a cat pissin' and we had a hell of a time gettin' home. Ruts sometimes six inches deep. Poor horse. Lord a mercy."

"Jingles, Poppy say bad words," Gloria June whispered in her cat's ear. Mawzy chuckled under her breath but decided not to acknowledge the comment.

"That horse we took to Fire Creek was the very one that took off with you on it when you was just three years old," Poppy added. "You was ridin' with Aunt Alice. She got down to pick some flowers and the horse bolted. Scared us all 'bout half to death. I don't know how, but you hung on until the horse finally stopped."

"Scared me too," Mawzy added. "Poppy, I'd just bet the route you and Mommy took to Fire Creek and the one we're on now are part of the Buffalo Trail. Can you imagine buffalo roaming this area? I learned about it in my West Virginia history class. Indians and English settlers traveled over the buffalo paths in the 1700s. There were supposedly buffalo roundups and stampedes not far from here. The beasts could bust through dense thickets of laurel up and down banks too steep for a man to travel over. They grazed along the Meadow River near Rainelle, right in our own back yard. It's been said there were over 60 million buffalo in North America at one time."

"Well, I'll be damned," Poppy said and became quiet as he pondered the past and his life with Mommy over the years.

It was love at first sight when he laid eyes on Elsie Mae White. He was in the dining room of the bunk house in a logging camp near Meadow Bridge. Elsie was 15 years old. She was helping her mother, who was one of the camp "cookees," prepare supper for the loggers.

Poppy was a looker so he caught Elsie's attention as well. He was 19. When Elsie brought a fresh plate of biscuits to his table he struck up a conversation. She was not only the prettiest but also one of the sweetest women he had ever met. She held that reputation until the day she died. She and her mother lived in Springdale, about eight miles from the camp and rode a horse to and from work. The

Poppy Walker third from left at coal mine in Bellwood, WV around 1917 as noted by son, Earl; below as a young man and with baby Mawzy and his wife, Elsie.

women had their work cut out for them. The loggers ate hardy as they had to fuel their bodies for the physical labor they endured ten hours a day, six days a week.

Poppy continued vying for Elsie's attention. She was captivated by his charm. Less than a year later they slipped off to Bristol, Tennessee to wed.

As newlyweds, they lived in Gentry where Poppy secured work as a foreman in a small logging camp. Mommy was hired as a "cookee" but only worked for a short time. Mawzy was born about 13 months later on November 5, 1907. Gentry, later renamed Layland, intersected with Gentry Holler when coal mining moved into the area and ironically was where Mawzy had just ended her marriage to Add.

Lumber operations in West Virginia were close to their peak during the early 1900s. By 1909 there were 1,524 mills in the state which produced almost 1.5 billion feet of lumber that year alone. Before railroads, it was quite a task to fell virgin timber and transport it to the mill. Many of the logs were huge. Red spruce was the most valuable in the area and could get 90 feet tall with a 4-foot diameter. White pine was abundant and grew over 100 feet tall. Horses and wooden tracks were used to get logs off the mountains. Loggers called "road monkeys" were assigned the job of clearing and maintaining a path for movement of horses and timber. Made Poppy tired, just thinking about how he had meandered from camp to camp to stay fully employed. Streams were used, if possible, to move timber to the mill for processing. If the stream was large enough, arks were built of logs with buildings on the top. A "town" with a bunk house for up to 100 loggers, a cook shack with a dining area and horse barns floated down the nearby Greenbrier River, herding a massive amount of timber.

Richard and Viola White, Mommy Walker's parents; right, Poppy and Mommy's cabin.

Poppy was so caught up in his thoughts, he was startled when Mawzy started talking again.

"What you thinkin' about?" she asked.

"Well, I was thinkin' about when me and your mother moved to Springdale," he replied and proceeded to tell the story.

Elsie's father, R. A. White, owned a general store in Springdale, which housed the post office. He was the postmaster for quite some time. Mr. White was a generous sort. Carried a lot of credit for families in need over the years even though he knew they'd never be able to pay him back. The house Mawzy would come to own sat next to her grandpa's store, though he was no longer the owner.

Mr. White also owned a lot of land in the Springdale area and gifted Poppy and Mommy 180 acres. He loaned them money to buy construction materials for a cabin and outbuildings.

The cabin they built was small – three rooms and a loft. It kept feeling smaller and smaller as more children arrived. Over the next 22 years 12 kids were born in that house, two of whom died.

The kitchen/dining/living area had an iron wood-stove and a fireplace. Two bedrooms were in the back of the house. Rope beds were constructed and topped with straw tick mattresses. The house had no insulation. Newspaper was used like wallpaper to help block drafts. The loft served as a bedroom for the three boys, Lawrence, Earl, and Chester, as they came along. Earl remembered seeing the sky at night through the cracks in the roof. Chester recalled snow blowing in on his quilt during winter storms. When it got freezing cold the boys ran downstairs several times a night to rekindle and warm up by the fireplace. Kerosene lanterns provided lighting. There was an outhouse and a natural spring nearby for water. Most of their land was across the road, so this is where they built a barn. Poppy purchased a horse for private logging on their land and plowing ground for a large garden.

"Mommy," Wanda yelled as she ran into the house. "I just saw Poppy's truck comin' round the mountain." Wanda, Mawzy's youngest sister, had waited on the front porch for over an hour in anticipation of their arrival. She flew back out of the house and down the lane waving her arms to greet them. She was so excited to have Eleanor there as a playmate. Wanda was six years old, and Eleanor was almost five. Except for Wanda and sister Jewell, who was nine, Mawzy's other siblings were fairly self-sufficient at that point.

So, Poppy's biggest worry at the time was getting Mawzy back on her feet again. Having young screaming kids running all over the place about drove him nuts. "Shut that damn kid up, will 'ya!" he was always yelling.

Gloria June had Poppy wrapped around her little finger in no time. "Where's Poppy's pet?" he called out. When she came running he lifted her up on his shoulders and carried her around the house and yard. She was the quiet one. Eleanor, Billy, and Wanda were invariably off on an adventure somewhere in the hills. Gloria June was too little to tag along. That Christmas when Santa Claus showed up at the home place, Gloria June was so afraid of him she ran into Poppy's arms. Poppy was her protector. "Go away, ole Santy, go away," Poppy instructed as he waved his arms to shoo Santy off.

"Rough and gruff with a soft spot" was Gloria June's description of him. Years later he teased her by picking on her children, David and me. When we came to visit, Poppy often looked at me and said, ""Who's kid is that anyway? That's the ugliest kid I've ever seen!" Or "That kid's got the blackest eyes I've ever seen!" Then he would belt out, "Black eye, pick a pie, blue eyed beauty. Green eyed greedy gut go around and eat the world up." This was often followed by "I'm gonna' get me some jawbones." Then he grabbed me and started gnawing on my jaw, making horrible smacking sounds. It didn't hurt bad, but scared me as I felt his beard rake across my cheek. Many a grandkid and great grandkid endured "jawbones."

Mawzy wrote in Gloria's baby book about her first fall, not long after they moved back to Springdale. *After Gloria June had gotten so she could walk fairly well, she found Aunt Jewell's little rocking chair in the bedroom. From this time*

93

on for several days no one could hardly pull her away from it. She just rocked and rocked and sang "bye baby." Well, this was all right, so long as she sat down and didn't rock too big, but as soon as she thought she had skill enough to stand up in the chair she wanted to stand up and rock. And it was this way that she got her first fall, that was worth crying over.

Watching Mommy slather cold cream all over her face fascinated Gloria June. One day when no one was paying attention, she decided to mimic Mommy's action. Down came the cold cream jar off Mommy's bedroom dresser. She opened the lid and proceeded to glob massive amounts of cream all over her face. She came out of the bedroom and into the kitchen saying," Ain't I pretty?" She was just too cute to get in trouble over that incident. However, when she kept getting into other people's powder and cream a spanking became necessary and was recorded as "first punishment" in her baby book. ...*at age 3 ½ she still likes to primp,* Mawzy noted.

Billy in his Sunday best at Poppy and Mommy Walker's home.

Mawzy had a heart-to-heart with Poppy and Mommy and asked Poppy to help her find a house where she and the kids could get established on their own. She told them she had contacted the Fayette County Board of Education to inquire about a teaching job. She applied and was told they would contact her if any openings came available. She reminded the board she had taught at Springdale School seven years prior. She was told her certification would need to be updated since she didn't have a college degree. Being the sole breadwinner for her family meant that her being a mother would not preempt her from teaching.

By spring, the Board called her. Enrollment at the Springdale School had increased enough that they decided to add another teacher. Mawzy was offered a position teaching first and second grade the fall of 1936, contingent upon passing the certification exam. She knew her future brother-in-law, Jim Twohig, who became Pansie's husband and was a teacher at Springdale put in a good word for her.

Frances Henry, the third teacher, was a descendant of Patrick Henry. Twenty some years later at the Springdale School, Julie, her daughter, used a letter of verification for Patrick Henry as a show and tell for someone famous. The kids were in awe. My brother, David, was a classmate. He showed his Davy Crockett coonskin cap Mawzy made for him from one of Poppy's old raccoon hides. Not authentic but just as valued. The kids of Springdale were lucky to have three teachers with such a commitment to helping them learn.

Mawzy in a moment of repose at Mommy and Poppy Walker's home.

To get recertified, Mawzy headed to summer school again. This time she enrolled at Concord College in Athens, West Virginia. Concord was founded in 1872 as a training school chiefly for schoolteachers.

Eleanor and Billy went with her. Add's sister, Mary, and her husband, Dallas, were still living in Gentry Holler and offered to take care of Gloria June. They missed her and knew it would be fun for their seven-year-old daughter, Dorothy, to help watch after her. So off to Gentry Holler Gloria went. Mawzy wrote about the separation as the "First Childish Tragedy" in Gloria June's baby book. *When Gloria June was not quite two years old she had to be parted from her mother. Mother was attending Concord College. This was some-what of a tragedy at first but she soon grew to love her Aunt Mary and Uncle Dallas very much.*

Mawzy continued the story in the "Second Birthday" page of the baby book. *Her second birthday came not long after the family were reunited on the return from summer school. Baby and mother were very glad to be together again... During the week of her birthday she spent with her Aunt Mary the one who had kept her all summer. They missed her so badly they had to have her visit them soon. So Aunt Mary got to make the little cake.* It was the last time Gloria June stayed with them, as Uncle Dallas died of appendicitis a year later and Mary and Dorothy had to leave Gentry Holler.

With certification in hand and a job secured, Mawzy was ready to move on to the next challenge. Once back at the home place she approached Mommy Walker.

Mommy, Poppy and grandkids Eleanor, Mary Jenny, Gloria June, and Billy

"I hate to ask, but would you be willing to watch Billy and Gloria June while Eleanor and I head off to school this fall?" Mawzy inquired. "Hopefully, it won't be for too long as you know Poppy thinks he's found a house for us. Once we're moved, I'll find a permanent sitter."

"Of course, I will. Your brothers and sisters will be headed off to school, so it'll just be your two here durin' the day. Besides, you sure have helped me out over the years. I'd be glad to see 'ya through this rough patch."

When Mawzy started teaching that fall, she was in a new school which had been built since her first stint at Springdale in the '20s. She spent the next 37 years of her life with this building as her second home and her students as her second family.

The school had nine steps leading up to the porch and main entry. Initially, there were two classrooms in the front section of the building – one room for 1st,

Above, the new Springdale School; Below, the strain of balancing her life as a professional woman and single mom was evident in Mawzy's school picture.

2nd, and 3rd graders and one room for 4th, 5th, and 6th graders. Five large windows per classroom, accommodated by 12-foot ceilings, provided abundant light and could be opened for ventilation when the weather was warmer.

In the back of the school was a large multipurpose room used mostly for play in inclement weather. When Mawzy was added as the third teacher, one side of this room was converted to a classroom. There were stairs in the center of the building, concealed by a door, which mysteriously lead to nowhere.

97

Each room was heated with a coal burning pot belly stove. The stoves were wrapped with a fireproof material to prevent children from getting burned if a ruckus happened to throw them in that direction.

A natural spring across the road from the school provided their water supply. Each morning, two students were assigned the job of carrying buckets of water from the spring to the school where they were emptied into a crock dispenser with a spigot. This was their old-fashioned water fountain. Two outhouses sat back in the woods behind the school. These were the same toilets the students used before the new school was built. Sears and Roebuck and other catalog pages served as toilet paper.

The new school is shadowed by the old school in the background on the right during an informal photo session. Photo contributed by Margaret Kraus.

Students brought their lunches from home and usually ate at their desk. Sometimes the multipurpose room was used.

After the new school was completed the old school was sold to the Church of Christ. Students were warned not to loiter around the old building.

By that winter Poppy had a firm commitment on a small house for Mawzy and the kids. It was on Gilkerson Road and was closer to the school than the home place. Mawzy purchased it from an elderly couple on a six-year contract for $1,000. A down payment of $300 was required with five annual payments of $120 and a final payment of $100 in year six. No interest was charged.

Mawzy's life as a single mom on her own was about to begin in the small, old house with dingy whitewashed siding. She would never miss a payment and was often ahead of schedule. In 1939, toward the end of the Great Depression, the couple wrote Mawzy a letter of appreciation.

Dear Mrs. Campbell,
Received your check for $70.00 on notes. I am attaching Note No 3 as paid and give you credit for $60.00 on Note No 4.
We sure appreciate this payment as we are in a very close place at present.

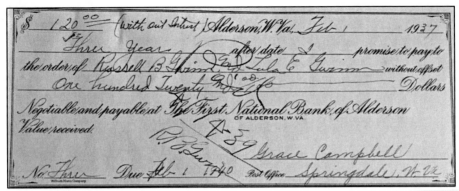

She kept all records of the house purchase in her safe deposit box. I am the keeper of the records now.

Times remained tough as the Great Depression lingered. Mawzy was lucky to have a job. A lot of people were desperate. Hobos frequented the area either jumping trains or walking from place to place in search of work and food. A stranger showed up at the home place one day. Aunt Sister just happened to be there at the time and came to the door. The fellow introduced himself as Walter Eaton and asked for food. "Looks like your name should be Walter Starvin, shouldn't it?" Aunt Sister joked. But she invited him in for a bite or two. The Walker family didn't have it as bad as many because they were farmers. There was never any want for food at the home place.

Mawzy remembered the story of how her grandpa White helped a poor woman with several kids who had just lost her husband. The widow came into his store and asked if he could donate a shirt for her husband's funeral and burial. He said yes I can do that. Then she asked for a new pair of pants. Again, he replied he could do that. After some thought, she asked for a new suit instead as the poor 'ole man had never owned a suit before.

He cleared his throat, as he often did when aggravated and said," Since you husband never owned a new suit I guess I can help you with that."

The widow started pushing him further by asking for a pair of shoes.

He replied, "If he is in a casket lying down with his feet covered up does he really need new shoes?"

One of the kids began crying so Mr. White gave in again. He figured there couldn't be anything else to ask for but he was wrong.

As the widow headed out the door, she turned and said since her husband was so well dressed, could they get him a new hat as well?

Mr. White cleared his throat one last time and replied, "NO, not unless you are planning to bury him standing up."

Appalachians love their story telling.

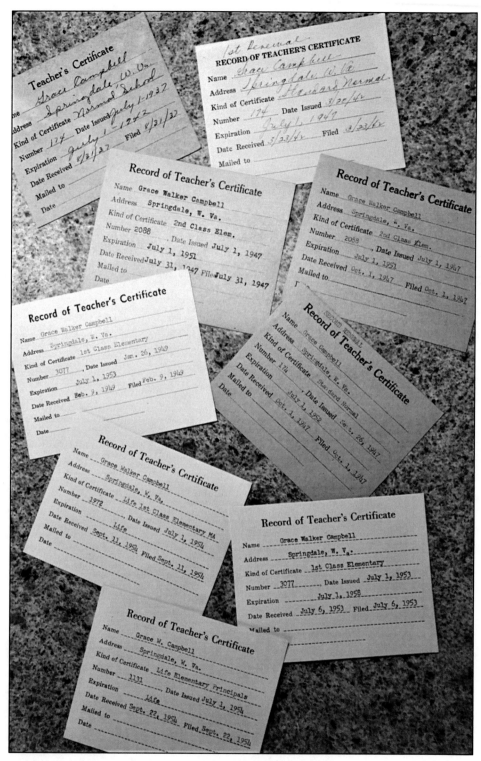

Years of certification renewals marked Mawzy's career.

"Your education is something no one can ever take away from you," was one of Mawzy's favorite tidbits of wisdom.

Mawzy was bound and determined to provide stability for her children and to make sure they understood the importance of their education.

She led by example. She continued going to summer school at Concord College to renew her teaching certificate via college courses and finally received her undergraduate degree in 1949.

She found a boarding house and took all three kids with her to Athens after the first year. Eleanor was old enough to watch Billy and Gloria June while Mawzy was in class.

From there she took West Virginia University extension classes in Rainelle and went to Morgantown for summer school until she got her master's degree and principal's certificate in 1954 when she was 46 years old. It was also the year of my birth.

She tucked away 13 teacher's certificates, three diplomas, and West Virginia University transcripts in her hope chest.

Mawzy's school photographs through the years.

CHILDREN LEARN WHAT THEY LIVE

If a child lives with criticism, he learns to condemn.
If a child lives with hostility, he learns to fight.
If a child lives with ridicule, he learns to be shy.
If a child lives with shame, he learns to feel guilty.
If a child lives with tolerance, he learns to be patient.
If a child lives with encouragement, he learns confidence.
If a child lives with praise, he learns to appreciate.
If a child lives with fairness, he learns justice.
If a child lives with security, he learns to have faith.
If a child lives with approval, he learns to like himself.
If a child lives with acceptance and friendship, he learns to find love in the world.

Source unknown

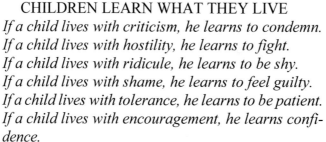

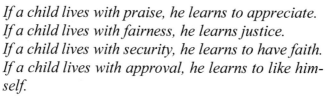

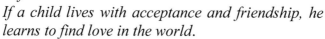

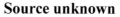

Mawzy's last class of students.

School Years

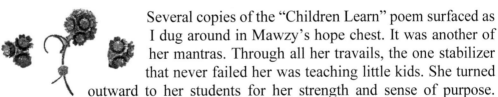

Several copies of the "Children Learn" poem surfaced as I dug around in Mawzy's hope chest. It was another of her mantras. Through all her travails, the one stabilizer that never failed her was teaching little kids. She turned outward to her students for her strength and sense of purpose. School was a place where her only focus was to provide an environment conducive to learning. It was a place where she could forget her troubles for a while. She thrived off the positive energy radiating from light bulbs coming on in the children's minds.

One of her students, Elaine, told me years later she would never forget Mrs. Campbell helping her when she was homebound for a month. "When I was in the first grade, I had water on my knee and had to have surgery," Elaine recalled. "Mrs. Campbell packed up each day's lessons and on her way home from school she stopped by my house to tutor me so I wouldn't fall behind. She left homework to be picked up and graded the next day." Mawzy wasn't paid extra. She did it because she cared.

Bud Harmon, a teacher at Springdale in the 70s said of Mawzy, "She never, never belittled a student or anyone." Bud became the school's principal after Mawzy retired.

School Days: The Community Hub

Some would call the little unincorporated town of Springdale a greasy spot in the road. Others would describe it as the middle of nowhere. Mawzy saw Springdale Elementary and its grounds as God's country and wanted to share it with the community.

In the late 1930s, not long after Mawzy started teaching at Springdale, she thought it would be good to have a formal dedication of the new school, coupled with a pie supper fund raiser to build a fence around the school yard. Having the school sit on the top of a hill without boundaries was an accident waiting to happen.

Articles in the newspaper told of the Carter Family traveling the area to do concerts for various schools and churches. They had recently completed a recording session in Bristol, Tennessee and were being broadcast on radio shows throughout the south. Mawzy loved their music as she could relate to their themes about the woes and joys of ordinary people. That their show was promoted

CARNIVAL SLATED
SPRINGDALE, Oct. 20 (RNS)—The Springdale Elementary School carnival will be held Saturday at the school, beginning at 7:30 p.m.

as "morally good" gave Mawzy peace of mind as she began her pursuit. She knew they would be a good calling card for the locals. As luck would have it, the Carters were available for a Saturday evening in the fall.

The day of the concert was glorious. Abundant sunshine. Crisp temperatures. Fall leaves so bright they seemed electric. People came. The school lunchroom was packed. The Carters belted out the chorus of "Keep on the Sunny Side" as their opening number. The crowd was ecstatic. "Wildwood Flower" was their encore.

Two of the band members, Maybelle and Sara Carter, had young children who traveled with them. The older ones took care of those younger. Eleanor was about the same age as June Carter and the two of them hit it off. Around and around the school yard they went playing "Ring Around the Rosie" and hide and seek with other kids. Little did Eleanor know she was playing with the future Mrs. Johnny Cash.

Christmas was a festive time at the school. In the earlier days, students put on a Christmas pageant for the community. Everyone looked forward to it as a kick-off to the holidays. In amongst Mawzy's old textbooks I discovered a small, well-worn book. The original cover was missing and was replaced with dark blue construction paper. Handwritten on the paper cover was "*A Christmas Play Book, Springdale School.*" Inside, school kids' names were written in the left-hand margin by many of the recitations, monologs, and dialogues. They were names I recognized from Mom and Aunt Eleanor's era. "A Christmas Lesson" was a dialogue earmarked for Mom and three of her classmates.

I found some of the parts a bit odd, but figured it was probably a sign of the times in the early 20th century. One caught my attention:

> *A Bad Man*
> *(For a tiny girl)*
> *There's a bad man lives on our street – He's awful bad 'cause when he sees me he says, "I'm goin' to steal you someday, I am, sure's pop."*
> *An' he scares me dre'fful bad.*
> *An' the other day - what you s'pose - he said he's goin' to write to Santy an' tell him to put me in his stockin' - the bad man's stockin' for a present Chris'mus eve.*
> *An' I told my papa an' he says he'll load up the gun an' if Santy tries to give me to that man for a Christ'mus present he'll shoot 'im full of duck shot.*
> *Santy better look out for my papa, he had!*

Mawzy must have found this one a bit odd too, as she hadn't written a name by it.

Students drew names for a gift exchange which occurred at the end of the pageant. One year Uncle Billy drew the name of a boy from a poor family. Mawzy helped him find a nice gift for the fellow. They picked out a starter Tinker Toy set. The recipient was so excited. Billy was pleased. When Billy opened his gift, all he got was a stick of gum. He was very disappointed. Mawzy used the opportunity to teach Billy "it's better to give than receive" and explained that's all the family could afford.

Pie supper fund raisers were still popular when David and I were in school. Not long before an upcoming supper, the school's janitor quit. Mawzy approached Louella, the school cook, to see if she would be willing to spiff up the school beforehand. She offered to pay her the same as her cook's wage. Louella agreed to do the work and said she would consider the position on a permanent basis if her husband could be hired as well. Mawzy was so relieved she agreed to hiring both. She knew Louella's husband had "black lung" from working in the coal mines and thought this may be a way to get him out of there.

At one of the suppers the four Jones boys and their dad showed up. The father was a tall, husky fellow and his boys were stairsteps of a similar build. As they entered the school, they bounded through the hallway toward the lunchroom.

"Me and my boys will eat 'er all!" the father boomed out in a voice that could be heard throughout the building. And boy could they eat. Their taste buds were a bit peculiar, though. They liked to put catsup on their Jell-O.

Several cake walks were on the docket as a part of the pie supper. The women of the community went all out to see who could come up with the most beautiful or original cake. Chances were bought for one's cake of choice. Those who purchased a ticket were called forward as each cake was featured. Music was played as the ticket holders walked around the perimeter of the lunchroom. When the music stopped, the person standing in front of the featured cake was the winner.

"Mawzy, can I have money to buy a chance on that butterfly cake?" David asked as he came running her way. "It's the best cake I've ever seen!" The cake was beautiful. It had been carved and pieced into a butterfly shape. The frosting was yellow with black trim, made to resemble a yellow swallowtail.

"It's for a good cause," Mawzy said. "Here's a dollar. Go buy your ticket now, then pay attention so you don't miss your turn." David hovered around that cake until it was finally his turn.

"All who have a chance on the butterfly cake need to line up now," the announcer proclaimed over the PA system.

Lots of chances had been bought on this cake. Besides its beauty everyone knew the creator, Gay Burns. Her cakes were second to none. David was so excited he was beside himself. The music started and chance holders began to parade around the room. Low and behold, the music stopped and guess who was standing before the butterfly cake? David had just won. He couldn't believe his good fortune. He took possession and for the rest of the evening he treated the cake as if it were an infant child.

The next day I thought it would be a good idea to have a piece of the cake to see if it was as good as it looked. I asked David's permission. He refused me as well as Mom and Mawzy. After a few days, Mawzy encouraged him to cut the cake so that it could be enjoyed before it got stale.

"That cake's going to end up harder than a bull's head," Mawzy said.

"Not gonna' cut the cake yet," David responded. "It's too pretty."

The cake eventually fossilized and had to be thrown away. As it was being dumped into the garbage, we discovered that Gay had meticulously used Dairy Queen spoons as skeletons for the butterfly wings. What creativity.

School fund raisers seemed to always include sending items home for the children to sell, as was the case when my Cousin Gary was in the fourth grade. He brought home six three-packs of pens to sell at $1 per pack. His first potential customer was his dad, Uncle Chester. After Gary made his sales pitch, Uncle Chester made a deal with him.

"Gary, if you can walk down to Poppy's house and get him to buy a set of pens from you, I'll buy a set too," Chester teased.

"I don't know, Dad. Poppy 's awful tight with his money. But I'll give it my best try."

Gary headed down the hill and around the pond to see Poppy. He walked into the house with the set of pens in hand.

"What you doin' here?" Poppy asked. "What ya got in 'ur hand there?"

"Well, Poppy, we're supposed to sell some pens for school and I was wonderin' if you'd buy a set from me?"

"I don't need any pens 'cause I never write to nobody."

"Ok then, I guess I'd better go see who I can sell some to," Gary replied.

"Wait a minute," Poppy said as he grabbed up his coin pouch. He dug around until he came up with coins to total $1. He handed the money over and Gary held out the pen set for him.

"I already told you I don't want none of them damn pens. Now get on out of here," Poppy said.

Gary left with a victorious grin on his face as he ran back home. Uncle Chester was flabbergasted at Gary's success.

"All I can say is you need to be a salesman when you grow up, Gary." Uncle Chester kept his end of the bargain and bought a set of pens too.

Mawzy sold candy bars at recess and lunch time to make money for school projects. Penny candy was an option for those with less money.

I liked going to the wholesaler with Mawzy as it was fascinating to see that much candy in one place. She let me help with the selection. I always pushed for Slow Pokes, Black Cows, Mary Janes, candy necklaces, and Bazooka bubble gum. The candy was stored in a locked cabinet in the back of her classroom.

Over the years stories were reported in *The Beckley Post-Herald* about activities being held at the Springdale Elementary School. One article told of a surprise birthday dinner for Rev. Roy Kessler, the pastor of Springdale Baptist Church. The school was also used for other church activities, especially while the new church was under construction.

Other community groups took advantage of the venue. The following December 22, 1962 *Post-Herald* article is an example:

Springdale Farm Women Have Christmas Dinner

SPRINGDALE (RNS) — The Springdale Elementary School was the scene for the annual Christmas dinner for members of the Springdale Farm Women's Club. The dinner was held Sunday evening with the families of the members and friends as guests.

Birthday Dinner Honors Pastor

SPRINGDALE (RNS) — A surprise birthday dinner was held in honor of the Rev. Roy B. Kessler, pastor of the Springdale Baptist Church, Saturday by members of the church in the Springdale Grade School.

The table was decorated with a three-tiered birthday cake.

Attending were Mr. and Mrs. Algie Burns, Mrs. Vena Walthall, Mr. and Mrs. J. O. McKinney, Mrs. Harry Peterman, Mrs. Bill Rookstool, Mr. and Mrs. Bill McKinney, Mrs. W. T. Webb, Mrs. Roy Kessler and son, Mike, Mr. and Mrs. Jack Benson and children, Mrs. Grace Cambell, Mrs. Gloria Alley and children.

Springdale Farm Women Have Christmas Dinner

Springdale – The Springdale Elementary School was the scene for the annual Christmas dinner for members of the Springdale Farm Women's Club. The dinner was held Sunday evening with the families of the members and friends as guests. Christmas decorations of greenery, candles, and a Christmas tree were used in the dining area. The tables were laid in white linen with arrangements of red and white poinsettias... An added attraction at the close of the diner was Santa Claus, being sponsored by the club members to give treats to the children. Gifts were exchanged by the members of the club while Christmas chimes and carols were played throughout the evening...

There were 72 adults and children listed in attendance.

Fourth of July picnics at the school were also organized by women's groups. Aunt Biddie was often involved. Games were arranged for the kids. The most anticipated was the greased pole climb for the prize of a five-dollar bill on top. It was a feat usually accomplished, likely because kids eventually wore off the grease in their attempts to make it to the top.

One year Aunt Biddie, Uncle Chester's wife, made her famous chocolate cake for the party. She had everyone guess what she had buried in the cake. The winner got to take the cake home. No one got the answer correct. It was Aunt Biddie's kidney stone, hermetically sealed, of course. It was a trick she pulled for years to come. On a recent visit she showed me her infamous kidney stone.

(See Aunt Biddie's chocolate cake recipe in appendix.)

The Jap Attack

Many of our boys have gone away,
Since that sad Pearl Harbor day.
They've gone to fight for the red, white, and blue
And for the protection of me and you.
Millions of boys are marching on,
Thinking of the triumphant song.
Hoping soon for victory,
So they can return to you and me.
The villainous Japs will crash like toys,
For killing our good American boys.
They should have known before the attack
That all ruthless people will get paid back.
Many of our boys will not return,
But for them we'll always yearn.
So to save some other boys lives
Buy extra bonds in the War Loan Drives.

From The Montrado, Meadow Bridge High School newspaper, January 1, 1945
Written by eight grader, Joyce Richmond

110

A Stiff Upper Lip

For the next two Saturdays after Mawzy took possession of her house, she loaded up Poppy's truck and had him take her and the kids there. She wanted it sparkling clean before moving in. The residue from burning coal had a way of permeating every nook and cranny so a good scrubbing was her priority. She placed and received an order of coal to be assured the bin was full. Mommy Walker gathered up some home canned fruits and vegetables as well as salt pork to help tide them over until Mawzy could get her own garden started in the spring. These goods were placed in the kitchen pantry along with store bought staples like lard, cornmeal, sugar, and flour. Each trip, any remaining space in the truck was filled with furniture. Mawzy's brother, Earl, followed along to help with loading and unloading.

On a cold snowy morning in late February 1937 Poppy helped move the last of Mawzy's belongings. After a year and a half of living at the home place and renting two other places, Mawzy and the kids finally moved into their own house for good. As they turned down Gilkerson Road, Mawzy's heartbeat accelerated with excitement. She looked over her property, silhouetted by the pristine snow-covered field and forest in the background, and felt a sense of peace. A new chapter in her life was about to begin.

That moment of tranquility was soon interrupted when the kids piled out of Poppy's truck and started running amuck. Eleanor was seven years old and Billy was five. Gloria June, who would grow up to be my Mom, was three. It didn't take long for them to release their pent-up energy. Billy scooped up a pile of snow and started making a snowball. Eleanor quickly caught on and did the same. Soon a snowball fight ensued. Gloria June stayed clear. She was more interested in throwing snow up in the air just to watch it fall to the ground again, while making sure Jingles didn't run off.

Poppy and Earl unloaded Mawzy's remaining possessions. Bossy, the cow, was fetched a few days later and secured in an area across the road where she could easily get water from the creek.

> **The Cow**
> *The friendly cow all red and white,*
> *I love with all my heart,*
> *She gives me cream with all her might,*
> *To eat with apple tart.*
> *She wanders lowing here and there,*
> *And yet she cannot stray,*
> *All in the pleasant open air,*
> *The pleasant light of day...*
> **By R.L. Stevenson**
> **(Used to accompany reading books as a part of Mawzy's course work)**

The house was small, about the size of the Gentry Holler house. The porch was elevated and accessible by four concrete steps on the east side. The front door opened into the living room. Two twelve-pane windows let in ample light. A potbelly stove filled the center of the room and heated the front half of the house. Earl stoked it with a wood starter and then coal shortly after they arrived. On the left side of the living room were doors leading into two bedrooms. Having only two bedrooms was not ideal for three growing kids. Gloria June and Eleanor were to stay in the front bedroom using the two twin beds from Gentry Holler. Gloria June ended up with Billy's bed, so he slept with Mawzy in the back bedroom, though he often ended up on the living room couch if Mawzy started snoring too loudly.

Opposite the living room entry was a half wall with an opening in the center, which gave the small house a more open feeling and led into the dining room. Mawzy had Poppy and Earl situate her wooden table and chairs in the center of the room. She placed a beautiful cream-colored tablecloth she had crocheted on top of the table. It was originally one of her hope chest items. She was proud of her work and silently thanked Mommy Walker for teaching her to crochet. Her Singer treadle sewing machine, mechanically powered by pushing a foot pedal back and forth, was positioned under the east and only window in the room. That machine saw a lot of fabric over the years in the making of kids' clothing, Mawzy's dresses and curtains. The right corner of the room housed a small desk where Mawzy prepared her school lessons after the kids were in bed. Their only closet was in the dining room and had a built-in ladder leading to an attic in the rafters. It became an exciting, but dangerous, hiding place for the kids. If Mawzy said it once she said it a thousand times, "Be careful up there. If you step off the rafters, you'll fall through the ceiling and hurt yourselves!"

The kitchen was north of the dining room. To the left of the entry was a compact white wooden free-standing pantry. Next to the pantry was the coal burning cook stove which also helped heat the back of the house. Perpendicular to the stove was a small sink and countertop with a dish rack for drying dishes. To the right of the sink was Mawzy's pride and joy, her white Hoosier baking center cabinet she bought with teaching money she saved while living at Poppy and

Mommy's house. It had a pull-down bin for flour storage on the top left side and double-doored shelving on the right. Below the bin was a built-in flour sifter with space beneath for a mixing bowl. The mixer was stored behind a roll back door. A pull-out enamel countertop separated the upper and lower cabinets and was where all the pie crusts, cookies, homemade biscuits, and rolls were created. Below the counter on the left was a large cupboard with two shelves. On the lower right were two utensil drawers and a bread drawer. An east facing window close to the baking cabinet provided lots of natural light. A door in the back of the kitchen lead to an outside stoop with an overhang.

Mawzy with a coal scuttle.

To the west of the house, Mawzy's property included a detached garage with a dirt floor and exposed rafters. The entry was closed off with old barn doors that latched with a cross bar. Though she had no car, the building was used for storage. Coal and wooden shoe heels were kept in bins in the rear of the building. The shoe heels were defective and were a biproduct of Rainelle's Meadow River Lumber Company. Mawzy was able to buy them cheaply to use for fire starters. Many a trip was made to the garage to shovel a bucket of shoe heels first, followed by buckets of coal. Winters were especially labor intensive, but coal was also needed in the summer to fire up the cook stove.

There was no running water. Mawzy kept her wringer washing machine in the wash house, between the garage and the main house. It stood on cinder blocks so as not to sink into the dirt floor. A bench pump, used to draw water from the well, and a basin sat next to the washing machine. Following the wash, clothes were placed in a galvanized tub for transport to the clothesline. Two wooden posts around thirty feet apart were driven into the ground on the back side of the house as a sturdy base for the line. Water was pumped not only for washing clothes but for drinking, bathing, and washing dishes. A water kettle was always being carried back and forth from the wash house to the main house. Beyond the bench pump was a root cellar and additional space to store items like a galvanized bathtub, gardening tools and canning jars. An outhouse was in the very west corner of the lot, about 25 yards from the house.

Move-in day was exciting and exhausting. As Eleanor and Gloria June carried their personal belongings into their room, an argument erupted over who got which bed. The iron twin beds, which had been purchased at the Greenwood Coal Company Store, were placed beside each other, with the heads toward the back wall. Eleanor plopped her suitcase on the bed closest to the west window.

"That's my bed," Gloria June said.

"Says who? I'm the oldest. I get to pick first."

"I don't like that corner. It's scary."

"Too bad, fraidy cat."

"I'm gonna go tell Mother you mean to me," Gloria June shouted and then started wailing as she ran out the bedroom door in search of Mawzy.

Billy was pouting because he didn't have a bed of his own, so he got in on the conflict. As Mawzy was carrying Gloria June back to the bedroom, he chimed in.

"Ya'll are a bunch of crybabies. At least you got a bed. You took mine away from me. Now I've got to sleep with Mother."

"Billy, I don't want to hear another word from you. This is the best we can do for now. You'll get your own bed some day before long," Mawzy emphasized as she was grabbing Billy by the collar. "Now go take the coal bucket out back and get some coal so it will be handy before we head to bed." Billy started to protest but when Mawzy put her hand on her hip and pointed her index finger at him he knew he'd best be moving on. Mawzy didn't like the situation either. She knew

Eleanor and Gloria June with their Shirley Temple dolls.

Billy was missing a father figure as Add was no longer around and Earl was not as accessible.

Mawzy helped the girls move their beds so they each had a bed by a window. The chest of drawers was placed in the corner Gloria June disliked. Once the furniture was rearranged, the girls proceeded to put their clothing items into the

114

rickety dresser drawers, with Gloria June mimicking Eleanor's actions. They proudly displayed their Shirley Temple dolls on top of the bed quilts Mawzy had made.

After things calmed down, Mawzy hung family pictures, displayed a few trinkets and put her own things away. Just before dusk she stoked the fire in both stoves and proceeded to fix a supper of biscuits with pork and gravy, home canned green beans and peaches. The Hoosier cabinet worked like a charm. She promised sugar cookies the next day. Not long after the kids were asleep, Mawzy headed to bed as well. She was bone tired. She prayed, thanking God for a roof over her family's head, for her teaching job to support them and for the help of her extended family. She cried herself to sleep as she agonized over what she could have done differently to save her marriage. Being a failure did not feel good to her. When around the kids she kept a stiff upper lip as she wanted to model her strengths, not her weaknesses.

The economy had been slowly working its way out of the Great Depression but took another sharp turn for the worse the fall of 1937. Mawzy took a 12% cut in pay. She didn't always get paid on time but was glad to have a job. So many others didn't. She racked her brain for ways to cut corners.

She started making more of the kid's clothes from cotton flour sacks. When flour companies realized how many sacks were recycled into clothing, they started printing patterns on them as a marketing technique. Dozens of patterns became available including baby patterns, florals and toys. Labels and sometimes instructions were printed in washable ink so as not to distract from the finished product. On one trip to the store in Rainelle for staples, Mawzy decided to send the girls on a mission. Billy had already wandered off on his own.

"Eleanor, why don't you take Gloria June to the flour aisle and pick out a sack pattern you would like for a skirt?" Mawzy asked.

Eleanor was excited they were given permission to take off on their own. By the time Mawzy caught up with them decisions had been made.

"Mother, I like this one. It has tiny white ducks all over it," Eleanor pointed out.

"Mother, lookie here. This one's a bear. Can you make me that bear? Oh, and here's one with cowboys on it. Get it for Billy," Gloria June added.

It didn't take long for Billy, Eleanor, and Gloria June to find fun and happiness in Mawzy's first home.

"I reckon that would be alright," Mawzy replied after a moment's thought. She didn't really need three bags of flour but knew they would eventually be used.

Over time Mawzy made tie back, flour sack curtains for all the windows in the house.

By spring, the whole back yard was plowed under for a garden. Mawzy was no stranger to raising crops as

she had worked many an hour in Poppy and Mommy's garden and her Gentry Holler garden. Between riding herd on the kids and getting her teacher's recertification in July she was able to raise and can a lot of vegetables for the fall and winter. Excess potatoes, carrots, turnips, and parsnips were stored in the root cellar.

Two apple trees were planted – one in the back near the garage and one in the east corner of the front yard. Mawzy also loved flowers. Hollyhocks lined the back of the house and were one of her favorites.

Over time, a lilac and rose bush were planted in the front yard and a flower garden of perennials and annuals, ringed by stones, gave the back yard color. The apple tree by the garage and the rose bush are still there. The apple tree in the front landed on top of the house after it was uprooted by a tornado in April 1974.

Food was plentiful but Gloria June hated anything to do with a vegetable. All she wanted to eat was puffed wheat. It was worrisome for Mawzy, so she tried a

scare tactic, "Gloria June, you are going to get in your swing one of these days and blow away if you don't eat something more than puffed wheat."

To stretch the coal supply, Mawzy banked the fire in the winter before heading to school. By the time the four of them got home, it was often freezing inside the house. She wrapped the kids in quilts, promised them a hot cup of apple cider and set about getting the fire started in the potbelly and cook stoves. While waiting for the house to warm up she often read them a story. One of their favorites was *The Little Engine That Could.* Mawzy liked it too. Gloria June begged for stories from her *Bible* story book.

Though financially strapped, Mawzy wanted to make the first Christmas in their new home special. One Saturday in early December, she planned an outing for them to go cut their own tree on Poppy and Mommy's land. They bundled up and headed out on foot to the home place. After settling on a tree, Poppy helped them load it in his truck and took them back to their house. The next day Mawzy popped corn, helped the kids string the popped kernels on a thread, then wrapped the string around the tree. They made construction paper ornaments, with Eleanor and Billy helping Gloria June since she was not old enough to handle the scissors on her own. Mawzy arranged for Santa to come to the house on Christmas Eve. She started looking out the window at the designated time, then yelled for the kids to come look for Santa. As he got closer to the house Eleanor and Billy were beside themselves. Gloria June was guardedly curious but when he got to the door she ran and hid as she was afraid of the man with the big belly and white beard. She remembered him from his visit to Poppy's house. Treats for the holiday included homemade candy and ice cream

Billy, above, and Gloria June, right, showing off their wheels.

made from snow. Mawzy's gifts to the kids were small, inexpensive toys and homemade clothing items. Poppy and Mommy helped by giving Billy his very own bed, Eleanor a sled and Gloria June a tricycle. A deal was made that the trike and sled were to be shared among all. It was a magical time.

Eighteen months later, a big Fourth of July picnic was held at Poppy and Mommy Walker's house. Mommy and her girls put forth a feast of fried chicken, potato salad, green beans, wilted greens with hot bacon dressing, cucumbers and onions in vinegar, deviled eggs, sliced tomatoes, buttermilk biscuits, homemade blackberry jam and cherry pie. Everyone loved Mommy's buttermilk biscuits. Said they couldn't be beat. After all were bellied up to outside, makeshift tables, the conversation turned to Mawzy's sister, Thelma, who had recently moved to Silver Spring, Maryland to take a job as a telephone operator at the Shepherd Exchange Telephone Company. Sister Pansie's boyfriend, Howard, said his brother also lived in Washington, D.C. area.

"Hey Pansie, we should go up there sometime to see Thelma and my brother, Bob," Howard suggested.

"Yur crazy as hell if you think I'd approve of you two takin' off together like that," Poppy interjected.

"It sounds like fun," Glenna said. "You know what. I could come along and be your chaperone. That is if Mommy would keep Mary Jenny for me. Gracie, maybe you could come along too since you're not taking any classes this summer." Two summers prior Mawzy had completed certification requirements for the Normal Course at Concord State Teacher's College which allowed her to renew her teacher's certificate for five years.

Mary Jenny had just turned three years old. Glenna, Mawzy's favorite sister, married Doctor Jett who was much older than she. They lived in the house just across the creek from Mawzy, where Dr. Jett operated his medical practice.

Glenna (Sister), and Dr. Jett

Glenna got pregnant not long after they were married. Unfortunately, Dr. Jett died before Mary Jenny was born.

"Eleanor and I could baby sit Mary Jenny and Gloria June," Wanda piped in when she caught wind of the conversation.

"I don't know," Mawzy countered. "I'm not sure you two would stick to your babysitting offer and there's the garden to look after."

"Gracie, you and Glenna could use a break," Mommy noted. "I don't mind keepin' your kids. They're gettin' old enough they're not much trouble anymore. The garden will be fine for a few days without you fussin' over it. I'm sure Thelma would be thrilled to see ya'll!" Mommy was concerned about Thelma living in a big city all by herself and thought a visit from family would be beneficial for all.

Right then and there plans for a week-long trip were made. Howard would be driving to Washington, D. C. with three Walker women in tow. The women's cost would be minimal as Howard offered to pay for the gas and they would be staying with Thelma. Three weeks later the four of them were on their way. It would turn out to be the trip of a lifetime for Mawzy.

Mawzy was almost 32 years old, in the prime of her life, and had never had a vacation or traveled far from home. Without responsibilities to weigh her down, her playful side emerged. Her hand-written travel log of the trip found its way into her hope chest. It was in a 3 x 5 booklet with a cork covering.

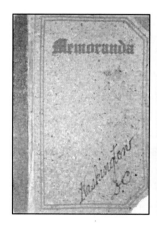

Mawzy's big adventure. Clockwise: Mawzy's trip journal, Pansie, Mawzy and Sister, Howard in front of car; The National Zoo, and a resident of the zoo.

Memoranda was imprinted in red on the front. In the lower right corner, Mawzy had neatly written in cursive - *Washington, D.C.* Her first entry documented a departure time of 9 a.m. on Sunday, July 23, itemized their route through the hills on narrow two-lane roads and into the D.C. metro area and noted a 5:30 p.m. arrival at Thelma's apartment. They made great time, especially without the benefit of a modern interstate highway. Mawzy wrote: *After supper, chased around over town. Went to D.C. and Georgetown to Howard's bro. Came home, talked, and ate; went to bed about 1:00 a.m.*

Monday was a big-eyed day with visits to the Washington Monument, the Lincoln Memorial, and the Arlington National Cemetery. Mawzy described the cemetery as a place *where the American heroes sleep.*

Thelma had Tuesday off work, so they all went to the National Zoological Park. Sometimes Mawzy's handwriting was hard to decipher. She took notes as she walked. Didn't want to miss a thing. Didn't want to depend on her memory at the end of an action-packed day. Her trusty Kodak camera also accompanied her every step of the way. At the zoo she noted: *Saw animals and birds from all parts of the world. Took two rolls of films.*

Mawzy was in awe of it all but she wrote the most about the Washington National Cathedral. *It is an impressive mass of 14th century Gothic and compares with most of the great cathedrals of Europe. It was started in 1907 and is only about one third finished; will be 1/10 mi. long when completed. It is not built by the Gov., but by contributions of people. Saw many people's tombs in here, one of which was Pres. Wilson's. The Rose Window in the north transept...tells the story of The Last Judgment. Christ is in the center. The other pictures above him represent the good things and the lower pictures the evil things...*

Because they were on a shoestring budget, most meals were eaten at Thelma's place. After Tuesday's tour she noted: *...we came home to Silver S. Had a grand dinner. After dinner went to Glen Echo Park. Went through 'hole' crazy house; Penny house; had fortunes told. Everyone was afraid to ride the roller coaster but Thelma and she didn't want to ride by herself. Ate Polar Bear frozen custard. Gol dern I like um. Came home and went to bed. Shore did now.*

The next day they toured the Museum of Natural History. Mawzy recorded...*saw within its stately walls all the objects of natural history; plant to geological and mineralogical specimens belonging to U.S. - Liked the Indians best.* From there they went to John Wilkes Booth's home and drove to Alexandria to see the construction of the new airport. The next entry reported the evening's events. *Wed night Sis and I went to a show. Pansie and Howard to golf game. Name of the show - Lucky Night with Robert Taylor and Myrna Loy... Shore did now.* It was a comedy of a rich girl teaming up with an intriguing and handsome homeless man. They ended up at Thelma's work to observe her in action. At day's end she wrote: *Took Thelma home after work 11: P.M. Told some nice jokes and went to bed - Gosh dern I like em. Nice egg sandwich.*

The economy didn't stabilize until the United States entered World War II. Young men were shipped overseas left and right. Mawzy saw neighbors and students from her earlier teaching days head off to war. It became even more personal for her when one after the other of her three brothers entered the military. The youngest, Uncle Chester, was the first to enlist in the service and joined the army.

While he was in basic training, he came home on leave. On his 10-day furlough he married his high school sweetheart Mildred Carter, affectionately known as Biddie because she was so petite. Mommy Walker fixed them a wedding dinner. Shortly after that, he was shipped overseas. Mommy was

Earl and Chester in uniform

121

Aunt Biddie and Uncle Chester as newlyweds.

a mess. When she got the news her baby boy was headed into battle, she sobbed," I'll never see my boy alive again." She was right. She lost her life shortly after Uncle Chester was almost killed.

Earl entered the navy and was eventually stationed in the Pacific Basin. He was a pharmacist's mate third class. He also survived. Said all he ever did in the military was pull teeth. His downfall came when he got home from the war. He had pined away for his sweetheart, Josephine, and was overjoyed to be with her again. They dated for seven years. He proposed marriage and bought her a diamond engagement ring. She led him on. He helped her get through college. She was Gloria June's roommate during Gloria's freshman year. Ended up she married a doctor she was also dating. She didn't have the guts to tell Earl, so sister Jewell broke the news. "I would rather have got news she died," was Earl's only comment. It broke his heart forever. He remained single and became a bitter man for the rest of his life. At one point he got a woman pregnant. She filed a paternity suit and won so he was required to pay child support. On his checks he wrote in the memo "for the little bastard" and eventually moved to Michigan to avoid making payments. Mawzy's son, Billy, and Earl remained close. Earl was like a father figure to him. Billy sought his company as much as possible as he got tired of always hanging out with the girls. He didn't want to become sissified.

Lawrence enlisted but had medical issues so was released from duty. So typical of sibling rivalry, Chester and Earl gave him grief and accused him of faking illness to avoid war.

Mawzy did everything she could for the cause. War bonds were heavily promoted. Newspaper ads suggested *"Everybody, Every Payday, 10%. You get back $4 for every $3 you invest when held to maturity (10 years)!"* Bonds could be purchased through a payroll saving plan or a bank Victory Club. There were local "Door Knocker" drives. Mawzy bought 10 cent stamps as often as she could at the Springdale post office, located in the Twohig's private residence. She walked by there all the time on her way to and from the Springdale school. The stamps were pasted in an official Stamp Album until enough were collected to buy a bond.

Victory Gardens were also touted to help the effort. Tons of food was shipped overseas with fewer workers at home to process it. In 1942, West Virginia's Victory Garden Council had a "Food for Freedom" campaign which was outlined in the Beckley *Raleigh Register*. Every rural family would be visited by a community garden leader. Civic organizations, 4-H Clubs and agriculture students assisted in the sale of seed packages. Eleanor, Billy, and Gloria June, as members of the Meadow Bridge 4-H Club, helped sell seed packets. For $1.25 one could

buy a bundle of seed packages for a 20 foot by 30 foot garden plot that would feed a family of five. Individually, the seeds cost over $5. Extension Service County agents gave presentations and provided pamphlets on growing techniques. A map of the best garden lay out was plotted for tomatoes, cabbage, cauliflower, peas, beans, cucumbers, citron, green onions, spinach, radishes, lettuce, corn, potatoes, onions, carrots, beets, and parsnips. Seed companies also offered guidance. The intent was to have families become more self-sufficient and provide excess produce for the war effort.

Victory Gardens were right up Mawzy's alley. She took advantage of all the program had to offer and gladly diverted some of her bounty to the troops. Community lots were encouraged. Mawzy pondered a Springdale School garden plot, but decided the soil was too clay ridden and rocky to yield much produce.

The program was a huge success. By 1943 there were around 18 million Victory Gardens in the United States alone. Other countries were also involved.

The summer of 1944 cast a bit of doubt over the success of Victory Gardens. The Walker family decided to venture out to nearby Babcock State Park for a picnic. Mawzy and some of her sisters began placing food items on a wooden picnic table. Victory sandwiches had been prepared.

"I'm starved," Lawrence yelled as he jumped in line and began picking up his food. He removed his sandwich from the wax paper wrapping. After taking the first bite he lifted the bread and peered inside where he discovered lettuce was the

only ingredient. "If this is the best our country can do, looks like we're about to get whopped!" was his conclusion.

Rationing was another nationwide program designed to protect needed resources and was administered by the Office of Price Administration (OPA). It started in 1941 with tires, then in 1942 with gasoline, neither of which concerned Mawzy as she had no car nor a driver's license.

That changed when sugar and coffee became rationed as they were two items Mawzy liked to have in ample supply. From there it became more and more complicated. Ration Boards administered

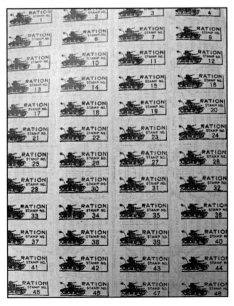

the program. One day after school in late February 1943 Mawzy pulled the *Raleigh Register* out of her newspaper box and a big article about the next wave of requirements grabbed her attention. She read:

> *"This week all families must live on the canned goods they have and next week, when sales are resumed, they take a new kind of ration book to the store. Everyone has 48 points to "spend" in March and families may pool their points. It will take, for example, 14 points to buy a standard size can of corn or green beans... Every family must send a representative to register for the new ration books."*

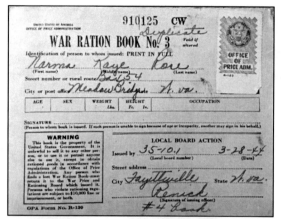

Mawzy figured there would be 192 points per month for her family. A long list of point values for canned, bottled, and frozen fruits and vegetables was printed. Red and blue wooden tokens were given as change to purchase rationed items in the future. Red could be used for meat and blue for processed foods. Mawzy sighed at the complexity of it all, cut the list from the paper for future reference, thought about when she could register for her ration books and was relieved she had food set aside from her previous gardens.

Eleanor started 7th grade at Meadow Bridge High School in 1942. The high school published a school newspaper, *The Montrado*, which was the former name of Meadow Bridge. Some said it was an Irish word meaning "long meadows." Others claimed it to be Spanish, meaning "mountain glen." Eleanor was proud to bring the paper home for all to see, especially if her name appeared. She and Mawzy's sister, Wanda, were best of friends, were in the same grade, and eventually got involved in the production of the paper. Mrs. Celeste Arritt was the sponsoring teacher. She held her students to a high standard and it showed in the newspaper, which usually received Quill and Scroll superior ratings. Every issue during the war included ads for war bonds. Dr. Seuss' "Starve the Squander Bug – Buy War Bonds" ads were featured. Students also wrote war related articles. They covered Ration Books and what to expect, lists of former students in the armed services and the importance of victory gardens.

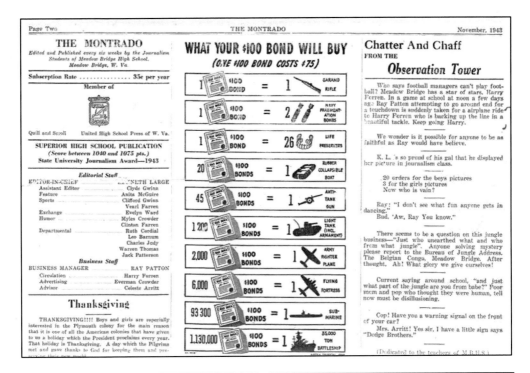

The "Squander Bug" is that unpredictable urge which tells you to go ahead and throw your money away—that just buying one more thing won't add to inflation, or help create a shortage of goods. Don't listen to the "Squander Bug." He's all set to gobble up every dollar he can. He thrives on your extravagance. Starve him with War Bonds!

Feature articles on the establishment of the high school Victory Corps were printed. Students in the 9th through 12th grades were asked to spearhead the collection of books, fats, hose, and tin cans; to sell war bond stamps; and to write to the troops. Eleanor was in the 8th grade so was too young to be in the Corp.

However, when Mawzy saw the article, she started saving her old hose with runs. Fats were being collected to use in the production of explosives. This was a tough one for Mawzy as she used her bacon fat for cooking. She reluctantly decided she would split each batch between her personal use and the war.

A *Montrado* article on a tin can drive was featured in one issue and was promoted as a contest where the boy and girl who collected the most cans received a medal. The article ended with a push to action as follows – *As everyone knows tin cans are vitally needed to help win the war. If you could only bring one tin can a day, it would soon amount to a lot. Don't just bring one, bring all you can. Just think, one tin can may help kill a Jap or a German.*

Another article, entitled *"Poor Hitler???"* had students responding to: *This is what we would do to Hitler if we had him all to ourselves.* Examples of replies were: *"Make a good dummy." "Use him for a dish mop." "Make two pieces of trash instead of one." "Put him in the back seat of my fresh air taxi and freeze him to death."* Mrs. Arritt's reply was *"Pour aqua regia acid down his trap."*

With millions of our men off to war, it became difficult for businesses to find enough workers to keep their operations going. Women came out of the household to fill occupancies across the country. They were the Women's Ordnance Workers, more affectionately known as "Rosie the Riveters" and their symbol became the WOW bandana. Meadow River Lumber Company in Rainelle started filling job openings with women. Mawzy found out about it, took the railroad motor car to Rainelle after school was out for the summer, made application, and was hired to begin making shoe heels the summer of 1943. The company's main war effort was building long ship beams for British submarine chasers. Men were pulled from the shoe heel job for the ship beam work. Mawzy had just renewed her teaching certificate the previous spring, so summer school was not necessary at this juncture. The extra money was welcomed as the kids were becoming more expensive to feed and clothe. Each morning during the week Mawzy and the kids would take off in the morning walking together. When they arrived at the Highway 20 intersection Mawzy would turn left toward the train depot to catch the motor car and the kids would turn right to walk to Poppy and Mommy's place to hang out with Wanda.

232-32-4803
SOCIAL SECURITY ACCOUNT NUMBER

GRACE LOUISE CAMPBELL
Springdale, W. Va.

WORKER'S NAME AND HOME ADDRESS

EMPLOYER'S NAME The Meadow River Lumber Co.
IF WORKER'S NAME IS CHANGED MAKE REQUEST FOR ACCOUNT NUMBER CARD BEARING NEW NAME ON FORM OAAN-7003 WHICH MAY BE SECURED FROM ANY SOCIAL SECURITY BOARD FIELD OFFICE.

While working at the lumber company, a friend told Mawzy milkweed pods were being gathered as stuffing for armed forces' life jackets. She came home that night and told the kids they could help their uncles and the other soldiers overseas by collecting milkweed pods, which were plentiful in the area, while she was working. She took them out behind the house to look for the pods so they would know what to do in the following days.

The war ended on September 2, 1945 with Japan's surrender, but American soldiers couldn't get home right away due to the logistics of shipping them back. The country got impatient and "Bring the Boys Back Home" became the rally cry. Mawzy scanned the newspaper every day for any news of when her brothers would get home. Earl didn't get back from the Pacific until the following April. When Chester got home in November, the household had changed. Mommy Walker was not there to greet him with a big hug and a home cooked feast. Though Wanda had stepped up as Poppy's housekeeper since Mommy's death, she was busy with high school studies and activities, so the home place had become a bit run down over the past year. Chester was glad to be back to his bride but was distressed. Back then it was called "shell shock." He knew it was a miracle he survived. Many didn't. The family gave Chester a picture of Mommy Walker in her casket. He was so torn up he refused to look at it then and never did. He went wild with drinking and carrying on for a while. He didn't talk much about the war for years but had nightmares until the day he died. Before his death he finally shared a bit of his experience.

Uncle Chester after the war.

At age 22, Uncle Chester was a "medic" for the 401st Glider Infantry 2nd Bn Co. G from Normandy to Berlin. He said he chose to be trained as a medic so he wouldn't have to kill anyone. He was the most decorated member of the family and wrote of his experience in a book titled *Glide to Glory* which showcased unedited personal stories from the airborne glider men of World War II. A summary of his story is as follows.

As their glider was headed into Normandy the morning of June 7, 1944, they avoided a mid-air collision with another glider and went between two trees which sheared off the wings, leaving the fuselage to plunge into the ground. When the glider hit ground, the floor was gone. As Chester's feet hit the ground it forced his seatbelt under his rib cage making it almost impossible to breathe. Someone cut his belt to free him. He then began tending to all kinds of injuries – broken legs and arms, cuts, and bruises. Both pilots were unconscious. Four men were killed. Two paratrooper medics helped. Out of 30 men, only 14 were able to move on to combat. They had landed somewhere between Chef-du-Pont and St. Mere Eglise.

They bivouacked near Chef-du-Pont in the late afternoon of June 8. By day-light of June 9 they got word they were going to attack the causeway. Having no combat experience, they had no idea what lay ahead. When they went as far as they could, everyone was ordered to get down as low as possible. They were half-way back from the head of the column. Chester said if their troop had been at the head, he would likely have been killed.

On the morning of June 10, the Allies' anti-tank gun destroyed the German tank on the causeway. Machine guns were going off in all directions. Mortar shells were plastering the area. By the time Chester reached the causeway there were many wounded soldiers for him to attend while avoiding being taken out himself. The carnage he saw that day cannot be imagined.

The Germans launched a counterattack after midnight but were pushed back, leaving the bridgehead intact. The next morning Chester's time was spent picking up bodies of men killed the previous day. His company held position until June 14. Their plan was to attack and take a road junction. The hedgerows were almost impossible to get through. They didn't get far before the Germans opened fire. Word traveled for a "medic up front." Chester started out crawling. When he reached an opening in the hedgerow, he raised up just as a mortar shell fell nearby. Shrapnel hit him on the right side of his face and he fell to his knees. A concussion knocked him out, but he soon recovered. Blood was flowing freely so he placed a compression bandage over the wound and got a blood clot to form. Then he realized his helmet was gone. At that point he understood why you don't wear the strap under your chin. He was evacuated to an English hospital for 20 days, then ended up back in training for the next air drop in Holland. The newspaper reported that his wife, Biddie, received a telegram stating that Pvt. Chester Walker was seriously wounded in France. Similar articles about those wounded in the war were common.

From there he went to Belgium in the Battle of the Bulge where he earned his second purple heart when a gunshot pierced his lung.

In 2020 a Presentation of Medals Ceremony was held in Chester's honor.

Biddie, as his widow, received thirteen medals for his service during World War II. A Certificate of Merit for outstanding performance of military duty was received.

"For heroic conduct in action on 30 September 1944, about four miles from Groesbeek, Holland. During a night counterattack, Private First-Class Walker, a Medic...moved from one wounded man to another administering first aid despite intense enemy fire. His coolness and continued devotion to duty under fire proved especially inspirational to the line troops."
Signed by James M. Gavin, Major General, U.S. Army, Commanding.

School Days: Nature and the Playground

In Nature's infinite
book of secrecy
A little can I read.
Shakespeare, Preface to *The Teaching of Nature Study*

The wooded arms of mother nature wrapped around Springdale Elementary, interrupted by only a highway curving around one side and the railroad tracks in the cut circling on the other.

A curved, unpaved road meandered up the hill toward the back of the schoolhouse. Mawzy walked or later drove this path which was about a mile from her house. In the early days when the weather was snowy, Guy, a retired coal miner and family friend, hitched a horse to a buggy

Snowed under but school was still in session.

with runners. He picked up Mawzy and several of the school kids to give them a ride to and from school.

Mawzy had a great love of nature and what better place to observe it than in the hills of southern West Virginia. One of her favorite college textbooks was *The Teaching of Nature Study*. I found it nestled among several other textbooks she saved. In the first section she underlined three passages that became some of the guidelines for her life's work.

"Nature-study cultivates the child's imagination..."

"Nature-study cultivates in the child a love of the beautiful..."

"But, more than all, nature-study gives the child a sense of companionship with life out of doors and an abiding love of nature."

A part of her course work was field study. I discovered an 82-page composition notebook chocked full of observations from her explorations.

She illustrated and wrote detailed descriptions of nine different birds' feet, feathers, and beaks. Birds such as hawks, owls and sparrows were featured. She described feathers as the bird's clothing.

129

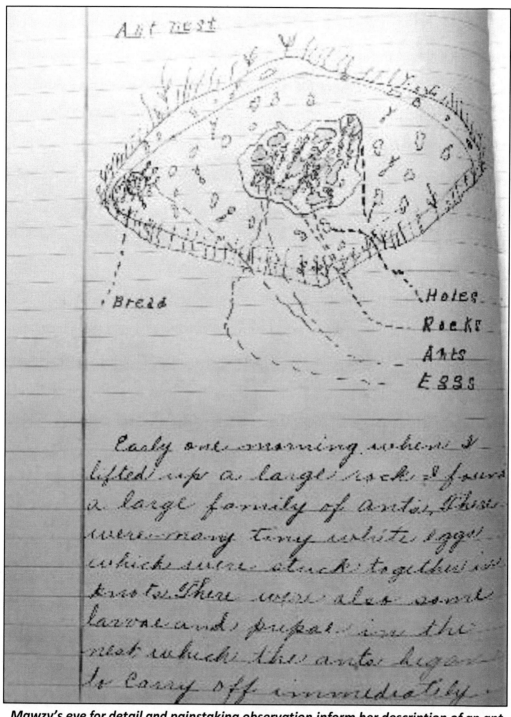

Ant nest

Bread

Holes · · · · ·
Rocks — — —
Ants · · · — · · ·
Eggs — · — · —

Early one morning when I lifted up a large rock, I found a large family of ants. There were many tiny white eggs which were stuck together in knots. There were also some larvae and pupae in the nest which the ants began to carry off immediately.

Mawzy's eye for detail and painstaking observation inform her description of an ant colony.

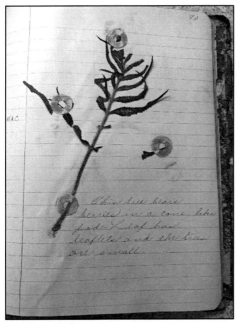

Mawzy turned her love of nature into hands-on coursework.

Fish, salamanders, snails, honeybees, ants, and grasshoppers were also studied, described, and illustrated. A chart of galls, abnormal growths on certain plants, was laid out on one page and included seven plants, such as goldenrod and milkweed. The shape of the gall and the parasite associated with it were noted.

Mawzy also gathered and pressed leaves from 32 different trees and described their structure. Specimens ranged from the sycamore tree to four different kinds of maple, from the tree of heaven to the pawpaw and Indian cigar tree and from

131

the ginkgo to the linden. Though fragile, most of the leaves remain intact. She made an "A" on the project.

Mawzy brought nature into the classroom through art. Generations of students cherished going on field trips in the spring in search of wildflowers and tree leaves to identify and press in their book. Finding a Jack-in-the-Pulpit was coveted by the students. Some of the field trips included a picnic. In her early teaching days when Gloria June, Eleanor and Billy were in school, she and the students walked along the crest of Springdale hill for about a mile until they came upon a natural basin the locals called Wallow Hole. Black bears, the state animal, came to bathe there, thus the name Wallow Hole.

On some outings, students extracted fungi from the sides of trees. Once harvested and back in the classroom, they etched a picture on the top and wrote their name on the back. The finished piece of art was placed on a shelf in the back of the room to dry. Each dried fungus was akin to a scrimshaw etching.

In the fall Mawzy harvested gourds from her garden, brought them to school and had the kids create animals with them. Swans, ducks, and geese were popular as they looked the most realistic.

In front of the schoolhouse was an upper playground about the size of a football field. There were grassy areas, areas of orange clay-laced dirt and rocky terrain.

The playground equipment was spread out straight away and to the left of the porch.

There were three seat swings with long chains attached to a metal pole. Swinging high enough to "wrap the pole" was attempted many a time. Though it couldn't be done, that didn't stop anyone. Once the swing reached the height of the pole it dropped back down with a violent jolt. The most promising results were double pumping with one student sitting and the other standing on the same swing.

Three seesaws sat behind the seat swings. They were made of green painted wood with a metal handle to grasp for stability. After the Beatles came on the scene in America, my friends and I sang "She Loves You" to the top of our lungs while we kept the rhythm with our ups and downs. "Boogie Woogie Bugle Boy" by the Andrews Sisters was Mom and Aunt Eleanor's favorite seesaw song. Next to the seesaws was a large, shiny metal slicky slide and merry-go-round. A monkey bar was later added to this area.

The most coveted piece of playground equipment was the hand swings. Each swing was a single long chain with two handlebars on the end. The top of each chain was attached to a rotating ring mounted on a telephone-sized metal pole.

Above, playground with swings and seesaws to left and lower ball field in distance. Below, Cousin Marty on monkey bar.

How do you like to go up in the swing,
Up in the air so blue?
Oh, I do think it is the pleasantest thing,
Ever a child can do!

Excerpt of *The Swing* by R. L. Stevenson taken from poems to accompany *Come and Ride, Tags and Twinkle, Good Times on Our Street and Friendly Stories* readers; submitted by Mawzy as a part of her course work)

If enough kids were on the hand swings, great heights could be achieved. Everyone took off running in the same direction until lifted off the ground by centrifugal force.

One morning before school, having achieved great success flying high on the hand swings, I moved over to a seated swing for a rest. Others moved in for their turn on the hand swings. There were four kids on the swings when right before my very eyes the center pole started to topple and fell to the ground. Fortunately for those of us on the seated swings the pole fell in the opposite direction. Three of the kids on the hand swings got up from the ground and appeared to be shaken, but alright. Mae was not moving. Her younger sister, Eve, came running over to see what was happening.

"That's my sister on the ground," Eve yelled. "She's bleeding." Eve started wailing as she hugged Mae and, in the process, got blood on her white blouse.

Mawzy was quickly summoned and the rest was a blur as we were instructed to head to our classrooms. An ambulance came to take Mae to the hospital. The school did not have a telephone at the time so Mawzy sent Cousin Marty and a friend to the closest home with a phone to call for an ambulance.

It was hard to concentrate on our studies that day. Eve was in my classroom and I couldn't help but stare at her bloodied blouse and worry about Mae.

That evening I overheard Mawzy explaining the accident to Mom. She was clearly distraught.

"I can't believe this happened," Mawzy agonized. "I just had all the playground equipment inspected last month and the report came back that everything met the safety check. How could they have missed the rust on the hand swing pole just below the ground? I should have paid more attention myself. From now on I surely will. I'm worried about Mae. I do hope she'll be alright."

Mae's parents were not happy, which was understandable, and this was particularly hard on Mawzy. All the gossip didn't help either. I even heard it from some of the school kids. Mawzy felt she had let one of her kids down. In her hope chest, she kept a letter from The University of Virginia Hospital concerning the prognosis along with a list of bills not fully covered by insurance. Fortunately, Mae eventually recovered from the fall.

The hand swings were never reinstalled. The pole and chains laid on the floor of the furnace room for years after the incident.

Where there are kids at play, accidents will happen. Though not as dramatic, several kids were playing a wild game of tag on a damp spring morning. The temperature was as high as it had been for months, so running on the thawing playground was treacherous. Richard was "it" and was in hot pursuit of my cousin, Rhonda. She ran around to the back of the schoolhouse, slipped on a soggy patch, and landed in the coal pile. In pain, she looked at her leg and saw a gapping bloody cut. Richard ran into the school and found Mawzy.

After seeing all the blood, Mawzy calmed Rhonda, told her everything would be OK, ran back into the kitchen through the back door and grabbed several wet cloths. She gently cleaned Rhonda's leg, wrapped it as best she could and helped Rhonda into her car. She instructed the other two teachers who had come out to see what was going on to ride herd on her classroom while she was gone. She hopped in the car, drove to Rhonda's house to pick up her mom, Aunt Biddie, and the three of them hightailed it to Dr. Davis' office in Rainelle. Doc cleaned the coal dirt out of the wound and stapled it together. Once fixed up, Mawzy drove Rhonda and Aunt Biddie back to their home then headed back to school.

"I have a doozy of a scar as a reminder of that day," Rhonda recalled. "I will always remember Aunt Gracie's TLC. Oops. I mean Mrs. Campbell."

On the opposite side of the playground equipment was an open area where hopscotch was played. A grid was drawn in the clay-colored dirt, a rock was procured by each participant and hopping commenced. A few of us decided to get in a round of hopscotch one morning before classes started. It had rained the night before, so we had to draw our grid on muddy ground. As I was maneuvering a particularly difficult hop sequence, I slipped and fell. I got covered in mud from head to toe. There was no way to go home to change clothes, so I cleaned up the best I could and was miserable for the rest of the day. At least I didn't get injured.

The hopscotch area was also used for hula-hooping and jump rope. In the winter, it's where we played "fox and geese" in the snow. In preparation, a big circle was stepped off in the snow and was then divided into eight pieces like a big pie. The center was the hub and was the safe spot. A fox was selected to start the game and chased the rest of the kids, who were the geese. Whoever the fox caught was then the new fox. If anyone ran out of the designated lines within the circle, they automatically became the fox.

The split maple tree was a popular hiding spot.

The lower playground, about half the size of the upper playground, was used mostly for softball games. Just beyond that space was a fence and a path that led to the highway near the railroad crossing.

On a wintery morning, I was walking with my friends, Miriam and Kay, toward the snow-covered lower playground. Suddenly, they both started laughing hysterically and pointing toward the ground.

"Look what happened to your skirt!" Kay snorted.

I looked down and to my horror my skirt was around my ankles. It had come unzipped and fallen down. I looked around for any boys nearby and pulled my skirt up as quickly as I could. It was one of my more embarrassing childhood moments.

"The hand-held bell was also used to declare the end of lunch and recess time," Bud noted. "The students took turns in the honor of ringing the bell. They would gleam proudly when it was their turn. Mrs. Campbell gave them the duty so each knew to have a good record so they could be the next bell ringer. Former students often commented on the school bell in fond remembrance."

Rainy days were the only time outdoor play lost its appeal. These days did provide an opportunity to polish up on a game of jacks. And there was a small group of us who worked on a plastic model of a human being. What a great way to learn about the placement of one's organs.

Mother's Day Greetings to Mother

P.S. Be sure to write me every chance you get. I would rather hear from you than anybody else. Don't worry about me because I'm trying to be good. Your one and only son, Billy

Postscript of a letter from Billy to Mawzy

Although it's seldom spoken of
  Throughout the busy year,
The sweet and kindly things you've done
  Are thought of, Mother dear;

And while it isn't mentioned much,
  It's always, always true
That all the finest things in life
  Are being wished for you.

Eleanor
Billy
Gloria

Eleanor, Billy, and Gloria June

Mawzy's Brood

During the war years, the area prospered. Mommy Walker begged Poppy to build a larger house with electricity, running water and an indoor toilet. She and the family had been cramped up in the homestead cabin far too many years. Poppy made her a deal; she could have her house, if she agreed he could build a roadhouse. Mommy reluctantly gave in. Lumber was plentiful and in high demand. Poppy was in the lumber and limestone block business and had three strong young sons to help. Lawrence was already working with him in the block business.

Poppy and Mommy wanted to get more involved in farming, so they also added other buildings onto their property. A chicken house was constructed for up to 60 chickens. Eggs were sold and traded. Behind the chicken house a machine shed was added. A granary for corn storage, a woodshed behind the house and a new barn closer to the house completed their spread.

The roadhouse was named The Dutch Colony. The front porch spanned the building, with an entryway in the middle. A huge intricate oak bar with six matching bar stools was centered in the back of the main room.

Behind the bar hung a large picture entitled "Custer's Last Fight" which was an advertisement for Anheuser Busch. It eventually adorned the wall of Poppy's living room once he gave up the beer business.

The expanded homestead and out- buildings.

Earl, Lawrence, and Chester

A hula girl lamp sat on the back bar counter. Earl likely brought it back from the Pacific when he was stationed there. When the lamp switch was turned on the hula girl swayed her hips which made her fringed skirt wiggle. The lamp also ended up in Poppy's living room. When the grandsons came to visit they always turned it on and lifted the hula skirt to see what was underneath.

Mawzy at Dutch Colony during construction. Below, Earl in front of the finished structure while home on leave.

Seven wooden booths sat in front of the bar – three to the left and four to the right. To the left of the bar was a door leading to a hallway which gave access to the kitchen, one cottage on the right and two cottages on the left. Bar food like hamburgers, hot dogs and fries was on the menu. The Colony's advertisement read, "Room on the Left, Room on the Right, Beer in the Middle."

Mommy was not enthused about the enterprise. As it turned out, she only entered the place once. She was helping in the kitchen. One of Earl's navy buddies was in town and they showed up at The Colony. Mommy came out to greet them and sat at one of the booths to visit for a minute.

When Poppy overheard Earl's buddy say, "Elsie, you're sure a pretty woman." he grabbed his brass knuckles, threw the fellow to the ground, and started pounding him in the face. If it hadn't been for Chester pulling Poppy away, he may have killed the guy.

From that day forth, Mommy referred to The Colony as the "hell hole." Mawzy's attitude was the same as Mommy's – she didn't care to be around alcohol as she felt it was the ruination of her marriage. She steered clear of the place as well. She had enough on her plate as it was with teaching, raising six, eight and ten-year-old and furthering her education. Until she had enough credits to obtain a bachelor's degree, she had to periodically take summer courses to renew her teacher's certificate.

Mommy enjoyed the extra space and the conveniences in her new house. One July evening, after they had lived there for almost four years, the mood was quite festive.

"A blackberry picking excursion was planned for the next day," Gloria June, recalled years later. "Mother and us kids went down home the night before to get a jump start on the morning."

"Mommy Walker was having a great time that evening, acting a fool and dancing through the house with a baggy hat on her head," Biddie, Chester's wife, recalled. "All the kids joined in on the fun." Biddie came over to visit with everyone.

Having had a hard day, Poppy quickly tired of all the commotion and went to bed. Eventually everyone else headed to bed to rest up for the big picking day. In the middle of the night Mawzy heard a strange noise and got up to see what it was. She saw Mommy disoriented and trying to walk down the hall, dragging her left leg. Biddie had been escorting her to Doctor Williams in Beelick Knob in an attempt to get her blood pressure under control.

Mawzy helped Mommy to the back bedroom and realized she'd likely had a stroke. Her left side was paralyzed. Panic set in. Someone called for an ambulance. By the time it arrived Mommy had had a second stroke which, at age 52, took her life. It was July 20, 1944.

"After the ambulance arrived, the medics pulled Mommy through the back window on a cot to prevent the kids from seeing her dead body," Biddie recalled.

Gloria June was nearly 10 years old at the time and remembered Mommy's death being "very sad and scary", as the excitement of the berry picking excursion turned into a tragedy. It was her first memory of someone dying who was important to her.

The funeral was well attended at the Methodist Church in Rainelle. Ministers from two different churches officiated and the Marfrance Quartet sang. Everyone commented it was a lovely service. She was buried at The End of the Trail in Clintonville.

Mommy Walker memorial

You cannot say, you must not say
That she is dead. She is just away!
With a cheery smile,
and a wave of the hand
She has wandered into an unknown land
And left us dreaming how very fair
It needs must be, since she lingers there;
So think of her faring on, as dear,
In the love of There as the love of Here,
Think of her still as the same, and say
She is not dead, she is just away.
I extend my deepest sympathy to you & family
© JAMES WHITCOMB RILEY

Mommy was the glue that held the family together, so her death was difficult for everyone. Wanda was the only child still living at home, so she helped keep the household going for the next three years until she graduated from high school. Her siblings, including Mawzy, pitched in when they could but had their own lives to manage.

141

Poppy was distraught. He realized how much he had taken Mommy for granted, as more of the responsibility at the home place fell on his shoulders. He regretted that only a week before he had been mean to Mommy.

"Mommy had a pot of oatmeal cookin' on the wood burning stove," Biddie remembered. "Poppy came through the kitchen and bumped into the pot handle. Knocked the pot to the floor. He let out a string of cuss words and proceeded to kick that pot all the way across the kitchen floor and clear into the dining room."

"See what I have to put up with all the time," was Mommy's comment to Biddie. It was the last time Biddie was alone with Mommy before her death.

Not long after Chester and Earl returned from the war, Poppy turned The Dutch Colony over to Earl. It was during this time Earl got involved with a woman who was doing laundry for The Colony. She's the one who filed and won the paternity lawsuit.

Since Billy and Earl were thick, Billy was given odd jobs around the place. Eleanor had a job too, after Poppy discovered he'd met his match. One day when Mawzy brought the kids down to the home place Poppy saw Eleanor walk in and asked, "Who the hell are you?"

"I'm in hell and I'm talkin' to the devil," was her quick comeback.

Mawzy wasn't thrilled with Eleanor or Billy working at The Colony. However, learning a work ethic trumped the location of the work. A little extra pocket change wasn't all bad either.

At the end of the evening, after The Colony was closed and the money counted, Eleanor was the courier. She hauled the money out of joint, crossed the road and climbed the hill to the home place. Poppy taught her how to shoot and care for a pistol, which she carried when transporting money. One Saturday afternoon before The Colony's opening time,

Dutch Colony ad in Montrado

Eleanor was cleaning her gun on the porch and a couple of boys around her age walked by and saw what she was doing. They made fun of her and said she didn't know anything about guns. She happened to see a cat going by, loaded the gun and shot the cat dead. The boys took off running and instantly had a new respect for her. They didn't mess with her anymore.

142

Billy, Gloria June, Wanda, Mary Jenny, and Eleanor on a trip to the fish hatchery in White Sulphur Springs. Below right, Eleanor and Gloria June; below left Eleanor, Billy and Gloria June in studio shot.

In her later years, Eleanor loved to tell the cat story and was still proud of her shooting skills.

Wanda and her husband Everett operated The Colony kitchen for a time. After Everett got out of the Navy, he ran a taxi service in Meadow Bridge and liked to stop at The Colony for a beer after work.

One night the fall of 1946 he stopped by when Wanda was working there. She was a senior in high school. They were both smitten. Before long they laid a plan. Over her Christmas break, she invited Eleanor to spend the night with her. They both snuck out the bedroom window, Everett picked them up and away they swept. Eleanor went along to witness their marriage as it was required in West Virginia for anyone under age 18.

They kept it a secret from Poppy Walker for a year. Everyone was excited about Wanda going to West Virginia University as a pre-med student. She got recognition as the first Meadow Bridge High School student to study for a medical degree. Everett drove his motorcycle to WVU to see her as often as he could.

The degree didn't work out. Poppy figured out the situation when Wanda became pregnant and started to show. He was rip-roaring mad and hated Everett who sneaked behind his back and took his baby girl away. Poppy lost his oldest daughter, Mawzy, and his youngest, Wanda, to Christmas elopements. While at The Colony, Wanda and Everett had two girls who often stayed with them in the kitchen, even as babies in a playpen.

The Colony became the family hub. Chester's four kids lived nearby and loved to go there with a nickel in their pocket to buy candy or popsicles from Uncle Earl. They schemed up a way to earn money for their treats. They set up a circus in their backyard and each came up with an act to perform. The oldest boy, Gary, climbed in a pheasant cage and carried on in there as the "Wild Child" act. Featured rides were the swing set and a large baby carriage being pushed at a rapid

Gloria June with cousins Norma Kaye and Mary Jenny.

speed down the side of the hill. Chester and Biddie paid 5 cents per child as their entry fee to the circus.

Eleanor was a tomboy in her younger years. She and Billy fought all the time but were often partners in crime. Gloria June wanted to tag along on their escapades, but they wouldn't let her. She felt she had just as much right to go running around as they did. It was too much like babysitting for them. So, she was always left home in the yard. At least she had her cat, Jingles, to play with and her best neighborhood friends, Polly, Ramona, and Betty Lou came over to visit sometimes. They played house in Mawzy's outdoor wash house and built a fire in the cook stove so they could make fudge. Sometimes they swam in a deep spot in the creek behind Betty Lou's house, but only if an adult was present.

While Sister coped with her husband's death, Mary Jenny stayed with Mawzy quite often. This also provided Gloria June with another playmate.

144

In the summer, Eleanor and Billy liked to jump the coal trucks as they headed up Irish Mountain. Once at the top, they played there for hours. One of their activities was rolling rocks down the hill into a pasture where cattle grazed. They called the process "cutting a rusty" as the rocks were a rust color. It was all a game until Eleanor almost killed one of the cows. The cattle owner approached Mawzy about the problem which put a stop to their travels up Irish Mountain.

Eleanor's fortitude was tested when one of the Fitzgerald boys saw her and Billy playing in the yard and came across the road to see them.

"Billy's a pretty tough guy, ain't he?" he asked Eleanor.

"He's not that tough," was Eleanor's response.

"I'll give you a penny if you go bloody his nose."

"Deal, if it's a shiny penny," Eleanor responded as she marched right over to Billy, punched him in the nose and proceeded to collect her nice shiny penny.

There was an abandoned coal mine drift mouth nearby that often filled with water in the spring after a rainy season. Eleanor, Billy, Wanda and a Fitzgerald boy decided it would be great fun to make a raft so they could row into the drift mouth cave. In secret, they took a few pieces of rough lumber from Poppy Walker's place and confiscated some of the tar Mawzy used to repair the roof. Once the lumber was wrapped together with grape vines, they commenced tarring cracks to waterproof their raft. After many days of labor, the raft was considered worthy of its maiden voyage, so they set out into the drift mouth. As they paddled further in it became darker and darker. The temperature dropped. There were turns to the left and right they had not anticipated. They quickly got disoriented. As they rounded one of the turns, they were in complete darkness. The ceiling became lower, so they had to bend over to avoid bumping their heads. Panic set in. They realized they were lost in the bowels of the mine. They attempted to work their way out of the cave. God was with them that day. After several wrong turns, they made the right one and a speck of daylight led them to the exit. It had started raining while they were in the mine. Had they been lost for too long they would likely have been trapped inside and drowned.

Mawzy knew nothing of the incident until the following New Year's Eve.

"Eleanor. Billy. Gloria June," Mawzy yelled. "Come in the living room." Once the kids were seated on the couch, Mawzy proceeded. "It's New Year's Eve so it's time again for each of you to tell me about all the mischievousness you've been into over the past year. If you come clean, you won't be punished." Mawzy stipulated. After their confessions, Mawzy liked to ask what they had learned from their blunders.

Eleanor and Billy proceeded to tell their raft story and Mawzy was so upset she reneged on her promise.

"You two are as ornery as they come," Mawzy said shaking her head. "I wouldn't have encouraged you to read *The Adventures of Tom Sawyer* if I'd have known you were gonna follow his lead. Eleanor you're just like Huck and Billy you're just like Tom. Do you realize that you almost lost your lives that day? Plus,

145

you took property that wasn't yours without asking. This behavior's not acceptable. I must go back on my word to help you understand that what you did was very wrong. Now I want both of you to go outside and bring me back a keen switch."

"It's not fair. You promised no whoppin' if we fessed up," Billy countered.

"Go on now. The sooner you get the switches, the sooner we can move on."

Billy selected his switch, quickly pulled out his pocketknife and cut a few notches in it to soften the blow. Mawzy caught onto his scheme when the switch broke with the first swat to the back of his legs and made him get another switch. He learned more than one lesson that day.

The following year Mawzy reneged again as the circumstances were just as bad. Billy, Eleanor and one of Billy's friends took Earl's truck without asking and stole some chickens from a nearby farmer. The friend was driving as Billy was throwing chickens in the back of the truck. The farmer caught them in the act and shot at Billy as he was climbing on the truck's sideboard. The three of them tore out of there for Babcock State Park where they cleaned the chickens and cooked them over an open fire pit. Much to their chagrin, the chickens were tougher than boot leather and tasted like cardboard.

Though Gloria June reported on her mischief each year, like pulling Jingles tail and not brushing her teeth, it was never deemed significant enough to warrant further reprimand.

Chores were assigned to each of the kids. Billy's primary responsibilities were to haul coal from the bin to the house and to keep Bossy's feed trough full. He also took care of three outside cats, who were kept around as mousers. Eleanor and Gloria June helped clean house, do laundry, and wash and dry the dishes. Gloria oversaw feeding Jingles. It was all hands on deck in the garden in the summer. When the kids were in school, homework always followed chores. Before Gloria was in school, Mawzy taught her to read while the other two were getting their lessons.

During the school year, once the kids were in bed, Mawzy turned her attention to lesson plans and grading papers.

All three of the kids were intelligent. Eleanor and Gloria June were more into book learning than Billy. All three had Mawzy as their first and second grade teacher. Because of Mawzy's early tutelage, Gloria completed the first and second grade in one year. Eleanor later told that Gloria June had the highest IQ ever recorded at Meadow Bridge.

Mawzy insisted the kids get involved in the local 4-H program, which had become more prevalent during the World War II era. Lucille, wife of brother Lawrence, was the club leader. Having a family eye on the kids when out of Mawzy's sight gave her some comfort. All three kids had their own small plot at as part of Mawzy's Victory Garden. "Feed a Fighter in '43" was the 4-H theme that year. They also participated in scrap metal collection. Mawzy said later she didn't understand why the United States sent scrap metal over to Japan so they could shoot it back at us. The milkweed pods the kids collected for military lifejackets dovetailed into a 4-H effort. The girls signed up for clothing and food projects.

Gloria June's sewing entry the summer before her senior year in high school was a poodle skirt which had just become quite the fashion. She won a ribbon at the West Virginia State Fair. The skirt was made of pink felt with a black and white cat appliqued on it, in memory of Jingles who had recently died. Her bobby socks and saddle oxfords completed the look.

Mawzy racked her brain to come up with a project Billy would find of interest. She poured through the project list with him and he finally chose a couple of projects – entomology and raising a duck. He was always on the search for bugs and became enamored with the idea of raising bees. When Uncle Earl got home from the navy, Billy approached him about helping build a beehive box. Earl gladly obliged. Billy did well with his bee project over the next three years. He even inquired about his bees in the letters he wrote to Mawzy when he was in the military. Not being the best of scholars, his grammar and spelling were poor. He asked: *How about the beas did you every take any honey from them or not. I guess you have by now though.* And about a year later: *So, the bees are still alive, they must be a pretty good bunch, because I had some once before and they died out right away, rember or not.*

Billy's duck project did not turn out so well. The duck disappeared and Gloria June was accused of turning it loose. She got in big trouble but swore to this day she was not the guilty party.

Gloria June was the most active 4-Her of the three. Her name was always showing up in the *Beckley Post-Herald*. By age 12 she started going to Fayette County 4-H camps and roundups at Beckwith.

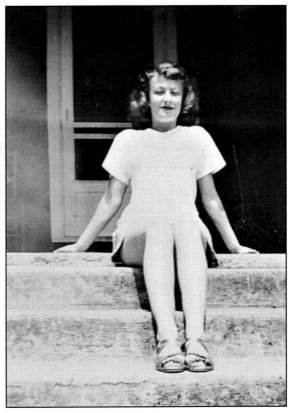

4-H camp bands; Gloria June at Jackson's Mill state 4-H camp.

147

Glamour Girls of 1939

KNOW THEM?

Calendar For April And May

The highlight of April and May will be a combination of picnics, plays and a minstrel. The dates are as follows:
April 18-19—"Scare Crow Creeps"
April 19-22—Easter vacation.
May 2- 3—"Let Me Out of Here"
May 7—Teach Day for Seniors
May 8—Senior party.
May 9-10—Coon Valley Minstrel.
May 13—Sr. Tacky Day.
May 16—Jr. and Sr. Banquet.
May 20—Commencement
May 21—Sr. and Jr. Picnic.

RELIHAN-BENNETT WEDDING HELD

Mrs. Julia Relihan, of Springdale, announces the marriage of her daughter, Josie, to Edis Bennett, of Roanoke, Virginia.

Mrs. Bennett is a graduate of M.B.H.S., and attended Concord College. She has been a teacher at the Meadow Bridge elementary school for many years. Future plans are indefinite pending the termination of the school year.

In World War II, Americans married more than 100,000 foreign brides; in World War I, only 8,000.

Bill's Barber Shop
Quick · Clean Service

NICK'S
The Hamburger King

Eleanor and Wanda in Montrado newspaper: below, Eleanor, Mawzy, and Gloria June with her infamous pigtails, Eleanor's basketball picture.

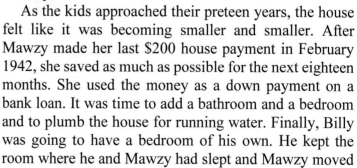

She won a "Lucky Penny" award at age 11; a "Heart H" award at age 14; regional "Healthiest Girl" in the Junior Girls division; and she served as secretary of her club for several years. She was selected as the county camp chief of the Delaware tribe and loved telling the story of having 4-Hers in her tribe raise their hand and say, "O Chief" before addressing her, which she followed with a "How-How." She also attended the state 4-H camp in Jackson's Mill.

As the kids approached their preteen years, the house felt like it was becoming smaller and smaller. After Mawzy made her last $200 house payment in February 1942, she saved as much as possible for the next eighteen months. She used the money as a down payment on a bank loan. It was time to add a bathroom and a bedroom and to plumb the house for running water. Finally, Billy was going to have a bedroom of his own. He kept the room where he and Mawzy had slept and Mawzy moved into the new bedroom which was added to the back of the house and aligned with the other two bedrooms. The addition was pieced together so that there was a small incline when turning from the dining room into this area. It was a pleasant space with the bed positioned under a window. Mawzy moved her cedar hope chest into this room. The bathroom was just off Mawzy's new bedroom. A toilet and built-in cupboards were on the far left. A small sink with a mirror above it anchored the other end. A porcelain bathtub and a small vanity table sat in between. There was a small window above the bathtub.

148

Gloria June would leave the braids behind in high school and blossom, while Eleanor became homecoming queen.

Enoch Cox, with the help of his oldest son, was hired to complete the addition. They also dug a hole and installed a coal furnace in the ground near the house. From there, a trench was hollowed out for the duct work leading to the house. The entire house was covered with asbestos siding so everything would match.

Once Eleanor and Gloria June hit junior high, they became involved in about every school activity imaginable. Wanda was right along beside them. Wanda and Eleanor were in the same grade and were like two peas in a pod. They loved playing basketball. Wanda was the captain of the team as a junior and senior. "Wanda was good because she was tall and rough," Gloria June recalled.

When Gloria June was in grade school, Mawzy always braided her hair into pigtails. As an adult the process was still engrained in Gloria's mind. "Once the braids were done Mother would give me a pat on the butt and send me on my way," she remembered. When headed off to junior high, Gloria's pigtails were still intact. One day she came home in tears and demanded Mawzy cut them off. Kids can be so cruel. *The Montrado* had come out that day and in a "Glamor Glimpses" article it stated, *Gloria June Campbell looks cute with those pigtails, which no one else has.* Off came the pigtails. Mawzy stashed a piece of each pigtail in an envelope in her hope chest.

By eighth grade, Gloria June had matured into a young woman. Her fashion status improved as the years went by. Her section of the senior class poem in *The Montrado* read *Gloria Campbell, a sweet young lassie, Wears clothes that make her look classy.*

Eleanor was more into drama. She signed up and often got a lead role in the high school productions. Gloria, being quieter by nature, was more likely to land a supporting role.

Eleanor was Homecoming Queen; Gloria was a runner-up two years. Both had their picture on the front page of *The Montrado* their senior year as popularity poll winners. They were always on the honor roll.

Brief Biographies was a feature of the school newspaper. Eleanor's was – *likes people who mind their own business; dislikes two-faced people; color, green; type of dress, sport clothes; ambition, beautician; favorite sport, basketball; best friends Jo Ann and Wanda; favorite flower, red roses; outstanding characteristic, very popular; outstanding ability, sewing; scholastic achievement, cheerleader; favorite musician, Dick Haymes.*

Being a beautician was appealing to Eleanor as three of her aunts had taken up the occupation and she found it so glamorous. Her sewing skills came from Mawzy's instruction.

In Gloria's senior yearbook, *The Monte Meade*, she was on almost every page. Her history was shown as class treasurer, yearbook staff, cheerleader, majorette, thespian, choir, 4-H, Girls' Athletic Association, Latin club, dancing, Future Teachers of America, and National Honor Society. She was voted most likely to succeed, best all around, most talented, and best dressed. Scholastically she was in the top ten of her class.

Billy's picture was featured in *The Montrado* when he was in junior high. Under the picture it read: *Billy Campbell, 7th grade's most popular boy, comes from Springdale, 4 feet 9 inches tall, weighs 98 pounds. Bill likes nothing but has a great desire to be a mechanic; he dislikes school very much.*

Billy Campbell — 7th grade's most popular boy — comes from Springdale — 4' 9" tall — weighs 98 pounds — Bill likes nothing but has a great desire to be a mechanic — dislikes school very much.

Billy as a middle schooler.

He never made the honor roll, but he did make the perfect attendance list on occasion, much to Mawzy's credit. He was on the basketball team, but he wasn't all that enthralled with the sport.

Football was more his game which he played from his freshman through junior years. Along with 4-H, these were his extracurricular activities, so his name and picture most often appeared in sports section of the school newspaper. Mawzy was grateful for the male guidance he received from Coach Arritt. He was an excellent football coach who became the school's principal.

School was Billy's platform for pranks. He and his two buddies, Jack and Bill, were always getting into trouble. During a football pep rally, they snuck under the bleachers and lit a firecracker. It was typical of their antics.

On another occasion, they decided to check out the Holy Rollers. Jack drove them to a nearby Saturday night service.

Standing L. to R.: Lawrence Judy, Darrell Goodson, Walter Ballenger, Darrell Goddard, Denville Shaffer, Eugene Jones, Roy Campbell, Ralph Judy, James Osborne, James Fowlkes, Billy McKinney.

Kneeling L. to R.: Carmen Castle, Benny Gwinn, Elwood Brown, Bill Estep, Charles Remley, Harold Goddard, Kermit Goddard, Billy Link and Vernon Shaffer.

Front Row L. to R.: Billy Campbell, John Estep, Dempsey Wickline, Rudy Gwinn, Billy Walkup, Herbert O'Connor, Clyde Smith, and Clive Redden.

Billy cut a different swath than his sisters at school. He was a member of the football team, (front row, far left), and played basketball. He benefitted from the stern guidance of principal and coach Arritt.

When the shouting and rolling started, the boys joined in with so much vigor they unintentionally turned the stove over and caught the church on fire.

The summer Billy turned 16, he got his driver's license and found a job driving a coal truck. He fudged on his date of birth to get a chauffeur's license for truck driving. Though born in 1932, his license

151

stated 1930. He wanted to save all his money to buy a car. "He worked from dawn 'til dusk to get that car," Mawzy remembered. By the end of the summer he had enough to purchase an old red Buick. He loved speed. Couldn't help himself. After reading the following article in the newspaper, he took off the evening of August 16 for the Hell-Driver's Car Show at the West Virginia State Fair in Lewisburg.

Beckley Post-Herald

Joie Chitwood and His Hell-Drivers will try for a new record, leaping a fast-rolling car over seven cars and a big bus. They will drive into flames, engineer thrilling crashes, and entertain Monday fair visitors with a show the like of which has never been shown in West Virginia.

As he sped down the first mountain out of Springdale, he missed a turn, ran off the road and slid down the side of the hill. His radio flew out of the car and was still playing at full blast alongside the road. He was not seriously injured but the car was totaled. The family felt that had he got hurt in the wreck, he would not have started feeling so invincible. He recalled in one of his army letters: *Well it don't seem like it but it has been two years ago today since I had the car wreck.* He did not give up on seeing the Hell-Drivers as he wrote later about going to their show in Columbus, Georgia. Earl claimed Billy had a total of 23 car wrecks, including the final one that took his life years later.

The fall of Billy's 16th year he and Jack decided to go on an excursion and ended up in Akron, Ohio. An accounting of their adventure was reported in the *Akron Beacon Journal* on November 25, 1947 and read:

Police Failed to Enter Spirit of this Occasion

"SOMEBODY'S SHOOTING up S. Main St.! Shots are being fired in every direction," a terrified voice shrieked in the telephone receiver of Police Radio Operator Harry Werner. Werner feverishly dispatched Cruiser men Raymond Pope and Griffin Greenert to the scene. Crack! Bang! Crash! Explosions road around the S. Main St. Hotel as Pope and Greenert screeched to a stop outside. The "shooting" seemed to be coming from the fourth floor. The cops rushed up there. Another roar and they located the room.

INSIDE WERE two youths, 16 and 17, calmly lighting firecrackers and throwing them out of the window to the street below. They were having a celebration, they said. They had boarded a bus in Springdale, W. Va., and came here through Pittsburg, Washington, D.C. and Richmond, Va. They had left home Friday to go coon hunting but changed their minds, drew $100 from the bank, and came to Akron instead. Both were sent to the juvenile detention home and wires were sent to their relatives in Springdale.

When the police brought Billy home, Mawzy first gave a sigh of relief and then ordered Billy to be taken to Pruneytown, a West Virginia reformatory for wayward boys, for a couple of weeks so he could think about what he had done. Back then, the threat of sending boys to Pruneytown if they didn't behave themselves was common. Mawzy saved the Akron newspaper article in her hope chest but tore out the part about withdrawing $100 from the bank. She could not bear to be reminded of hard-earned money going up in smoke.

Mawzy was beside herself. She thought she was doing everything she could to raise Billy right. One evening after school when the kids were still at their 4-H meeting Mawzy walked over to Sister's house. Sister and Mary Jenny were back in Springdale to visit family and check on their property, which was vacant at the time. When Sister answered the knock on the door, she was surprised to see Mawzy.

"Lordy, Gracie, what you doin' here? I figured you'd be gettin' supper ready by now."

"Got a minute?" Mawzy asked. "I sure could use a shoulder."

"Sure. Come on in and have a seat. You look tired. What's on your mind?"

"You know, my girls are doing pretty well," Mawzy noted as she wrung her hands and sighed. "Eleanor has given me a fit or two but overall, she's a good girl. Gloria's an angel. But I just don't know how to handle Billy. He's out of control. Whoppins' don't phase him and neither does being grounded. Not having a father around has been hard for him. I think he's afraid people will call him a sissy because he lives with a bunch of women. Maybe that's why he feels he has to be so rough and tough."

"He's had Earl's help sometimes, hasn't he?" Sister asked.

"Yes, but if you look at the men in his life, Earl, Poppy and his father, Add, I think they're more the problem than the solution, if leading by example has anything to do with it."

"Gracie, I see what you're sayin'. You have your hands full, don't you? You're a good mamma and a good provider. Don't ever think any different. You're doing the best you can. Hopefully, your guidance will eventually shine through."

"I sure hope so. Suppose I'd better get to fixin' that supper you were talkin' about. Thanks for listening. Always helps to talk it through. A prayer or two doesn't hurt either, does it?" Mawzy said as she gave Sister a hug and headed for the door.

Another of Billy's escapades was not discovered until he came clean in a letter he wrote to Mawzy when he was in the army. He confessed,

I neaver did have any bones broke I don't guess, just lucky I racken. You remember the time you thought I had my arm broke and had it exrayed. Well I'll tell you about it now. Well it wasn't broke at all. I stopped at Earl's comeing back from the doctor and Ralph Woodridge wrapped it up for me so I wouldn't have to take six week tests at school. We took a little bord and whittled it down and made

153

the splint and he wrapped it up then. We used about all of the gause and tape that Earl had down their. I waited until all the tests were over at school and then I took it off. Remember you got after me when I took it off, you said it hadn't had time to get good and well yet. I really got a bang out of that. What do you think about that, a pretty slick trick huh…

Eleanor graduated from high school in 1947 and expressed an interest in attending Concord College. She wanted to follow Mawzy's footsteps and take course work to become a teacher. Though specified in the divorce decree, Add provided very little financial assistance in raising the kids. Mawzy requested help with the kids' college, but he did not come through.

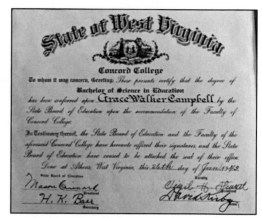

Mawzy's degree

Mawzy's frugality served her well. Eleanor graduated from Concord in three years as she went to summer school with Mawzy who was working on her bachelor's degree at the same time. Mawzy graduated with a bachelor's degree just eighteen months ahead of Eleanor.

The summer before his senior year in high school, Billy convinced Earl to take him to the Beckley Army Recruiting Center where he ended up enlisting for a three-year term. Billy had had enough of school life. When he got home that afternoon, he filled Mawzy in on his plans.

"I'll swan Billy, what have you gone and done now?" Mawzy asked. "You only have one more year left of school. Getting a high school diploma is so important for so many jobs. You're barely seventeen years old. Why don't you just tough it out and finish school first?"

"Mother, you know how much I hate school," Billy countered. "Just think. You won't have 'ta hound me anymore about gettin' my lessons. My mind's made up. If all goes like I hope, I'll be leavin' for basic training on August 30." Mawzy's nest was starting to empty out.

Billy (center), while in the Army, always found time to check in with Mawzy.

Billy completed four months of basic training at Fort Knox,

Kentucky. From there he headed to Fort Benning, Georgia for combat training, then was assigned a carpenter's position working on a dam. Once the dam project was over, he passed the fireman's exam and began firing boilers at a steam plant that provided heat and hot water for the barracks and mess halls. His last job at Fort Benning was driving a 2 ½ ton truck. He noted: *I like to drive pretty good just like always. That is a truck just like the one Chester used to have.*

When the Korean War started, Billy headed overseas. Mawzy was worried sick he would end up in combat. The casualties of World War II were still fresh on her mind. She finally got the letter that gave her some peace. Billy wrote: *When I wrote you the last letter I was at Camp Drake ready to go to Korea, but now I am 100 miles from their and I am not going to Korea. I am assigned to a ordnance outfit now and it is non combat... I guess that I was just lugkey. About 98% of the boys coming over seas are going into the infenty in Korea...* Later he wrote *I saw a Sgt... the other day and he told me that about all of the boys we were with at Benning got killed in Korea...*

In Tokyo, he worked in a carpenter shop as a part of the reconstruction project and finished his military career there as a mail clerk. He commented on his job: *Look at me, my work isn't as hard as carring in a bucket of coal.* He claimed his ability to use a typewriter kept him off the front line. His Aunt Lucille, Lawrence's wife, taught his typing class in high school.

While in the military, he wrote over 60 letters to Mawzy. She saved all of them in her hope chest. Most were written while he was stationed in Japan. She savored each but was disappointed with his poor spelling and grammar. She questioned whether she should have pushed at bit harder with his studies. It was obvious from his letters Mawzy kept urging him to finish high school.

Shortly after arriving at Ft. Knox, he wrote: *I can't finish my high school until I get out of basic training, but I'm sure going to do it then.*

A week later he updated: *By the way I have seen for sure about finishing my high school and I can and I also can get a diploma from M.B.H.S.*

A week after that: *Mother I want you to get Gloria J. to see how many high school credits I have and what I need to get credit in... I may be able to finish my high school up down here and if I can I am going to...*

Once settled at Fort Benning he followed up: *I seen about my H.S. credits and I can't get the Boligy class right now... I think that I will take a course by mail...*

Finally, a year later: *I got my test papers back on my Biology course... and I made satisfactory... It sure was a hard test. When I get my credits I will have to write to Madison, Wisconsin to get them forwarded on to M.B.H.S. Was glad to here about what Mr. Arritt said about giving me a whole credit. Well if he just knew how hard that I worked on it... I'm still wondering what he thinks about giving me credit on the Fireman's course that I took. I registered for another course... It's a Auto Machine course, I am going ahead and take it anyway even if they do give me credit on the outher.*

After necessary credits were earned, Billy got anxious for his diploma and inquired about his status on numerous occasions. He teased Mawzy in a June 1951 letter. *So you got my diploma for me huh. Well if I had of finished before I came in the army and had of been their to get it myself, I was going to play like I was sick and let you go down and get it anyway.*

Billy could be quite demanding. In his very first letter he asked for the best padlock Mawzy could find for his footlocker and wanted it mailed the next morning. He asked for money several times. When he was in Georgia it was hot, so he wanted all his summer clothes sent to him right away after alterations had been made to a pair of his pants.

He begged for Mawzy and Gloria June to write him more often. He missed Gloria June and was always inquiring about school happenings. He coveted the treat boxes Mawzy sent to him, which were filled with cookies, candy, and cake. At one point he wrote: *I wouldn't care if you sent me a box of candy and cookies every week.* Mawzy solicited Gloria June's help in filling the boxes going out the door.

Inquiries of Earl were scattered about in his letters. He had borrowed Earl's truck before leaving home and wrote: *Has Earl every come and got his truck yet and was he mad because I nevery brought it back to him.* He was aware of Earl's paternity court case and asked: *How about Earl and his trial. You didn't say anything about it in your letter, has he had it yet or not.* He indicated getting and answering letters from Earl. He asked about Earl's sweetheart: *So Josephine wanted me to write to her, well I wish that you would send me her address... So her and Earl are still going to geather, he has been going with her for a long time now hasn't he.*

Billy continued to be full of mischievousness and had no reservations about sharing it with Mawzy.

He sent a message to Gloria June in one of Mawzy's letters: *Gloria June there is a great big fat boy down here and I think that I will bring him home with me to see you like Cutler did that time for Polly.*

He also pulled Gloria's leg in a letter he wrote to her. *They have been giving us 2 shots every Friday seince I have been here. They broke a needle off in my arm Friday and I will have to go and get it taken out in the morning I guess and I know that it is going to hurt.*

Many tales were imparted about how he and his army buddies were "pulling a fast one" or "playing a good one" to shirk some of their duties. He shared that he had just missed going A.W.O.L. from one of his excursions.

He confessed to turning over a neighbor's outhouse in Springdale the previous Halloween and was wondering if anybody had completed the task in his absence.

Mawzy was concerned about Billy's drinking. While still in basic training at Fort Knox he tried to put her at ease: *Mother you said not to spend any of the money for beer or whiskey. Don't worry about me drinking any because I have made up my mind not to drink any at all... All the boys smoke except me... That is one good thing you done for me, by not letting me every get the bad habit of smoking.*

Billy's infectious good humor and home training made him a popular GI.

Long before, Mawzy caught Billy and one of his buddies smoking in the wash house. Her thrashing with a keen switch must have worked.

Surprisingly, he did mention drinking when he was stationed in Tokyo. *We had a company picnic last Sunday down on the beach here below Tokyo and everybody had a good time... We had fried chicken and most any thing else that you would want to eat... Oh yes one more little thing 200 gallons of draft beer. Ha! No one got too drunk but we all had a good time.*

Billy wrote a lot about his girlfriend, Eleanor, who he met in Georgia. He spent a lot of time with her, went home to meet her parents and even mentioned the possibility of getting married. Yet, he was always joking about other women. He told stories in his letters that made Mawzy uncomfortable because they brought back memories of the letters she received from Add about his flirtations when they were dating.

Mawzy's hope chest contained treasures from Billy's sojourn in Japan such as the lacquered album above. The silk bomber jacket below was found in Mawzy's garage attic.

I am writing to eight different girls now and you ought to read some of the answers I get from them. All of them live in W. Va. but none of them too close to home. One of them has a new Buick car she said. Thats the one I am going to see when I come home I think. Then if I can borrow her car I will go and see some of the rest of them. Ha! Ha!

I have been going with two different girls pretty steady and I had a date with both of them last night...

He told how he and a buddy took the first girl to the other's place of work. The first girl was left in the car while they went inside to see the other. When Billy and his buddy left, the girl inside followed them, discovered the girl in the car and a fight broke out between them. Billy said he just sat back and laughed at them. *I believe it is just a bad as some of the messes the G. J. and Eleanor get into sometimes,* he concluded. On the outside of the envelope Billy had one of the girls leave a lipstick kiss.

While in Tokyo he wrote: *Yes I go out with a Jap girl every now and nen. I'm just like all the rest of the GIs they all do, officers or enlisted men, married or single they all go out with them.* Billy became quite fond of one of the Japanese girls. She even wrote him a letter once he got back home from the service. She called him rosy cheeks.

It wasn't all play for Billy. He was proud of the recognitions he received. Early on he got a medal for his M1 rifle sharp shooting skill and made the highest score in his platoon firing a machine gun. He was selected as one of the best soldiers in his company to be in a big Armistice Day parade. He was awarded a Korean service medal.

Mawzy inquired more than once about his rank and when he would get promoted. He tried to explain to her, but she didn't understand so she asked for his commander's address. His response was: *I don't see why you wanted to know that unless you are wanting to write and ask him something about me. Just allways remember I get his mail first ... and if you ever wrote to him, I could always find out whats in before he ever seen it. Company Commanders are busy enough with out people writing them and asking a bunch of silly questions... Oh, yes I can change jobs and companys and make Sgt with in two or three more mounths...but I don't think I will do it. So I think that I'll be a happy cpl instead of a unhappy Sgt.* At one point Billy got demoted, but never revealed why it happened.

Billy was fascinated with the goods that could be purchased in Japan at a fraction of the stateside cost. He wanted to share his discoveries with his family. Talked about buying a bunch of toys to send to his cousins. He wrote:

Name something that you would like to have from over here and I will try and get it for you. I saw some jackets yesterday that I would like to have so I expect I will get me one and sent it home for you to keep for me. I expect Gloria June would like one too so I will get her one... Then a week later*: Well I got a thing or two to send home today... I got three jackets, two cigarette lighters and a albon – I guess that's the way you spell it, anyway it is a thing to put pictures in... The albon is for you...*

The reversible silk bomber jackets were burgundy and cream on one side and black and cream on the other. Full bodied dragons, dragon heads, raptors or scenes were embroidered on the backs and fronts with Japan embroidered on the back. The jackets became a hot item. Other family members started requesting one of their very own. So did Gloria's boyfriend, Charlie. Billy said she could give Charlie his jacket and he would get another one for himself. I found two of the bomber jackets in an old trunk in Mawzy's garage attic.

Mawzy kept the wooden lacquer album in her hope chest and it housed a lot of pictures taken while Billy was in the army. On the front cover was a red map of Japan. Scenes, including mountainous terrain, were painted around the border.

Mawzy asked Billy to send her a bathrobe and some china dishes. Gloria June requested a silk scarf. Billy obliged. He wrote in a letter to Gloria: *Remember Mother wants a bathrobe and I can't find one big enough for her. All of the people over here are little, but I think I know where I can get one made to fit her.*

ELEANOR CAMPBELL

On numerous occasions Billy urged Mawzy not to worry about him. Stacked up on top of her other worries was her concern over his love of cars and his reckless driving.

Only five months after joining the army he started yearning for another car. His letter turned out to be uncanny: *I am thinking about getting me a car this pay day. Used cars are pretty cheap down here. What do you think about it. I guess you will say that I will kill myself if I get a car but I don't think that I will...*

A bit later he wrote, *I am going to save all the money that I can between now and some time next winter. And then I want you to help me get a car. What do you think about it, will you help me or not...*

Once in Japan Billy and a buddy decided to pool their money to buy a car. *No I don't drive fast over here, the roads are no good and there are to many M.P.s. So don't worrie about me having a wreck.*

While Billy was in the army, life moved on in Springdale. The fall of 1950 was joyful. Mawzy honored Gloria June with a sweet 16 birthday party at their house. There were 25 in attendance including Gloria's boyfriend, Charlie. It was reported in the *Beckley Post-Herald* and was a milestone for Gloria. She even wrote to Billy to fill him in on the details.

At this point in the three women's lives, it cost an arm and a leg just to keep all of them in hosiery. Since Mawzy didn't drive, she made a lot of purchases via mail order. I found many a cancelled check made out to The Wilburn Hosiery Company.

Eleanor graduated from Concord in August 1950, procured a job teaching the second grade at the Minden Elementary School and became engaged to her college boyfriend, Jack, that October.

Jack grew up in Beckley, so the engagement made a big splash in the *Raleigh Register* as did coverage of the November 5 candlelight wedding at Beckley's First Christian Church. There was a flurry of activity and excitement around the household as the plans unfolded. Gloria June was thrilled that Eleanor chose her as the only attendant. Mawzy made Gloria's dress. As was so common in the era, it was described in detail in the *Register*.

Miss June Campbell... chose an ankle length gown of pastel pink net over satin. The scalloped neckline was gathered with net to form the cap sleeves. Her head dress was a bandeau of yellow, pink, and white chrysanthemums and she carried an arm bouquet of mixed chrysanthemums.

Eleanor's wedding dress was purchased as Mawzy just didn't have the time to make two dresses on such short notice. The *Register* reported, *She appeared in an ankle length gown of white satin fashioned with a fitted bodice which fastened down the back with self-covered buttons. Under the full skirt she wore a hoop and the inset yoke of white net was appliqued with flowers. Her only jewelry was a single strand of pearls worn under the Peter Pan collar. Her headdress was of white satin as were her elbow-length mitts and she carried a net fan covered with white pom-poms and gardenias and centered with a white orchid.*

Mawzy on Eleanor's wedding day; below, Eleanor the blushing bride.

Years later Eleanor modeled her gown for a PTA fashion show in Atlanta where she and Jack eventually moved. The dress was then given to their maid, "Snooks," who altered it for her own granddaughter. "Snooks" was the aunt of Gladys Knight of the famous "Pips."

Eleanor was given away in marriage by Uncle Lawrence, Mawzy's oldest brother. Her father, Add, did not attend the wedding but some of his siblings made a showing. Though Eleanor had been close to her father when she was little, he had not been around much after the divorce. The invitation read *"Mrs. Grace Campbell requests the honour of your presence..."*

After the ceremony was over, Eleanor hid in a Sunday school classroom and cried because she was afraid of what married life might be like. Mawzy, in a panic, tracked her down for the reception and assured her all would be fine. The *Register* described

Mawzy *receiving guests for the reception wearing a dress of navy crepe with matching accessories and a gardenia corsage.* It was a fairytale wedding and ended up being the only one in which Mawzy played a part.

John Alley, a man thirteen years Gloria June's senior, had his eye on her. Young, sweet, beautiful, innocent Gloria June. She was a junior in high school. He had watched her march up and down the football field in her majorette uniform and cheer for the Wildcats at basketball games. He loved seeing her cheer.

"Meadow Bridge on the gridiron, The gridiron's hot, You can't beat us with the stuff we got. So you boogie to the left and you boogie to the right. And the Meadow Bridge Wildcats Fight! Fight! Fight!"

John Alley; Gloria June as a cheerleader.

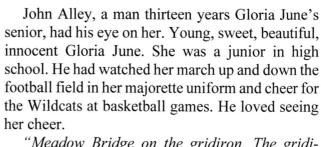

It was her favorite cheer. Years later, after her memory was compromised, out of the clear blue she started chanting that cheer.

John got wind of a party being thrown for the Meadow Bridge basketball team and weaseled his way in.

He made all the right moves and caught Gloria's attention. According to the *Beckley Post-Herald* there were over 50 people in attendance and as luck would have it Gloria's boyfriend, Charlie, didn't attend. John could be the life of the party, especially when he'd had a nip or two. He loved to dance and he drove a cool car. He bragged about being a World War II veteran stationed in India where he played a part in the construction of the Ledo Road between India and China. Told her he would show her his medals some time. He offered her a ride home and coaxed her into going on a drive with him the following Sunday.

When Gloria June got home that night, she told Mawzy of the encounter and that he was coming on Sunday to take her for a drive.

"Gloria June, what are you thinking?" Mawzy grilled. "John's almost old enough to be your father. And from what I gather, he nor his father have a very good reputation. They're known to hit the bottle. Believe me, you do not want to get involved with the likes of that."

"Mother don't worry so much. It's just a car ride. He wants to take me over to Hawk's Nest State Park. That's all. Come on, it's no big deal."

It turned into a big deal. Much to Mawzy's dismay, they dated all through Gloria June's senior year at Meadow Bridge High. Charlie was out of the picture as he went into the service. According to one of Billy's letters, John gave Gloria June his military medals, almost as if they were a promise ring. His drinking gave Gloria some pause on occasion, but he always let her take his car if he was too lit to come along. A few weeks after Gloria's high school graduation John invited her to go with him, his sister Patti and brother, Bob on a two-week trip to see their sister, Evelyn, in Miami Beach, Florida.

Gloria begged and Mawzy balked. In the end, Mawzy gave in. It was all so glamorous in Gloria June's eyes. She was only 16 years old. She'd never been to a beach or seen the ocean before. She'd barely been out of Fayette and the surrounding counties. The trip was documented in *The Raleigh Register*.

She and John took a day trip 30 miles north to Ft. Lauderdale. That evening John was drinking and having a wonderful time. Gloria June was fascinated by it

Gloria June and John in Florida.

all. They passed by a wedding chapel and he suggested they elope. She declined. Thought he was joking. He kept working on her, even after they returned to West Virginia. She started to soften up to the idea. Perhaps an older man was just what she needed. A father figure of sorts. To make up for the one she did not have growing up. And he could be a lot of fun. Maybe his drinking would subside once he was more settled.

Shortly after their return from Florida, Gloria's attention shifted to preparing for college. Like Mawzy and Eleanor before her, she headed to Concord College for a teaching degree. That fall she moved into the dorm and became engrossed in her studies. She tried out and made the college majorette team.

It was all over in the blink of an eye, Mawzy thought as she came home from school the fall of 1951 to an empty house. Gloria was off to college, Billy was in the army half-way across the world and Eleanor had started a life of her own with her husband, Jack. She still saw Gloria on weekends sometimes and Eleanor came

The romance between John and Gloria June bloomed.

by to visit but it was not the same. She had expressed her loneliness to Billy in a letter she wrote to him when he was in Japan. His response was:

You say you are by yourself now huh. Well if nothing don't happen I will be at home next winter... If I can get me a pretty good job, I will stay I guess... I guess it would be best for me to be at home with you seince Eleanor and Gloria June are both gone. But I don't have the least idea what I would work at if I was at home do you.

John went to Athens to see Gloria June as often as he could and continued suggesting they get married. Her quiet demeanor made her easy to manipulate and she finally gave in to his proposal. They eloped one weekend in Lebanon, Virginia, about 75 miles from the campus. She gave him one stipulation. She insisted they keep the marriage a secret for the time being. He gladly agreed as neither of them was looking forward to Mawzy's reaction. She ended up pregnant and knew it was only a matter of time before their marriage would become public knowledge.

John cared for Gloria which was revealed in two recently discovered letters.

Thursday Eve.
El Rancho
Good Morning Beautiful:
Seeing you last night and knowing that you are still mine has made it possible for me to be away from you until Fri evening.

As I told you last night, this week has been forever.

I did everything but cry Tuesday evening when Delbert left me here alone. Walking the floor might help some people, but it sure don't help me.

Something like this eases the pain more than anything. I think writing to you every night will do the trick. Starting Thursday you will be hearing from your husband real often.

The only time that I might fail will be because of working late or being there with you. How does this sound to you?

164

...Just think after we sleep tonight there will be only a few hours of waiting.

Darling, I don't know how this is making you feel this Thursday morning. All I know is I love you so much that its like talking to you here tonight. Sure was nice of Delbert to let us use his car. That's more than Dad or Helen would have done. Well gorgeous you had better get out of bed and eat breakfast so you will feel real good today.

I love you with all my heart and live to be a million and it never changes.

Your ever-loving husband,

Johnny

Friday Nov. 2, 1951

Around 5 P.M.

Hi gorgeous:

Here so soon? I look like hell but feel pretty good. Have just about froze my giz off today.

Had to start early today to make some extra loot for you and <u>*her*</u>*. Any kicks from* <u>*her*</u> *yet? It won't be long I bet ya!*

Was it ever cold in this barn last night. Del and I slept so close together I had to get up when he did. We were froze together.

I have been thinking of you constantly today. Afraid my babies would forget that there might be ice on some parts of the road yet. Can always bet on you – can't I?

Honey I'll be with you shortly. Have to get our a---s in the saddle if we get back to Athens before it snows...

Love ya!

When Mawzy got wind of the marriage, her first inclination was to get it annulled. When she found out Gloria June was pregnant, she knew it was too late. Her heart ached. She, more than anyone else, feared what was coming. She also felt guilty for not paying more attention to Gloria June's comings and goings and for letting her go to Florida with the Alleys.

Books and Babies

First tooth, second tooth, third tooth and more,
Courses on Shakespeare and the American Civil War.
First word, second word, third word - what joys,
Textbooks lost in a pile of baby toys.
First step, second step, third step - skinned knees,
In between working on college degrees.
Birthday cakes, a wagon, and a baby doll,
Who'll be teaching school next fall?
Baby rattles, pacifiers, and a tiny swimming pool,
Along with extension classes and going to summer
school.
Santa Claus, the Easter bunny and one more test,
Evidence of all stored in the hope chest.

Myra Alley Kingsbury

166

Mawzy at dining room table with Billy, Billy Boy and Myra on her lap, celebrating David's 3rd birthday.

Books and Babies

When Gloria June and John married, they dreamed of finding a place of their own. John had depended on his dad, the superintendent of the Alaska Coal Company mine in Beelick Knob, for work and financial support. Rode on Big John's shirt tails all his life. He was, after all, the favorite child. Liked his cars and was a sharp dresser.

Plans went awry when Big John remarried and Helen, the new wife, made it quite clear it was time to cut the apron strings. John, Jr. lost favor with his dad and his inheritance as well. He moved into a shack with his buddy, Delbert, near Beelick Knob where they mined coal.

Living at Mawzy's house became the easiest option for the newlyweds. Due to her pregnancy, Gloria June dropped out of college after the first semester with 16 credits under her belt.

A selection from a tub full of books found in Mawzy's garage attic.

Even with the distraction of Gloria's pregnancy and a son-in-law under foot, Mawzy pushed forward with her own education. The winter of 1952, she enrolled in graduate school through West Virginia University and took two extension classes in Rainelle - Criminology and Introduction to Anthropology. She saved all WVU transcripts in her hope chest.

Though aggravated with the circumstances, Mawzy anxiously awaited the arrival of her first grandchild. She was glad school was out before the baby arrived as it meant she would have more time for doting. When Gloria's contractions started, John had already hit the bottle. Mawzy didn't have her driver's license, so John called his younger brother, Bob, to take them to the hospital in Richwood, which was 45 miles over hill and dell. Bob rushed from Beelick Knob to Springdale, picked up Gloria, John and Mawzy and made it to the hospital in time. The delivery was difficult. Gloria June gained so much weight during the pregnancy that she could rest a plate on her belly. Forceps were needed to get the baby's head out of the birth canal, but he finally made it into the world and was named David Glenn. He was a big boy. Weighed in at almost 10 pounds. Had a big head, which measured 22 inches around. He was a wrinkled, mashed up, red hued little fellow. Gloria was convinced she was having a girl, so was quite surprised. In David's baby book she itemized gifts received. In the remarks she wrote: *Most of these things were received at a shower before baby came. It was given by Jewell, Pansie and Wanda* [Mawzy's sisters] *... Most of the things at the shower were for a girl. But we fooled them...* Not to worry. The girl's baby clothes were stored away and brought back out when I came along 18 months later.

A few hours after David's birth, John was called to the nursery viewing area. Mawzy came along. He looked over all the babies. "Oh God, I hope it's not that one," he said. "He is ugly as hell." Turns out that was David. Gloria wrote other people's comments in David's baby book.

"He's a fine big boy," John Alley Sr. said.

"He is an Alley alright," Helen Alley said.

"He is awful ugly," Mawzy said.

"I don't know if he will ever look any better," Cousin Mary Jenny said.

"Look at 'ol' Dave Alley," Pansie said.

"I think he is a pretty boy," James, Pansie's husband, said.

"He sure is big," Wanda said.

An early bath for David, posing with a proud papa, Mawzy with her pride and joy.

"He has big feet," Dad's friend, Delbert said.

"He is cute," Gloria's friend Patsy said.

"I think he is sweet," Cousin Norma Kaye said.

"He looks like a doll baby," her mother, Evelyn, who was Mawzy's sister, said.

"He sure is a big baby," Uncle Earl and his girlfriend, Josephine, said.

"Our baby was the largest one in the hospital while I was there," Gloria noted.

David still gets a chuckle out of his debut. He quickly became the apple of Mawzy's eye. She was overly concerned about his misshapen head. As soon as he came home from the hospital, she spent a goodly amount of time every day rubbing his head in the hope it would become more rounded. He tended to be sickly in his early years. Mawzy took him to a wedding shower and one of her colleagues asked him how he was doing.

"Not doin' so well," he replied like an old man. "Got low blood." He was anemic. During that time doctors still made house calls. Dr. Dunbar, of Meadow Bridge, was the local house doctor. David had so many doctor visits that when he saw Dr. Dunbar coming he ran to the couch, pulled down his pants and put his butt up in the air for a shot.

Doc Davis, our family doctor, had his office in Rainelle. He was in his late 50s by the time my generation hit the scene. He was a slight man with a short, narrow mustache and wire rimmed glasses. He looked like Hitler but was soft spoken and well respected in the community and in medical circles. He was busy, as he doctored workers at the Meadow River Lumber Company, various coal mines and the railroad. His waiting room was ominous to us as kids. It had a high ceiling, dark heavy wooden walls and waiting chairs and a large matching counter in the center of the room. When Doc was ready to see another patient, his Nurse Keaton stuck

Dr. W.B. Davis, veteran Rainelle doctor, physician, counselor, and most of all, humanist, is shown in a pensive mood as he contemplates D-Day, July 20, 1974, the day he hung up white coat, put aside his stethoscope and went home to "cut the grass."

Meadow River Post, *Rainelle, WV, July 1974.*

her head out the door of his office and yelled in a nasally voice, "Next." If someone did not rise immediately, she kept repeating "Next" until she got results. On one of my visits, after giving me a shot in the arm, Doc said, "You have the toughest hide of any kid I've ever seen." I wasn't sure if that was something to be proud of or if I had a skin problem. As I sat in the examining chair, I could see into the back room which housed row upon row of tall shelves filled with every kind of elixir and pill imaginable. With his own apothecary, it was a one stop shop. Mawzy held him in high regard and saved both his retirement announcement and obituary in a scrapbook of clippings in her hope chest.

Uncle Buddy Rose, one of Mawzy's brothers-in-law, was our dentist and officed in Rainelle as well. My teeth were soft so I always had a cavity or two and had them filled without any deadening as I was afraid of the Novocain needle. What pain when he hit the nerve, plus the drill was slow moving and felt like a jack hammer in my mouth. I finally agreed to Novocain and was disappointed I had lived through more trauma than was necessary. Uncle Buddy, like so many of my relatives, was a character. He was a fast, reckless driver. "Look out, Spider Rose is coming," could be heard anytime he was out on the road.

Gloria June had to grow up fast. She was 17 years old, still a child herself. Yet she now had the responsibility of her own child and a husband who had not stepped up to the plate as a provider.

One Saturday when Mawzy was working in her garden, Gloria came out with David in her arms and plopped him down in his play pin. She went back in the house to grab a basket of laundry to hang on the clothesline. Mawzy decided it was time for a candid discussion.

"Gloria June, we need to talk," Mawzy said as she pulled up another bunch of carrots. "I'm not going to chastise you for what's transpired. What's done is done. Though you won't remember, your father and I had some of the same issues you and John are having now. Alcohol ruined my marriage and I fear it's going to do the same to yours."

170

David with Gloria June at Babcock State Park; David and John

"I know Mother," Gloria sighed as she shook out another diaper to hang on the line. "I'm sorry for the shape I've put us in. I just hope things will improve with John's work."

"It's not that I don't like John. I just don't like some of his ways," Mawzy continued as she wrestled green beans off the vine. "You can't always change someone else, but you can shore up your own situation. I'll help you as much as I can, but it's important you continue your college education. You have to be able to take care of yourself and your baby boy."

"You're right. I'll call tomorrow to see about enrolling in classes this fall."

"You won't regret it. When you finish up with the laundry come on in so we can get these beans ready to can while David's still napping."

That fall it was back to college for Mawzy and Gloria. Mawzy took two extension classes in history, studying the United States-McKinley to New Deal and the American Civil War. Gloria completed 16 hours for both the first and second semester. She decided to major in English education. With both in college, there was seldom a time for the next four years when the dining room table was not cluttered with textbooks and a stack of freshly laundered diapers.

For on-campus Concord College classes Gloria commuted a little over an hour over the hills each way in John's baby blue Chevy convertible. David was two months old. On those days, her friend, Betty Lou, babysat David until Mawzy could pick him up after school.

Eleanor with Debbie; below, Annie, Billy, Billy Boy.

Betty says she can still remember Gloria stopping by her house that winter wearing a baby blue coat with a white fur collar which matched the car. Betty said she looked pretty in both the car and the coat.

In June Mawzy left home for summer school at West Virginia University. Uncle Earl drove her to Morgantown every Sunday and came after her every Friday so she could be home with her family. She loaded up with six classes focusing on psychology, health, and supervision.

With Mawzy in summer school, Gloria and John were on their own with one-year old David. It was during this time Gloria realized how much she depended on Mawzy for guidance, childcare and running the household. She was beginning to understand the importance of providing for herself and her children. She was pregnant with me by that time.

Mawzy backed off her course work during the next school year. She only took one class per semester as there were too many distractions in her life.

Aunt Eleanor had moved to Atlanta and was pregnant with her first daughter by the time David was born. She was the most independent of Mawzy's children. She was still teaching elementary school and Uncle Jack was with army intelligence. They were living at Fort MacPherson at the time of Deborah's birth in February 1953. It is a miracle the little one survived as she was a breech birth and the umbilical cord was wrapped around her neck. Mawzy couldn't be there for the birth because of all her responsibilities at home, at work and with her studies. Jack's sister-in-law, Mary, was able to help.

172

Billy came back home after being discharged from the military, got a job driving a coal truck and helped Uncle Earl at The Dutch Colony. He became sweet on Annie, who was from Leslie. She and her sister, Josie, worked at The Colony. Annie and Billy ended up getting married. When they were in the family way, Billy decided it was time to look for a more stable job. A high school buddy of his had recently moved to Ohio to drive a bus for the Cleveland Transit System. When he was home over the holidays, he stopped in at The Colony for a cold one. Told Billy the Transit Authority was looking for more drivers. Billy was interested. He already had his chauffer's license.

Annie gave birth to Billy Boy at her home in Leslie in January 1954. A month later Uncle Billy took off to Cleveland to apply for a bus driver's position and find housing for his growing family. Annie and Billy Boy moved in with Mawzy. Gloria was due with me at any time. Over the next 11 months it took a team effort to handle three infants while Mawzy was teaching and Mom headed to work and then back to college full time. Annie was the daytime babysitter. The three women were always playing musical chairs. Who was studying now? Who was teaching school? Who was watching the babies? Who was preparing meals? Who was doing laundry? Who was cleaning the house? Who was bringing in the coal and stoking the fire? Who was picking up the toys? Who was working the garden?

Gloria June applied for a temporary teaching certificate after she completed her second year of college. John was not doing any better in the "providing for his family" category so Gloria felt the need to help with expenses. She taught one semester the fall of 1953 at the Backus Mountain one room school where Mawzy had her first teaching job so many years before. She told me that I got to go to school with her every day, in her belly. She recalled Mawzy telling of carrying Billy to school in her belly when she taught at Kathryn, near Gentry Holler.

The February night I was born Dad had taken a nip or two and when Mom's water broke his first comment was, "You're not having the baby yet, you just peed your pants."

He was wrong, and they almost didn't make it to the Richwood hospital before I was born. I was small and David had paved the way for me 18 months earlier.

When they brought me home, the house was crowded.

There was Mawzy, Mom, Dad, David,

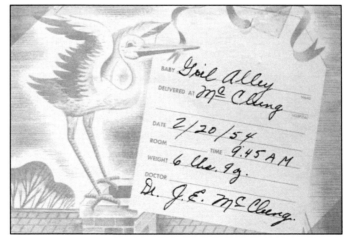

Gloria June and Myra

Aunt Annie, and Cousin Billy Boy, who was only one month older than me. Because of the tight quarters, there was no room for my basinet. I slept in the second dresser drawer from the bottom in Mom and Dad's bedroom, but they assured me it was always left open. Maybe that is what made me feisty, like Aunt Eleanor whose beginnings were in a dynamite box in Gentry Holler.

David was not all that excited about having a baby sister. I was a curiosity though. One day when I was fussy, he decided I needed to be fed. He went to the kitchen, grabbed a can of peaches out of the pantry, marched into the bedroom and threw the peaches in my dresser drawer. Fortunately, the can didn't hit me.

Mawzy was on the home stretch of finishing her master's degree. She went back to West Virginia University for a second summer session to finish 12 hours of administrative course work. By

Annie and Billy Boy

July she had enough credits to qualify for her Life First Class Elementary and Life Principal's Elementary Teacher's Certificates. She graduated with her advanced degree in August. 1954 was a big year for both me and Mawzy.

We spent a lot of time outside my first summer. Mom and Annie sunbathed on Mawzy's quilts. Billy Boy and I were with them, crawling around and learning to roll over. David was a bit more of a challenge as he was walking by that time. He was getting really tired of not having all the attention.

Cousin love—Myra and Billy Boy

He decided he wanted to be the tiny boy again, so he grabbed my blanket and climbed in his red Radio Super wagon Mawzy gave him the previous Christmas. He covered himself up and pretended to be taking a nap. Mawzy had recently returned from summer school. She came out of the house about that

174

David and Uncle Billy

time, saw David in the wagon and had a good laugh. David had worked his charm once again.

Mom took a break from college the semester I was born, but by fall she started extension classes again. Mawzy was teaching and Annie was still taking care of Billy Boy, David, and me. Uncle Billy got the job with the Cleveland Transit System but came back home as much as he could to be with his family.

Just before Christmas he made a down payment on a house, came home for the holidays, packed up Billy Boy and Annie and off to Cleveland they went. Mawzy was happy for them but hated to see them leave. Mom told me I hated to see them go too. She said after they left, I would call out and go looking all over the place for Billy Boy. He was my bud.

Billy Boy and Myra in their Easter finery.

David and Uncle Jack playing with Christmas train set.

Eleanor, Jack, and Debbie came home that Christmas as well. They stayed with Jack's parents in Beckley since Mawzy's house was so crowded. Eleanor was surprised by all the chaos. There was never a quiet moment nor a space to call your own. Her heart ached for Mom and the predicament she was in. One afternoon when the kids were taking a nap, she approached Mom.

"Gloria June, I hate that you don't have a home to call your own," Eleanor sympathized. "Hopefully, this will change before long."

"I hope so too, but I have my doubts," Mom countered. "I love Mother dearly and I appreciate all she's done for me, but I fear my situation is aggravating her to death and money is tight right now."

"Maybe I could help. Why don't you let me take Myra to raise as my own? She and Debbie could be like sisters. Since Debbie is a year older, Myra could wear her clothes after she grows out of them."

"Circumstances would have to be a lot worse than they are now before I'd ever consider giving up my little girl," Mom said without hesitation. "Things will be better once I finish college and start working on a regular basis."

"I understand, but if you ever change your mind, the offer stands," Eleanor responded as she reached for Mom's hand and gave it a squeeze.

I wonder what Mom thought of the offer. It may have seemed an insult to her. Did Eleanor not think Mom was capable of raising me? The conversation with Eleanor may have made Mom feel she was taking advantage of Mawzy. At the time, Eleanor was better off financially as Jack was now a junior executive for General Motors in Atlanta and she was still teaching school.

After Billy's family left and Mom resumed college, her best friend, Betty Lou, babysat David and me. She was like our second mom. We loved Betty, but we were a handful at times. She will never let us forget the time she went to the freezer on the back porch and we locked her out of the house. She kept yelling for us to let her in and heard us giggling. After letting us know she meant business, we became afraid of the repercussions and unlocked the door.

My temper and stubbornness always got me in trouble. Betty Lou called my outbursts "bull fits." My worst "bull fit" was at Betty's house. Mom dropped

David and me off before heading to school and wanted a hug and kiss goodbye. I refused. After Mom left and I watched her head down the driveway I decided I had made a terrible mistake and wanted to make amends. It was too late, so I proceeded to cry at the top of my lungs, ransack Betty's living room and knock over and break one of her lamps. I got my butt popped that day.

Mom liked to get me all spiffed up, but she said in no time I was disheveled. I hated having my hair combed. It hurt, so I went around half the time with tangled hair. They nicknamed me "Little Huss."

One evening when Mom was studying Shakespeare at the dining room table and smoking a cigarette David approached. He was three years old.

"Mommy, what's 'at book? Can you read me a story?" he asked.

"Double, double, toil and trouble; Fire burn and cauldron bubble," Mom belted out, as she was studying Macbeth. She laughed and tickled David on the belly.

"I don't like 'at story. I want the three bears story," he pouted and started to walk away.

"Make you a deal. I'll read about the bears for your bedtime story."
Mom kept her promise and read David *The Three Little Bears*.

When she was done, she tucked him in bed and asked him to say his night-night prayer. It was the same prayer Mawzy recorded as Mom's first prayer in her baby book. He shut his eyes tight, put his hands together and proceeded:

Now I lay me down to sleep.
I pray the Lord my soul to keep.
If I should die before I wake.
I pray the Lord my soul to take.
God bless Mommy and Daddy.
God bless Mawzy.
God bless Rosie and Bill.
God bless little sister, Billy Boy, and everybody.
Amen.

Rosie and Bill were Betty Lou's parents. Bill took a shining to David. He was like the boy Bill never had. Took David to do farm chores all the time. Even made David a little side car for his horse drawn mowing machine. On one visit David was "helping" Bill feed castor oil and turpentine to a cow to relieve its trots.

The cow coughed up the mixture and it landed all over David's face. David was in a panic.

"Oh, Bill," David yelled out. "I'm killed. I'm killed Bill. I'm killed."

David with Bill at Easter.

Bill busted a gut laughing, but assured David he would be fine as he gently wiped David's face off with his shirt sleeve.

Mom was winding up her college education. She went full bore over the summer and completed her student teaching at her alma mater, Meadow Bridge High School in the fall. She taught elementary education in the morning and two ninth grade English classes in the afternoon.

David in Bill and Rosie's yard, David on Bill's truck. Below, Anne, Steve, Billy Boy, Mawzy, and David relax during the Cleveland trip.

Over Christmas break, Mawzy decided to take David with her to see Uncle Billy. Billy and Annie recently had their second child, Stevie, and Mawzy was anxious to meet the little fellow. She thought David and Billy Boy would have a good time together and she was missing her boy.

They took a train from Prince to Cleveland. Mawzy was a bit apprehensive

about traveling so far with such a young child. At the train station she bought David a little plastic train set, consisting of an engine, two cars and a caboose, to help keep him occupied on the trip up and back.

Billy was excited to show Mawzy around the big city of Cleveland. They went to the iconic Higbee's upscale department store in Cleveland's Public

Above, Mawzy, Anne and Billy out for a night on the town; bottom, Billy and Billy Boy greet a new addition, Steve.

Square. Years later it was the location of scenes from the movie, "A Christmas Story." Higbee's always amazed with their holiday decorations. David was big

eyed with it all. He saw a life-sized, stuffed polar bear decorated for Christmas and thought it was real. He ran over, pointed to it, and started yelling. "What's 'at bear doin' in here?" When he didn't get a response he yelled even louder, "I said, what is 'at bear doin' in here?" Mawzy finally explained it was stuffed just like his teddy bear at home.

When everyone was settled from that episode, they moved on to the shoe department. David saw a pair of high heels and pointed at them. "I want that pair of shoes for Little Huss," he said to a clerk who was standing nearby. "Mawzy let's get these for "Little Huss." They decided it was time to get out of the store and move on. That evening Mawzy, Billy and Annie got dressed up, went out to dinner and then to see "The Man with the Golden Arm" starring Frank Sinatra at The Hippodrome Theatre.

This is around the time Mawzy got her nickname, as she was riding herd on David and me while Mom was going full bore with her studies.

Mom made the dean's list both semesters her senior year and was named a princess in the May Festival, just as Eleanor had been. She graduated from Concord College the spring of 1956. That fall she drove 3 ½ miles to Bellwood for her first full time teaching job in a one room schoolhouse with 25 students. The next year she was hired by Meadow Bridge High School to teach physical education and English. Mawzy was so proud. And continued to be as Mom started working on her master's degree three years later. They took five of the same classes, so Mom used Mawzy's textbooks and referred to her notes.

Mawzy sometimes worried over Mom's marital problems with her sisters. Evie and her husband, Dr. Buddy Rose, had a daughter close to Mom's age, Norma Kaye. The summer of 1958 they invited Mom to travel with them to Disneyland and Hollywood. They wanted to help Mom recapture a bit of her childhood.

Mawzy encouraged her to go and offered to watch us kids. It was a whirlwind trip which included stops along the way at Yosemite National Park and the Grand Canyon. I was beside myself that I could not go along. I was too young to understand the family dynamics. David and I both received a post card from Mom while she was gone. Mine read, *"Hi Myra. Things here look like a fairy story. Be good and I'll find you something pretty here. Love, Mommy."*

Gloria June's Bellwood school-teacher picture. Below, John babysitting Myra and David.

She bought me a stuffed Goofy, my favorite Disney character. David was into Zorro, so Mom brought him a Zorro costume which included a black hat, a mask, a cape, and a chalk-tipped sword. A lot of chalk marks showed up over the property for a while.

Mawzy was happy to see Billy more settled. In her hope chest was a letter she had saved - an accolade to Billy from the Cleveland Transit System:

Your courteous actions have been noticed. These courtesies, together with the fact that your riders have commended you to us is, we think, proof that human beings ae not as cold and indifferent as they sometimes seem. We hope you keep up the good work... There are enclosed five patches... We feel that you will be proud to wear this courtesy insignia which "Identifies The Lady and Distinguishes The Gentleman."

People always told him he looked like Jackie Gleason who was a bus driver on "The Honeymooners" TV show. On one of his routes, Billy stopped at a railroad crossing. A hoodlum came over and attempted to rob the bus. Billy hopped out of the bus, tore off the railroad crossing arm and beat the man out of the bus with it.

With fewer financial responsibilities, Mawzy decided the time was right to get her driver's license and buy a car. Dad helped her pick out a blue 1956 Chevy. She was like a kid in a candy store. At age 49 she finally had wheels of her own.

Billy had not lost his love of cars and speed. Shortly after he bought his first new car, he ran into a restaurant window in Cleveland and totaled it. Luckily, he was not seriously injured. Billy Boy was mad at his dad for ruining their new car.

After their third son, Randy, was born, Billy and family decided to move to Chattanooga, Tennessee. Randy's middle name was Earl after Uncle Earl. Ironically, as an adult Randy ended up looking more like Earl than his siblings.

Billy went into business with one of his Mason buddies. They were partners in the Chow Now Drive-In restaurant. Billy's interest in restaurants stemmed from fond memories of The Dutch Colony in Springdale.

Soon after there was another move, this time to Gadsden, Alabama, where Billy managed the Noccalula Bowling Alley snack bar and later became part owner of a local drive-in restaurant. He named the drive-in after Billy Boy. When we saw pictures, David and I were in awe that our cousin's name was up on the

The Billy Boy drive-in restaurant; memorabilia from his Chow Now eatery.

Mawzy admiring her grandkids: David holding Randy, Myra, Stevie, and Billy Boy. Below, Eleanor, Deborah, and Jack on left; Billy roughhouses with his boys on right.

marquee of the building – The Billy Boy Drive-In Restaurant, "Home of the Whatta Burger."

We went to visit Billy's family with Mom and Mawzy over Christmas in 1960. It was an awesome trip. Billy had the record, "Splish Splash" by Bobby Darin and played it over and over. He loved that song and so did Mom, We kids thought it was hilarious and danced all around the house like a bunch of banshees anytime it was playing.

On Christmas Eve Uncle Billy gave David, me, Billy Boy and Stevie $5 each and sent us to the Falls Drug Store in pursuit of Christmas gifts for each other. It was an interesting process as we found things and tried to hide them from each

182

other so they would be a surprise. The escapades continued when we were given wrapping paper, ribbon, and tape to finish the task. If anyone were looking for Mawzy, she could usually be found in the kitchen.

Billy's family was enjoying life in Alabama. A fourth son, Danny, was born the fall of 1962. Annie was a stay-at-home mom. Billy loved those boys. He loved nothing better than to rough house with them at home.

Yet Billy also missed his home in the hills of West Virginia. He and Annie packed up the kids and came back to Mawzy's house at least twice a year – usually at Easter time or in the summer and around the Christmas holidays. Eleanor and her family sometimes joined in on the visits.

Not long after returning from Mawzy's the Christmas of 1962, Billy wanted to test drive a friend's sports car. One evening after work, he called another friend, Donald, to go with him. It was his last car ride. Following are excerpts from the January 9, 1963 front-page article in *The Gadsden Times*.

Head-On Crash Near Noccalula Claims 2 Lives

Two Gadsden residents were killed and another in the hospital as the result of a two-car head-on crash on Noccalula Road near the top of Lookout Mountain at 9:45 p.m., yesterday. Police said William Gene Campbell, 30, ... died instantly in what Accident Investigator Homer Lee Garner termed "one of the worst wrecks I've ever seen." A passenger in Campbell's brand-new car, Donald Eugene Smith, 29, ... was rushed to a local hospital with serious head injuries. Smith died about 1 a.m. ... Garner said Campbell's late-model sports sedan apparently crossed over the center line on the second curve up Lookout Mountain and struck the Freeman vehicle which was coming down the mountain. According to witnesses Garner said, Campbell had just shifted gears and was attempting to get back on his side of the road when the crash occurred... Mr. and Mrs. Charles Smith, the parents of Donald Eugene Smith happened to be passing the accident shortly after the collision. They stopped and asked if anyone was hurt and were told a Smith boy was in it, but he had several children. Knowing their son had no children, the Smiths went on home, only to be called from the hospital and told their son was in serious condition...

Other stories surfaced. In one, a pothole was to blame when the driver coming down the mountain swerved to miss it. No one will ever know for sure but interestingly enough the pothole was filled the following day.

The police dropped off Uncle Billy's bloody clothes at their house. The boys found them.

There were two funerals – one in Gadsden and one in Rainelle. Uncle Billy was buried the day after Billy Boy's 9th birthday at The End of the Trail

Cemetery, not far from Mommy Walker. Annie was left with four boys, the youngest of which was only 14 months old.

She had a mess on her hands with the restaurant businesses Billy left behind. She was devastated. So was Mawzy. All hope for Billy's happiness and success was shattered.

Annie worked part-time at the Billy Boy Drive-In for about 18 months after Billy's death. Four years later Billy's partner paid her $10,000 for Billy's share of the drive-in. She invested the money in a CD and took the interest to help supplement her income.

Billy's last Christmas with his boys. Below, Billy's boys.

The army provided Billy with a $5,000 life insurance policy. When he left the service, he decided to let the policy lapse. Mawzy tried to get him to keep it but he refused so she paid the premiums and made herself the beneficiary. After Billy's death she used the proceeds to help cover his family's expenses.

Mawzy did all she possibly could to help Billy's family. Over the next five years, while the boys were younger, she took the bus to Alabama every Christmas and went a couple of summers. She made Annie's house payments as was evidenced by cancelled checks stored in an old shoe box and discovered in her garage attic. Three years after Billy's death, she even pleaded with Billy's other business partner in Chattanooga to return Billy's seed money for the Chow Now restaurant. Annie had only received $100 per month from him for about a year. Mawzy kept a copy of the hand-written letter she sent him in her hope chest.

Dear Sir,

I don't want anyone to think I am interfering where I have no business – but from all indications Annie Campbell, my daughter-in-law is not getting enough income through Social Security and the small veteran's check to provide the necessary things for her family. She feels she made a mistake in two ways in letting you have the money from the Billy Boy Drive In – 1st she needed it for other things at present (especially since she was squeezed out of the Snack Bar business) 2nd she does not have any legal papers showing that she has any interest in a business in Chattanooga.

If you were the friend of Billy's as he thought you were I hope you will realize what that money means to them especially those poor little helpless children and return the money at an early date. If for any reason it is impossible to do that now, please have some sort of a legal paper prepared to give her. I don't believe you would want to let that much money go without something to stand good for it yourself. No matter how good one's word is there is always a possibility that something might happen before the settlement is made.

I help them all the time, but I don't know how long I will be able to do so. I went to visit them Christmas and tried to help them have a happy one. I bought a refrigerator, lamps, clothing, food, and toys. Last summer I helped pay a hospital bill for the baby. I send packages and money right often. Eleanor and Jack help them all they can and that is all the help she has.

As you probably have heard Billy say, his daddy didn't help but very little to raise them and of course he wouldn't help with his grandchildren. They have some good neighbors that do little things for them. [One of Billy's Mason brothers] got the boys a race car set. They played with it almost all day Christmas.

Annie is an honest person and would do nothing to hurt anyone. She is really hurt because she never hears from you all. She and Billy both thought so much of you and your wife. So I plead with you again to do something about their money you have.

Would also appreciate it if you would pass the word to Buddy that there is a widow and four children in Gadsden, Alabama who need the money he owes them on the house Billy let him have.

I am expecting to get some response from this letter in the near future.
Yours truly,
Grace Campbell

A response came back to Mawzy which she also stored in her hope chest. Claims of owing creditors and the business being in the hole ensued. Nothing ever came of Mawzy's attempts to recover these assets for Annie and the boys.

Billy's boys loved Mawzy so much and recognized her love for them.

Remember how Billy had to sleep with Mawzy when she first moved into her own home in Springdale? Ironically, I ran across this letter from Billy's son, Randy, in Mawzy's hope chest.

Dear Mawzy,

Thank you for the dollar. I hope you have a merry Christmas. In not long we will get out for two weeks. It will be Christmas vacation. Tell David and the others – hope they have a merry Christmas too.

P.S. THANK YOU FOR THE MATTRESS

From – Randy Campbell

Mawzy bought twin beds and mattresses for all four boys the Christmas after Billy was killed.

Years later, Billy Boy reminisced about Mawzy's impact on him. He stayed with her the summer after Billy's death. She had him do chores every day, like mowing the lawn and weeding the garden and paid him for his labor. When they went out for a drive, Mawzy let him sit next to her and put his foot on the gas pedal. On one occasion he got too exuberant with the accelerator and they went through the neighbor's yard so that was the end of that activity. On one of their road trips, Mawzy drove him to see his grandpa, Add Campbell. She stayed in the car. "I felt uncomfortable," Billy Boy recalled. "I was in a stranger's world."

"Mawzy was the one who made me proud I was a Campbell," he added. "She was a piece of sunshine."

Mawzy handed down a sense of family that bonded the cousins as tightly as did the ties that kept Billy, Eleanor, and Gloria June united. Above, the cousins, including Aunt Annie, Randy, Stevie, David, Myra, and Billy Boy gather on Mawzy's porch.

School Days: Hot Lunches Come to Springdale

In Mawzy's early years of teaching, students brought their lunches to school. On many occasions lunch bag contents were sparse. Some kids showed up with no lunch at all. This was particularly true when the coal miners were on strike.

"Is that all I'm a gonna get?" Mawzy overheard one little boy say as he peered into his bag.

"That's the blackest banana I ever saw," was another's lunch time lament.

Mawzy wanted all the kids well fed so worked diligently to start a hot lunch program. Some schools in the area already had hot lunches. She knew her school principal's position for the 1953-54 school year was secure, as she was on the home stretch of completing all her course work. To get a jump start, she attended a hot lunch training meeting the spring of 1953 in Fayetteville, where the Fayette County school administrative offices were located. This gave her the tools needed to move forward. She learned that in addition to commodity food donations the National School Lunch Program offered financial aid.

To take advantage of federal government assistance, Mawzy's first step was to find a cook. One day after school, she walked to Louella Patterson's house in

Louella Patterson

Meadow Bridge, which was three miles away. Shortly after rapping on her door, Louella surfaced.

"Hello, Grace. I wasn't expecting to see you. How are you doing today? Come on in and have a seat."

"Thanks, Louella," Mawzy said as she stepped inside the house and sat down on the living room couch. "I've been thinking a lot about what the kids are bringing in their school lunches. I worry some are just not getting enough to eat. I want to start a hot lunch program. I know you're a good cook. Heaven knows you've had enough practice with six children and a husband to feed. I was wondering if you would consider being our school cook?"

"I appreciate you thinking of me," Louella said, "but I'll have to think about it. I'm not sure I could do the job justice and still keep up with everything I have to do here at home."

"That's all I can ask," Mawzy said as she headed out the door to walk home.

Mawzy started to orchestrate fund raisers for the needed fixtures, equipment, and appliances. The Springdale Parent-Teacher Association held a pie social that fall and raised $140.41. That was a start. A Halloween carnival was also held and featured cake walks, a bake sale, a fishpond, grab bags, target shooting and fortune telling. Through these events, civic association donations and retail contributions there was enough raised to start feeding the children hot lunches the winter of 1954.

Initially Mawzy asked parents to provide a plate, a glass and silverware for each of their children, as there was no money in the school's budget for these items. Until Mawzy could get some lunch money in the coffers, she often took dollars from her personal account to cover the cost of the groceries. She was a meticulous recordkeeper and had many a cancelled check made out to the school lunch program. She bought eggs for herself and the school from Enoch Cox, who had also helped her with remodeling and the maintenance of her house.

Louella, after much consideration and discussion with her husband, decided to take the school cook's job. She felt the extra income would be helpful for the family, especially during miner strikes. She did love to cook. And cook she did for 26 years until the school closed. All meals were made from scratch for around 60 students. She did all the menu

- At least two ounces of meat, or a substitute such as cheese, eggs, dried beans or four tablespoons of peanut butter
- One-half cup each of two vegetables or a fruit and vegetable
- Two slices of bread and butter
- Pudding, cookies or some other sweet

The lunchroom with Louella, Bud and visitor. Photograph provided by Bud Harmon.

planning based on the federal government's requirements as illustrated in the accompanying box.

Louella went a step above guidelines as she almost always made homemade rolls. The kids told her she made the best biscuits, but they were yeast rolls. She claimed her secret was the commodity powered milk. Cheese, hamburger, and green beans were frequent staples received as commodities for the school. Once a week a grocery truck backed up to a window in the rear of the school and handed food in to Louella. These were groceries purchased in addition to commodities received.

"Mrs. Patterson's kingdom was all within the kitchen," Bud remembered. "She was the chief cook and bottle washer. She would fill and place each tray on the tables and all the students had to do was sit and eat. Seconds were available. Sometimes we had a lunch guest. Mrs. Patterson always treated them royally."

Louella and Mawzy planned special meals around Thanksgiving, Christmas, and Easter holidays.

"One odd thing I recall clearly was over a period of two years every time Mrs. Patterson was in the cooking stage for Thanksgiving or Christmas turkey, the electricity went off," Bud said. "We were suspended for a couple of hours before service was restored and enjoyed the delicious meal even more."

The grand finale was always a picnic the last day of school. Mawzy wanted to reward students for another year of accomplishments. My favorite picnic games were the sack and three-legged races. My least favorite was Red Rover as I was often considered the weak link for the opposing team to pass through. When they did, I felt I had let my team down. The picnic always ended with fresh cut watermelon to enjoy. Seed spitting contests ensued.

I ate Louella's cooking for six years so I can vouch for its goodness. The rolls were delicious. So were her no bake chocolate cookies, made of oatmeal, cocoa, and peanut butter. There was one secret Louella kept. If any cookies were left over, she allowed the kids to sneak them out of the lunchroom to snack on later. Once all the children were seated with their lunches before them, Mawzy led her flock in saying grace. With heads bowed, all sang in unison, "God is great and God is good and we thank him for this food. Amen."

On a day when baked potatoes were on the menu Ralph, one of the Jones brothers, asked the kids at his table a question.

"Can any of you take this paper straw and poke it all the way through a raw potato?" Ralph inquired.

"No and I bet you can't either," Bobby challenged.

"Mrs. Patterson, can I have a raw potato?" Ralph yelled. "I promise I won't make a mess."

With a bit of reluctance, she obliged. Ralph picked up a straw with his right hand and put his right thumb over the top of one end. He held the potato between his fingers and thumb with his left hand, drew the straw back and drove it straight through the potato. Everyone was amazed. Necessity is the mother of invention. The Jones boys didn't need store-bought toys for their entertainment. Through knowledge and practice they developed skills to come up with their own creations. They made the best paper airplanes of anyone in the school. A competition was often held with planes being thrown off the school porch. Most wouldn't make it to the bottom of the stairs. The Jones brothers' planes soared up to 200 feet if the wind was right.

Springdale Elementary School's kitchen received scores above 90 out of 100 on sanitation inspections. Mawzy's belief was "If you're going to do it, do it right." Louella agreed. "They liked to joke about being written up for storing toothpicks in the cupboard with the dishes," Bud recalled.

Over time Mawzy was pleased with the benefits of the lunch program as she could see improvements in many of the students' health and performance. She could tell they weren't as scrawny.

Only a few months after the hot lunch program got off the ground, the school was burglarized, as it was quickly deduced food was stored there. On February 20, 1954, the day of my birth, the *Beckley Post-Herald* posted the following article:

Quantity Of Food Is Stolen From School

Local officials were still without clues late this afternoon which might lead to the solution of the robbery last night of the Springdale school.

Rainelle State Police officer, Tpr. B. H. Cassell reported that someone entered the school some time during the night, and missing from the hot lunch kitchen are three sacks of flour, 22 pounds of cheese, 40 pounds of hamburger, a case of canned beef, and a quantity of canned goods.

Cassell stated that entrance to the building was gained by opening the window of the girls' toilet. A lock to the kitchen door was also prized open.

The principal of the three-room grade school, Mrs. Grace Campbell is absent from her duties due to illness.

Mining jobs were beginning to fall by the wayside due to the onset of mining mechanization and some of the mines being depleted of coal. Break ins may have been a perceived solution for some to help stave off hunger.

Commodities could not be sold or given away. If there were excesses or the commodities were getting dated, they had to be thrown away. Mawzy "threw them away" in a culvert down past the lower playground by the railroad tracks after she discretely let needy families know of the discard location.

"Because the school had no telephone, Mrs. Campbell excused herself five or six times a year to go to her house and call the board of education," Bud said. "Most of the calls had to do with the hot lunch program. We finally got a phone installed the fall of 1971. It wasn't ideal as it was on a four-person party line. Never knew who might be ease dropping on the school's business."

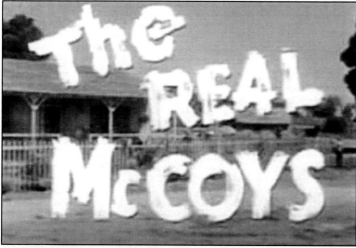

"I wish I wasn't cursed with the McCoy charm."

"Luke, for a kid that couldn't say Mama until he was four years old, you sure turned into a gol' durn flapjaw!"

"Little Luke, there's a dish of soap in the kitchen. Why don't you go have it for lunch?"
Lines from Grampa Amos in *The Real McCoys* TV show

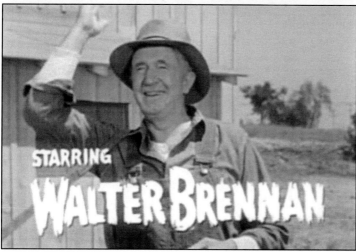

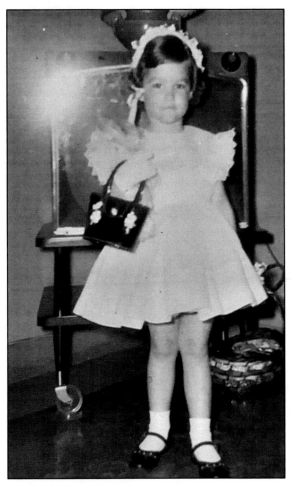

The Arrival of the TV – No Brag, Just Fact

David and I were beside ourselves with excitement. It was Saturday morning and our new black and white television set had just been delivered. I was three years old and David was four. Mom bought it for us kids with her first paycheck, though everyone enjoyed it immensely. I got in trouble with Mawzy on delivery day. I kept getting in the installer's way as I was flopping around on a cushion in the floor and inadvertently showing my underwear. I was embarrassed after I realized the inappropriateness of my behavior. It was my first lesson from Mawzy on how to properly behave.

We got a signal from three stations. WOAY, transmitting from Oak Hill, was the first station in southern West Virginia and the only reliable one for us. At midnight it went off the air after the Star-Spangled Banner played while a picture of a large US flag waved back and forth on the screen. Black and white stripes popped up after the song ended.

There were random tests of the Emergency Broadcasting System. CONELRAD, an acronym for Control of Electromagnetic Radiation, was a system used to alert the public of a national emergency, like an atomic bomb. When the siren blasted on the TV, we weren't sure if it was an attack or a test until informed after the fact. I didn't like these tests as I was afraid it was a sign the Communists were coming to take us over. A friend told me her cousin was behind the iron curtain. I didn't know what she meant. I don't think she did either. The Cold War was on and even though I didn't understand what it was, I did know fear and recognized Khrushchev as the enemy. We heard about it almost every night on the news. The television opened the world to me, a life to date so sheltered as to cover only a small radius.

The TV's picture tubes had to be replaced periodically. Junior Thomas, who owned a nearby appliance store, made house calls to install the new tubes. Television reception was controlled by an outside antenna which ran about five feet above the roof line of the house. When the TV wigged out David and I banged our heads against the back of the couch.

"Come and fix it, fix the TV," we shouted over and over in sing song fashion.

"OK, OK," Mawzy replied. "I'll go outside and turn the antenna. Stand in the doorway where you can still see the TV and tell me if it's working." She gave the antenna a twist then yelled, "Did that do it?"

We yelled back, "Not yet." After two or three tries she usually regained our reception. Weather often wreaked havoc with our plans as the TV was our backup on rainy days.

"Ah one and ah two and…" on Saturday night we settled in to watch *The Lawrence Welk Show*. Everyone in the household had a beau or girl on the show except me. Mawzy was enamored with the organist, Robert Ralston, Mom with the accordion virtuoso, Myron Floren, and David with Janet, the youngest Lennon sister. I occasionally got bored, not having a focal point, and went off to play on my own. My beau was Little Joe on *Bonanza*!

Mawzy loved *The Real McCoys* starring Walter Brennan. He played Grampa Amos, who was originally from the hills of West Virginia but moved to "Californy" to the family's inherited farm. He reminded her a bit of her dad, Poppy Walker. She also watched Brennan in *The Guns of Will Sonnett*. She chuckled at and impersonated his often-used line "No brag, just fact."

Mawzy didn't understand film editing, so she was amazed to see a cat dancing in a Meow Mix cat food commercial while singing, "Meow, meow, meow, meow..." She didn't think it was possible to teach a cat to dance the cha cha cha.

Lassie was probably our most coveted show as a family. David was beside himself when Zorro made a cameo appearance on *Lassie*. Zorro was David's favorite action hero and had his own TV show which David always watched.

One summer Mawzy, Mom, David and I took a big trip to see Uncle Billy's family in Gadsden and Aunt Eleanor's family in Atlanta. After Sunday supper at Eleanor's house Mawzy laid down for a rest.

"Where's Mawzy?" David asked as he walked into the kitchen where Mom and Eleanor were having a cup of coffee.

"She's down for a nap," Eleanor said.

"I gotta' wake her up. It's almost time for *Lassie* to start."

"No, David, don't do that. We've had a big day. She's tired," Eleanor insisted.

"Well, don't blame me if she's mad because she missed *Lassie*," he responded as he stomped away. Mom and Eleanor snickered and decided to let David go wake up Mawzy.

The first special program we saw was *Hansel and Gretel*. It scared me and after watching it, I had another recurring nightmare. I dreamed David and I went to a Meadow Bridge High School football game with a family friend. When the game was over, we headed out of the stadium and got separated from the adults. We were pulled into the concession stand by a witch who was stirring a cauldron of boiling water. Her plan was to boil and eat us. David escaped. Just as the witch grabbed me to throw me in the pot, I always woke up in a panic from the dream.

The most anticipated television event of the year was *The Wizard of Oz*. It was right up there with Christmas in terms of excitement. We watched it every year. I loved the cowardly lion and the way he always played with his tail when he was nervous. I still like to quote him, "I'm gonna fight ya with one hand behind my back. Gonna fight ya with my eyes closed...."

The day of the show we kept asking how soon before it would start. A plentiful array of snacks was prepared. Fresh popcorn was made. I can still see Mawzy pull out the old heavy pot with the cracked wooden handle, fill it with popcorn and oil, hold the lid handle with one hand and the pot handle with the other and rake the pot across the hot stove burner until the last kernel popped. It was the best popcorn ever. David and I were each given a saucer with a dollop of butter and a spoonful of honey on it which we stirred with a spoon until blended. Our stirring chant was "Baby ribbon, baby ribbon, baby ribbon...." I have no idea what it meant but it gave us our cadence to blend the concoction.

One year after all the snacks were prepared and we were anxiously awaiting the show, the TV went on the blitz. Gloom and doom entered the scene. Try as she might, the rotation of the antenna wouldn't do the trick, so Mawzy saved the day by making it a special game night with Monopoly as the grand finale.

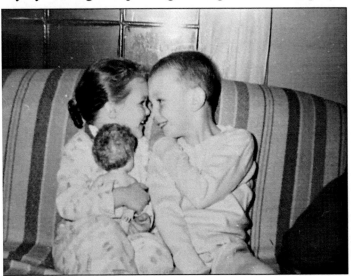

Whether it was *Captain Kangaroo* weekday mornings or Saturday cartoons, David and I were known to wage battle against each other during some of the commercials.

Once the show started again, we always became best buds with an arm around each other.

The creek by Mawzy's house wasn't just to play in. It had a soothing effect. May have dissipated a battle or two. In the summertime, with the house windows opened, we heard it babbling in the background as we sat on the couch watching our Saturday morning cartoons.

Woody Woodpecker, Mighty Mouse, Felix the Cat, Popeye and *Heckle and Jeckle* were favorites. Clips of *Laurel and Hardy* and *The Three Stooges* between cartoons was the slapstick icing on the cake. When Mawzy heard our belly laughs, she knew either *Laurel and Hardy*, which we called "fat" and "skinny" or *The Three Stooges* were on.

I still remember my Felix the Cat Wonder Books. I was mesmerized by the book's added feature where I flipped the pages to watch Felix dance in the upper right-hand corner of each page. I turned the pages over and over to watch his moves.

I really looked forward to *The Flintstones*, which was the first animated prime time show and came on Friday nights at 8:30. *The Jetsons* hit prime time soon after. I found it fascinating that these two cartoons came out about the same time - one from the distant past and one into the distant future.

When David and I were a little older, there were three shows that caught our attention. One was *American Bandstand*. We hopped all around the living room in an effort to mimic the dancers. We got a kick out of *The Beverly Hillbillies*. Though we knew they were making fun of us, we couldn't help but laugh at their hillbilly antics. We were gripped by *The Twilight Zone, "...*a fifth dimension beyond that which is known to man..." On one of the episodes a boy fell between his bed and the wall and slid into a different universe. I still don't like to sleep in a bed where I face close to the wall.

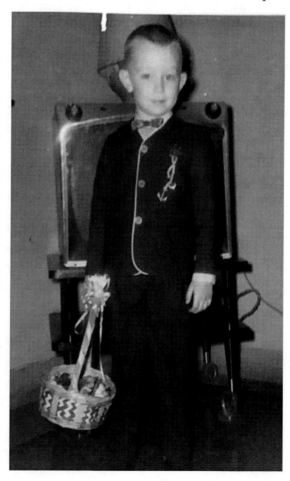

David got to be on TV when he was in the third grade. His name was drawn to be a contestant on WOAY's *Kiddie Quiz*. Mawzy and Dad took David to the Oak Hill station. Dad's interest was a rare occasion. Mawzy said he was like a bird on a hot rock during the show. The game show host periodically asked the contestants questions about themselves.

One of the questions was "What does your father do for a living?" Mawzy was petrified that David would say, "He drinks a lot and plays cards." Thank goodness David did not get that question.

I didn't get to go. Mom and Mawzy thought I was too young to take along, so Mom stayed home with me to watch as David proceeded to win prizes when he answered questions correctly. As a contestant he was given a large cowboy hat to wear and sat on a tall chair so that his legs dangled as he was quizzed. He made a good showing and won several prizes. The question he missed was, "What is the Milky Way?" His answer was "a candy bar." The right answer was "the galaxy."

After David answered one of his questions correctly, he asked for a Lestoil doll as his prize. Lestoil was a high-powered cleaning liquid. The marketing of their dolls was ingenious as they were sold for $1 plus a Lestoil label. They became the rage. By 1958, over 700,000 dolls had been mailed to customers. I heard him say he wanted the doll for his teacher. Mom thought he said he wanted it for his sister. I was excited in hopes Mom's hearing was better than mine.

When David came home with all his prizes, his favorite being a battery-operated truck with a flashing red light on the top, I must admit I was a bit jealous and felt left out.

But what really tore me up was seeing the Lestoil doll and discovering it wasn't for me. She was beautiful with a porcelain face, curly blond hair, and a full skirted dress of purple and yellow plaid. A shiny yellow sash and wide brimmed hat completed her outfit. I hoped upon all hopes that David would change his mind and give it to me. But it was not to be. He was polishing the apple. Mrs. Spencer, his teacher had hinted about the doll prior to the show. Years later, David said he was sorry for giving the doll to her. I reminded him that at least he was thinking of someone besides himself.

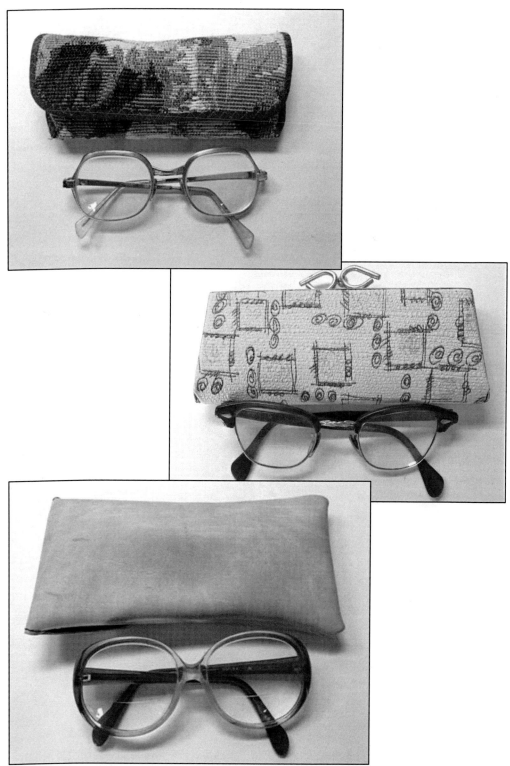

Mawzy always kept an eye on her students; attentiveness and decorum shaped her educational philosophy.

School Days: Discipline, Safety, and Learning Go Hand in Hand

Mawzy could tutor an individual student even as she kept an eye on the rest of her class.

 Milk was a key component of the lunch program and by 1956 additional federal money was available for its purchase. During that time, kids at Springdale Elementary were given all the milk they could drink. Allowing milk out of the lunchroom came to a halt after one of the students charged into the school over the noon hour in search of Mawzy.

"Mrs. Campbell you won't believe what's goin' on outside. Some of the kids are throwin' their milk cartons against the side of the schoolhouse to watch 'um explode!"

Mawzy would not tolerate disorderly conduct or wasted food. She walked briskly out of the building and around to the back of the school where she caught five kids in the act.

"George. Brenda. Sam. Cathy. Bobby. Follow me." They obeyed and each got three swats with a Ping-Pong paddle. They were then ordered to go to their seats for the rest of the day.

My brother, David, got the Ping-Pong paddle twice. The first time was when Mawzy asked the second-grade students to draw a picture of a man or woman and to do the best they could. David proceeded to draw a stick man but gave him three legs to make him more anatomically correct. Mawzy came over to look at his progress.

"What is that?" she asked upon on seeing the "third leg." She took the drawing away from him, put it in her desk drawer and ordered him to come to the front of the room where he got three licks with the paddle.

The second time was when he attempted to give Julie, a girl he was sweet on, a kiss. Mawzy usually left the classroom right before lunch to go to the restroom so she had some privacy. After she departed, David seized the moment, got up and proceeded to Julie's desk. Mawzy came back into the classroom just as David was bending over to give Julie a peck on the cheek. Out came the paddle again, not so much because of the kiss but because he disobeyed by getting out of his seat.

The black leather barber's strap was reserved for those who got in really bad trouble. It dangled on a large nail in the back closet of Mawzy's classroom. It was about 18 inches long and 4 inches wide. It was a quarter of an inch thick and was spooky to look at if the closet door happened to be open. If you did something that warranted the strap, you were taken from the classroom and out into the hall-

The cut

way. The other teachers came to Mawzy with their errant students, as only Mawzy could use the strap. Once the child was out in the hallway, those left in the classroom were so quiet you could hear a pin drop as breaths were held until the sound of that first crisp whop. There were always three whops.

One of the most common causes for the strap was going into the cut, a deep and narrow ravine carved into the side of the hill to make way for train tracks. It wasn't far from the schoolhouse. Mawzy had a fence built all along the cut to provide some protection. The strap was her way of letting the kids know there were still dangers when getting too close. She knew firsthand as, in her early years of teaching at Springdale, one of her students got his arm cut off by a train when he snuck into the cut. He was one of her more difficult students, would not mind her and once chased her around the potbelly stove with a shovel.

Throwing rocks at trains passing through the cut was also strap worthy. The CSX Railroad

200

contacted Mawzy to complain. They told her rocks hitting the fan could cause serious damage and warned if it didn't stop, they would notify the police. Cousin Gary was one of the first to get the strap for rock throwing.

Gary got the strap a second time for peeping in the girl's bathroom window. He and a couple of his buddies built a makeshift plank high enough so they could see through the window. After climbing up the plank, they got big eyed when they saw someone headed down the bathroom hall. Low and behold it was Mawzy. She caught them red-handed and saw Gary flying through the air as he jumped off the plank. Busted. Strap time for all involved.

Mawzy played no favorites with family members which included her own children, some of her siblings' children, David and me. She requested that we not call her Mother, Aunt Gracie or Mawzy when in school. We were instructed to always address her as Mrs. Campbell, just like the other students.

I got in a bit of hot water with Mawzy in the girl's bathroom. There were no stalls, just three toilets lined up on one side of the room and a couple of sinks on the opposite side. After lunch one day, a friend, Sarah, and I were sitting on the pot and I asked her a question.

"I know you have more pairs of shorts, but I was just wondering why you always wear the red ones?"

Mawzy was coming down the narrow bathroom hallway and overheard me. She held me by the shoulder until Sarah left the room and then explained that the question was not appropriate. I realized then that Sarah probably didn't have many other pairs of shorts and that I had hurt her feelings. I felt terrible, as that was not my intent.

Mawzy would not tolerate sleeping in the classroom. If she discovered a student snoozing, she would ask for help.

"Who wants to wake up Hubert?" she called out one day. Hands instantly went up in the air.

"Wayne, your turn." Wayne got up, walked over to Hubert's desk, and started to turn it over. Hubert came awake with a start and caught himself before the desk capsized. This technique worked every time.

On the other end of the spectrum were those students who had trouble staying in their chairs. One student was so bad he wandered around the classroom. Mawzy's solution was to tie him to his desk. Disruptions to learning would not be tolerated.

Mamma Bear would be a good description for Mawzy as she took the safety of her "cubs" seriously. A stray dog showed up in the school yard over the lunch hour. He kept hanging around day after day and started to pester the kids, probably because he was hungry. Mawzy tried to shoo him off as she worried he might bite someone. Finally, she approached three sixth-grade boys, gave them a rope and asked them to get rid of the dog. They took it to the abandoned outhouse behind the school and hanged it. They drug it back into the woods for the buzzards to eat and returned to the classroom. Problem solved. One less worry.

201

*"Life's riches other rooms adorn,
but in a kitchen home is born."*

The above quote is on the back cover of Mawzy's well-used *Betty Crocker Picture Cook Book.* The book was so worn, the cover had to be reattached with duct tape. *Betty Crocker*, along with the *Searchlight Recipe Book,* made frequent appearances on the kitchen counter. You can tell which recipes were her favorites by the amount of telltale splatter left on the pages. A few of her favorite recipes are included in the appendix.

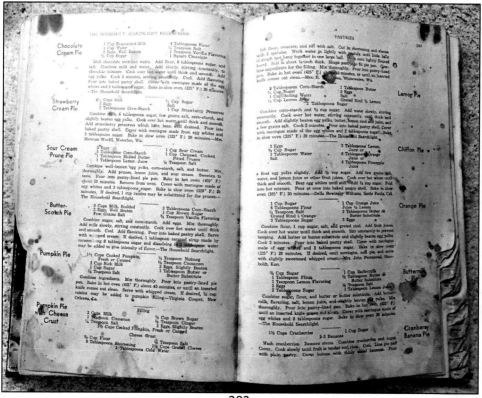

Mawzy was almost always happy in her kitchen kingdom. Her Hoosier baking center is to her right. Below, Myra loved being near the good stuff.

Mawzy's Kitchen

When Mawzy was home, she spent a lot of time in the kitchen and it was where she seemed happiest. I could always hear sounds coming from there – sizzling, pounding, chopping, dough smacking, sifter grinding, mixer running on various speeds, timer going off, dishes rattling, banging of cupboard doors and the oven rack being pushed in and pulled out.

Another sound was that of song. Mawzy loved to sing while she cooked.

One of her favorite songs was "You Got to Quit Kicking My Dog Around" by Jimmie Driftwood. She like to add "Dog I, dog I, dog around" to the end of the song.

She also enjoyed "The Doughnut Song" which tells

203

the story of a kid who attempted to buy a donut with a coal company scrip coin and was rejected. Mawzy could relate to scrip coins with their odd-shaped holes and an imprint of the mining company's name. The coins could only be spent at the mine's company store.

When Mawzy was in a melancholy mood, she turned to the chorus of "Worried Man Blues," by The Carter Family. She sang, *"It takes a worried man to sing a worried song... I'm worried now but I won't be worried long..."* over and over. David became concerned about the man in the song and approached Mawzy.

"What's going to happen to that man? Why won't he be worried anymore?" David inquired.

She had fun with Little Richard's "Tutti Frutti" but she preferred to sing "Rootie Tootie" instead. Patty Page's "How Much is that Doggie in the Window?" and "Dance with Me Henry" by Etta James also surfaced.

The kitchen was a cozy space. The walls were rough two by fours painted a pea green color. White cupboards and appliances helped brighten the room as did the natural light coming through the east window. The free-standing pantry just inside the kitchen door was a popular place for David and me to pilfer as good stuff was stored here. Even in later years it was the first place we went when we came to Mawzy's house. Her bag of old-fashioned horehound cough drops was kept on the second shelf, but we thought they were so nasty Mawzy didn't have to worry about us eating them up.

Beside the pantry was an electric stove. The coal burning stove had been replaced when duct work was installed for the house. Mawzy kept the bacon fat can, which was metal with a strainer in the top to catch dregs, on the stove for easy access. Bacon fat was used for frying and in some recipes. It's what made brown beans so delicious and was another example of her effort to minimize waste.

We seldom threw out leftovers. We called consuming them "eatin' up the shame" because it was a shame to throw them out. The family expression originated from Mawzy's sister, Aunt Jewell, during the Great Depression era.

"What you fixin, Mawzy? I asked one evening as I came in from playing in the creek and saw her standing by the stove frying something in a pan.

"They're frog legs. You've got to try 'um. They're quite tasty."

"No way am I gonna eat those frog legs!"

"No, I was just kidding, they're really chicken legs."

I ate a leg or two only to be told they really were frog legs. I was mad that I had been duped. "Bull fit" time. I must admit they did kind of taste like chicken.

Mawzy's Hoosier baking center cabinet was still intact but showed wear and tear from years of food preparation. The paint had worn thin in places and the enamel countertop had a large chip on the left side. She always kept at least five bags of sugar stored in the bottom cupboard. Because of the Great Depression and the sugar shortage during World War II, she tended to hoard staples.

One of the Hoosier utensil drawers housed the dreaded cake turner. This along with a keen switch were Mawzy's chosen kid whipping tools. The switch was always taken from the bush behind the house. It was the same bush Mawzy used for Eleanor, Billy, and Mom's switches. The switches were long, thin, and nimble and stung like the dickens on the back of my legs. I got the cake turner once when I disobeyed the "don't go inside any of the neighbors' houses" rule. I was playing by myself in the yard when my friend, Shirley, stopped by to see if I wanted to join her for a round of hopscotch. That was a no brainer. I loved hopscotch. Once our round was finished,

The bush of doom, where the switches came from.

Shirley invited me to come to her house, two doors up the dirt road from us. She said her Mom would braid our hair. I'd never had my hair braided before, so couldn't resist the temptation. Once inside and about half way through the braiding process, I heard Mawzy hollering for me. Uh-oh. Busted. Cake turner time.

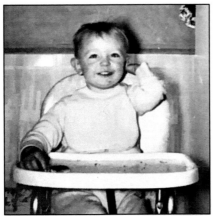

On the south side of the kitchen was a small wooden table with four matching chairs. The table was often covered with a vinyl tablecloth for kid proofing. I think it was mostly for me, as I spilled my milk a lot. I can still hear Mawzy say as she poured my milk, "One glass to spill and one glass to drink." She gave up and replaced the table with one made of Formica and chrome. Much more child friendly. The room was too small to place all the chairs around the table, so the table was pushed against the wall opposite the Hoosier cabinet and the fourth chair sat under the window.

For a few years that chair was replaced by a highchair for us kids in the household. There was a mouse hole at the base of the wall under the window. I checked the hole quite often, half with fear and half with curiosity to see if

205

I could spot the little feller. The fourth chair was witness to a traumatic event for me. Aunt Jewell and Aunt Sister were visiting. When Mawzy's sisters came they always sucked the air out of the room with their rambunctiousness and laughter. Mawzy was the meeker, milder one but she enjoyed the frivolity they brought to the table.

"Boy, we sure use to have some crazy times down at Poppy's house, didn't we?" Jewell said as she reminisced about the holidays there. "Gracie, why didn't you come down more often and join us?"

"Jewell, ya'll got mean when you started drinkin'," Mawzy said. "Just like Poppy. I never cared for that kind of bantering. And you know how I feel about alcohol."

"Yah, we could get pretty wild, couldn't we? It's those brothers that started it."

"You always were the sensible one, Gracie," Sister chimed in.

"I suppose. Sister, how are things goin' for you in Charleston these days?" Mawzy asked.

"I'm keepin' busy with my private duty nursing," Sister answered. "But I've gotta' tell 'ya, I had a hair-raisin' situation the other night."

"What in the world happened?" Jewell asked, all ears.

"I got up in the middle of the night to pee," Sister started in. "As I was sittin' on the pot, I looked over into the shower and you'll never guess what I saw."

"Somebody didn't break into your apartment, did they?" Mawzy gasped.

"No, there was this huge spider crawlin' on the wall," Sister answered. "Now you know how petrified I am of spiders. Well, I went and got my gun and shot him right there on the spot."

"You're kiddin', right?" Jewell asked.

"Nope."

"Why didn't you just take a towel and whack him with it?"

"Wanted to make damn sure he was good and dead!"

Mom was sitting in the chair by the wall, taking it all in. I was vying for her attention and was trying to crawl up her leg. It didn't work so well and I fell to the floor and chipped my knee cap. A wailing ensued.

The refrigerator was housed in the laundry room. Two things you could always find in the fridge were commodity cheese and cod liver oil. Mawzy brought excess cheese home from the Springdale Elementary School, where she was principal. It was yummy and became a staple in the hot lunch commodity program to help maintain dairy prices, beginning in the 1950s.

On the opposite end of the flavor spectrum was the dreaded oil. It was always in the door on lower shelf in the back corner and seemed a bit sinister. David and I were fed a tablespoon of the stuff when we didn't eat everything on our plates. After a few doses, I had no problem cleaning my plate. Fear of that nasty oil is probably why I was never pencil thin. David on the other hand, being anemic and a finicky eater, had a much closer relationship with the oil.

Mawzy still planted a large garden behind the house each spring. Having grown up in hard times, she continued to be as self-sufficient as possible. Not only did she raise a lot of vegetables, which she canned, but she also harvested apples from her trees and went foraging for blackberries in the summer. Blackberry picking was not one of my favorites. I did not like the briars on the bushes and called them "blars." I was also fearful of running into snakes as we were in dense areas on the hillsides. It took forever to get my small bucket full, partly because I kept eating along the way. There is just nothing better than a wild blackberry eaten right off the bush, unless it is Mawzy's blackberry jelly. I've never in my entire life had any jelly that was better.

Us kids' favorite foods growing up were fried bologna, brown beans and cornbread and hominy and wieners. Mawzy made the cornbread in a cast iron skillet, which gave it a nice crispy crust. She often made us fried apple pies and peanut butter cookies. Even now when I see a peanut butter cookie, I can still smell Mawzy's cookies baking in the oven and see her using a fork to crisscross their tops.

Billy was always a welcome sight at Mawzy's table.

On one of Uncle Billy's trips home, he brought us a boxed pizza mix and toppings. We had never had pizza before. Didn't know much about it. Mawzy fixed it for us. It was such a treat it became one of our favorites.

There was often a milk competition between David and me. We were convinced the first pour from the jug was the best, as it had more "glug, glug," the bubbly noise the milk made coming out of the top. So, the argument was over who got the first pour.

207

One day when Mom was mixing Cool Whip for a Jell-O topping, she yelled for David and me.

"Hey kids, you want to lick the bowl?"

"Yay," we yelled as we came running into the kitchen at breakneck speed.

Mom handed us each a beater which we proceeded to lick dry. Next, she put the bowl on the table for us to share.

"I'll get a knife to divide the bowl," David said as he pulled a knife out of the silverware drawer and laid it across the middle of the bowl.

"Grab us some spoons, too," I said.

With spoons in hand, we began digging into the bowl. Our method of division was flawed as we could sneak our spoon under the knife.

"Hey, stop getting over on my side of the bowl," David yelled as he reached over with his spoon to my side to take back his share.

"Mom make David stop eating on my side of the bowl," I countered.

"You started it first."

Mom came back in the kitchen, took the bowl, and handed it to David. "Here, you eat this," she ordered.

"How come he got it all?" I whined.

"Your turn is coming," Mom said as she proceeded to whip up a fresh bowl of Cool Whip. "Here. Now sit there 'til you eat it all."

Funny how it just didn't taste the same when there was a bowl full to wade through. These were the days we got on Mawzy's nerves.

Mom used to get me to eat my breakfast by fixing me "good bites." They consisted of a small bite of an over easy egg, a chunk of bacon and a piece of toast, all stacked on the end of a fork. There was absolutely no problem getting me to finish the meal, with one exception. I refused to eat the egg if it had any "splitters." A word of my creation, "splitters" were the overcooked lacy, tough, scratchy edges. I still don't like "splitters."

Uncle Earl knew Mawzy was always ready to cook up the squirrel he bagged.

One of Mom's favorite breakfast items was a leftover biscuit split in half, buttered, and placed on a saucer. She then proceeded to pour coffee over the biscuit like gravy. She loved her coffee.

"Anybody home?" I heard someone yell so I went running to the front door. It was Uncle Earl standing there holding a couple of squirrels he had shot. "Gracie around?" he asked as he dangled the critters by the tail. "I was wonderin' if she'd cook these squirrels for us."

"She's in the kitchen with Aunt Sister," I replied. "I'll go get her for ya."

Mawzy was happy to cook the squirrels.

"You got a nut pick I can use?" Aunt Sister asked as we sat down to eat. After one was located, she picked the squirrels' brains out and ate them. I was totally grossed out. At least she didn't blow through the squirrel's skull to make it whistle after the brains were eaten like Poppy Walker did. This is a hillbilly delicacy I decided was not for me.

Another hillbilly favorite I avoided was ramps, a pungent wild leek, that tastes like a cross between garlic and onion. They are frequently prepared with scrambled eggs, but Mawzy didn't cook them very often as there was no one to go up into the mountains for their harvest. Flavorful or not, once consumed they permeated your system to the point you walked around reeking like a monster clove of garlic for the next three or four days. For West Virginians, spring is considered official when ramps come into season. There are still ramp feeds all over the state, with the largest being in Richwood where I was born.

School Days: The Start of the Day

It was a school day morning at Springdale Elementary. At 6:30 a.m. the only thing that could be heard from the school grounds was the sound of an electric push lawn mower. Mawzy was mowing the grass and it was another of her efforts to conserve resources when and where she could. She wore an old house dress and flat shoes so as not to soil her school clothes.

The grass was quite dewy that morning, so she had to stop often to clean the caked grass from the underbelly of the mower and the blades. Time was slipping away before students would arrive. So, when the mower clogged again, she attempted to clean it without taking time to stop the motor, not following her own rule of "haste makes waste." As the blades sliced into her hand, she jerked back three bloody fingers. The mowing would have to be finished another day. She ran into the schoolhouse kitchen where Louella, the cook, helped her clean, disinfect and bandage her fingers.

"Thanks for fixin' me up," Mawzy sighed. "No time for coffee in my old green mug today, I'm afraid. I need to change into my school clothes, comb my hair and try to look presentable before the kids show up."

As the kids arrived their priority was play time in the

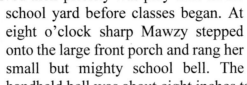

school yard before classes began. At eight o'clock sharp Mawzy stepped onto the large front porch and rang her small but mighty school bell. The handheld bell was about eight inches tall with a black wooden handle and thick brass base. When Mawzy's retired Bud insisted she keep the bell so it now rests in her hope chest.

"Flag salute," Mawzy yelled. Everyone knew the routine. They formed two lines parallel to the porch banisters. Became silent. Faced the large US flag attached to the left pillar of the porch. Placed their right hand over their heart and began.

I pledge allegiance to the Flag
of the United States of America,
and to the Republic for which it stands,
one nation under God,
indivisible, with liberty and justice for all.

Once completed all moved quietly up the stairs and into their classrooms. There were two grades per room. Mawzy's room was the first one on the left just past the water fountain and was where she taught the first and second graders. Third and fourth graders filed into the room on the right, opposite Mawzy's room. The fifth and sixth graders walked straight forward to the room in the back. All rooms had a large bank of windows which provided abundant natural light.

The boy's bathroom sat just beyond Mawzy's room and the girl's bathroom was on the opposite side. The kitchen and lunchroom were in a large area in the back of the building to the left. The kitchen was separated from the lunch tables by a counter between the two.

The water was so iron-laden, it had a red tint. Tasted terrible and left stains in the water fountain, kitchen and bathroom sinks, and the toilets.

The school floors were unfinished tongue-and-groove hardwood and were cleaned by the janitor weekly with a green sweeping compound. Coal was the heat source for the school, initially via potbelly stoves then later through a central steam boiler system. "Took at least two hours before you heard the cracking of the baseboard fin tubes and knew heat was on the way," Bud recalled. "There was a two-man crew who kept the coal in goodly supply and got the fire going in the morning. I stoked the fire on occasion. A fire was needed the whole school year, even in the spring and fall, to take the chill off."

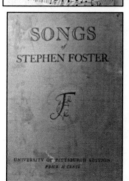

In the 1950s and early 60s the man who remodeled Mawzy's house, Enoch Cox, was janitor of the school. He also had his kids help.

One of his boys, Wayne, remembered working at the school. "Dad got the fire started on school day mornings," Wayne recalled. "Us kids cleaned every day after school and kept the fire stoked over the weekend so the pipes wouldn't freeze. Dad was paid $57 per month. He paid me $10 per month. Mrs. Campbell was old school. During the day if the fire got low, she wasn't above heading down to the basement to shovel coal into the furnace. She didn't want the kids to get cold."

In Mawzy's room the day often started with songs. She felt it helped kids transition from play to schoolwork and was also a mood lifter. "She'll Be Coming Round the Mountain" was a favorite. It was derived from the African American spiritual song "When the Chariot Comes" and made its way into Appalachia in the 19th century.

She liked Stephen Foster, known for his parlor and minstrel songs. "Old Susanna" and "Camptown Races" were popular. The kids loved to belt out the first verse and chorus of "Camptown Races."

De Camptown ladies sing dis song,
Doo-dah, Doo-dah
De Camptown racetrack five miles long,
Oh, doo-dah day.
Gwine to run all night!
Gwine to run all day!
I'll bet my money on de bob-tailed nag,
Somebody bet on de bay.

The third and fourth grade teacher, Mrs. Spencer, settled students by reading a chapter from a book. My favorite was *The Boxcar Children* by Gertrude Chandler Warner. Some days we would beg her to read just one more chapter before our class work began. Some days she obliged. Some days she didn't.

Mrs. Cozort, the fifth and sixth grade teacher, usually got down to the business of instruction right away. She provided concessions in other ways. For example, the boys in her classroom were allowed to bring their .22 rifles to school in the fall and store them in the closet in the back of the room. Mrs. Cozort collected all the shells which she placed in her top desk drawer until school was dismissed. The boys would then collect their munitions and head out for a squirrel hunt as they made their way home.

After singing, the next activity of the day in Mawzy's room was a student cleanliness inspection. She asked for two volunteers, a boy and a girl. Hands were always raised high in the hope of getting picked to help. The selected boy was the "doctor" and was given an old stethoscope to drape around his neck. The selected girl was the "nurse" and was given an authentic white starched nurse's cap to wear. Mawzy had obtained both items from Aunt Sister who was a nurse.

All students were asked to place their hands on the top of their desk. The doctor and nurse for the day walked around to each student and examined their hands and fingernails. If hands or nails were dirty, the student was sent to the bathroom to wash up. Mawzy wanted to help students distinguish between clean dirt and dirty dirt – surface vs imbedded dirt. Inspections were her way to get the point across. Many students over the years experienced the inspection. One time Uncle Billy, being the prankster he was, sent Betty Lou to wash up when she really didn't have dirty nails. He laughed while she fumed.

During the late 1950s a state law was passed requiring student immunization. Free clinics were held monthly throughout Fayette County. Proof of diphtheria, smallpox, typhoid, and polio was needed within one month of entering school. All clinics were off site for Springdale Elementary. However, when boosters came along, they were given at the school. First thing in the morning, students lined up in the back of the fifth and sixth grade room and proceeded to pick up and eat their sugar cube booster. Much nicer than the needle.

Teaching two grades in one room meant jockeying student activities back and forth. Students in one grade were often called up front to a kid sized wooden table for reading and art while students in the other grade were given an assignment to do at their desk. When I was in second grade and we were reading at the front table about various occupations, Mawzy asked us what we wanted to be when we grew up. Truck driver, coal miner, nurse and teacher were common answers. I said I wanted to be an actress. Not sure where that came from.

"You've done well with your lessons today, so we have a little time before the lunch," Mawzy noted. "Who would like to tell a story?" Up the hands went. She selected a student to come to the front of the classroom. She wanted students to get comfortable speaking in front of others.

"Mikey, your hand's raised. Come on up. What story would you like to tell today?"

"Can I tell the one about Peter Rabbit? And when Mr. McGregor wanted to turn him into a kind of a rabbit pie?"

"Yes, that's a good choice and one of my favorite Beatrix Potter stories. Go ahead." Beatrix was a natural scientist and conservationist so Mawzy saw her as a kindred spirit.

I loved to tell stories so would always raise my hand enthusiastically to be called upon. Because of my tendency to provide excessive details, Mawzy quickly learned to call on me last. This way recess was a natural breakpoint for my story to end.

When John Alley left his family, Myra wadded up this photo and threw it away. She then retrieved it, smoothed out the wrinkles, and cried.

*I remember when I was
The twinkle in my daddy's eyes.
Then he left one day
Without saying goodbye.*
From "Daddy Why?" by Heidi A. Hopson

Last Ditch Effort

Dad's drinking and lack of responsibility were becoming less and less tolerable to Mawzy, which put an additional strain on Mom and Dad's marriage. Dad wanted to be a provider, but his drinking coupled with coal mine strikes and layoffs made it difficult. Mawzy had to co-sign for a car loan so Mom would have a reliable ride to work. Dad tried to put forth a good front.

On days when he wasn't working, he usually couldn't be found. He liked to dabble in gambling - playing "penny ante" in Bellwood with the coal miners there. Someone came to Mawzy's house looking for him.

"Where's John Alley?" they inquired when Mawzy answered the door.

"Playing "nickel ickel" in Bellwood," Mawzy responded as she got a bit mixed up about the name of the game. It became a family joke after that.

On a July night in 1958, just before bedtime, Mom called for David and me.

"Come with us," she said. "Your Dad and I have a surprise for you. We're moving."

Their hope was to make a new start.

"Nickle ickle," a game of penny ante in Bellwood, photo provided by Biddie Walker.

"Is Mawzy coming with us?" David inquired. "Because if she's not, I don't wanta go."

As for me, I was excited as I envisioned us traveling afar to a new and exciting place. Was I ever disappointed when our trip took us about 200 yards around the corner to Aunt Sister's house. Since Sister now lived in Charleston, Mawzy approached her to see if she would rent her Springdale house to Mom and Dad. She agreed and set the rent at $40 per month. Mawzy helped pay the rent on occasion. I found one of Mawzy's cancelled checks made out to Sister for $80 in 1960. After that Mawzy made it clear to Dad this was the last time she would help them out of a bind.

Sister's house brought back pleasant memories for Mawzy. It is where Mom had taken her first steps. In Mom's baby book Mawzy wrote: *She would see some object, while standing and wanting it very quickly was soon induced to walk a few steps after it. These first steps were made while she with her brother, sister and mother were keeping house for Aunt Glenna and Uncle Dr. while they were on their trip to Minnesota.*

The house was shoved into the side of a very steep hill. There wasn't much of a front yard, but the back was flat and quite expansive. It bordered the creek parallel to Mawzy's road so you could see her house from that vantage point, except in the summer when all the trees' leaves were at their fullest. The house was three stories high but looked like only one from the road because of the way it was positioned on the side of the hill. The main floor was where we lived, but David and I liked to explore Dr. Jett's old office and the bottom floor. We found remnants of a former life there such as tools, dishes, an old pair of roller skates that attached to your shoes and a vintage medicine cabinet full of crusty medicine bottles and medical instruments.

216

A nice front porch wrapped around the west side of the house. Front porches were coveted in West Virginia, as a favorite past time was porch sitting to observe nature and watch passersby. Mawzy liked to quote one of her college professors from New England who said, "I have never seen anyone sit as gracefully on their front porch as West Virginians do."

The front door opened into the living room and from there straight back to the kitchen. The kitchen was small but had windows on two sides so was much brighter than Mawzy's kitchen. Off the living room was a hallway which provided access to the bathroom and two bedrooms on either end. David and I had twin beds in the bedroom to the left. Mom and Dad's bedroom was to the right.

David did not adapt well to the move as he was homesick for Mawzy. He was always begging to go spend the night with her and often did. I missed her too, but not like he did.

On school days Mawzy stopped by the house to pick up David. Before I was old enough to go to school, Mom took me to Betty Lou's house. Every so often I went with Mawzy and David. Mawzy sat me down at a table in the back of the

Myra and David during Easter at Aunt Sister's (Glenna's) house.

classroom and gave me work to do, like coloring pictures. I often found myself listening to her instruction. I was quiet as she made it perfectly clear I wouldn't be able to come back if I disrupted her classes.

We had some happy times on that hill. Betty Lou, and her husband, James, often came over on weekends to play cards with Mom and Dad. James was one of Dad's drinking buddies.

My most vivid and best memories of my father were when we lived in the Aunt Sister house. It's where we became best of pals. When he wasn't drinking, he was a happy go lucky jokester who loved to sing and dance. That's the man my Mom fell in love with. She said he was one of the best dancers she had ever seen. One of his favorite songs was *Jambalaya (On the Bayou)* by Hank Williams. I can still see him flopping around as he sang the chorus. Another song he liked was *One Bourbon, One Scotch, One Beer* by George Thorogood. That one I don't remember.

He was always teasing me when he talked about "back when he was a little girl living in Pennsyltucky." Said he was born a girl but turned into a boy when he started playing in the coal pile. His favorite nickname for me was mattress mouth. My goofy nature and my rhythm I inherited from Dad.

The back yard became a wonderland. We built our croquet court in grandiose fashion, then on many occasions whacked away at the wooden balls with our mallets. Dad strung lights on posts he installed around the court, so play could be continued into the night. As dusk approached, nature's chorus began with frogs, crickets and katydids competing for attention. An occasional whip-poor-will would sing his distinctive chant. It could be beautiful unless you were trying to sleep then he could keep you awake half the night with his incessant chorus. Lightening bugs assisted in the court lighting and sometimes we took a break to see how many we could catch in a jar.

Our swing set was moved from Mawzy's yard to our back yard. The neighborhood kids always came over. We were the only kids in the neighborhood with a swing set, so it was a drawing card and a luxury David and I took for granted. As adults, some of our friends still reminisced about playing with us on that swing set.

One night as we were heading toward the house after a backyard session, Dad pulled out a package of chewing tobacco. "There's a surprise in the bottom of the pouch," he said. "Do you want it?"

What little kid doesn't say yes to a surprise? The offer sounded akin to a Cracker Jack box with a prize inside. So, I said "Yes!!"

"Here ya go," he said as he dug deep into the pouch, pulled out a wad of something and handed it to me. I popped it in my mouth expecting a sweet, delicious morsel only to quickly discover I had been tricked into taking a chew of tobacco. I gagged and spat that crap out of my mouth. Nasty! Duped again. Why

Myra with Lassie and Gloria June.

218

were people always trying to trick my taste buds? That he laughed at me added insult to injury.

Mom and Dad got us a dog. He was a small collie, so we named him Lassie. We loved him so much. He was always there to greet us when we came home and was our backyard mascot. He came to a bad end. We found him lying part way under the porch, dead. Dad figured he had been poisoned.

We had a pet snake of sorts. On the lower level of the west side of the house was a massive amount of wooden lattice which covered an earthen storage space for lawn mowers and tools. There was a mammoth black snake who liked to weave his body through the slats and bask in the afternoon sun. I was afraid to get close to him but could observe him by looking down from the porch. Dad wanted to keep him around in the hope that he would be a good mouser. We named him Blackie.

Just beyond the lattice was an old cut stone pump house. It covered a natural spring and was how Springdale got its name. We were not allowed to go near it, for fear of a snake nest or falling down the well.

Myra, David, and Grandma Annie

"Want to go with me while I wax the car?" Dad asked one day. I quickly jumped on the opportunity and it's the only time I remember going somewhere with him alone. We went to Springdale's Sacred Heart Catholic Church lot. Dad parked in the shade, turned on the radio and proceeded to sing along while doing his work. I played around the old oak trees and collected acorns for my dolls. It was a magical time for me.

We took a vacation to Tampa, Florida to see Dad's mom, Grandma Annie. She moved there after her divorce to be close to her children who had migrated to the area. Annie went through the same thing with Big John as my Mom was enduring with Dad. After she first discovered Big John was cheating on her, she gathered up her daughters, sneaked to his love nest and proceeded to hurl rocks toward the windows. Many of the windows were broken. Big John came running out of the shack to see what the heck was going on. Busted! Grandma Annie let him have it as she threw rocks at him and left him for good that day.

For Dad, the apple didn't fall far from the tree. Big John Alley was known to take Dad out drinking and carousing with him at a relatively young age.

The long drive to Florida was dreadfully boring, but the beach was a blast. It was the first time I had ever seen the ocean and playing in bucket upon bucket of

David and Myra enjoying themselves in Florida; the postcard sent to Mawzy.

sand was a thrill. David, being lighter complected than me, got a terrible sunburn. He was slathered with mustard plaster so we could go back to the beach the next day. The plaster was so uncomfortable he kept sneaking into the ocean to wash it off.

David sent a postcard to Mawzy from Florida. It was mailed to Cleveland where Mawzy was visiting Uncle Billy and family. He wrote, *"Dear Mawzy, I watched Lassie Sunday. It's fun in Florida. Bet it's fun too where you are. We went to the park. Love, David."* When we left Florida, the drive home was just as boring.

One night, after Dad had hit the bottle way too hard, he and Mom got into a fist fight in the living room. Hands were pounding and voices were screaming. It scared David and me half to death. David decided to take matters into his own hands. He went into our bedroom and came back carrying our little space heater over his head.

"If you guys don't stop fighting, I'm going to hit you with this heater," he proclaimed, trying to look big and act brave.

"You wouldn't hit me, would you?" Mom asked in alarm.

"Yes, I will if you don't stop." This was enough to halt the combat. I stood behind David the whole time, big eyed with my mouth shut tight.

On a Saturday morning a couple of weeks later I got up and found Mom in the kitchen making my birthday cake. "Where's Dad?"

"He's still in bed. Why don't you go and wake him up?"

I headed into their bedroom and proceeded to pounce on Dad. "Wake up Dad. It's time to get up," I pleaded. With his head face down in the pillow, he barely acknowledged my presence, so I continued to pester him. I jumped up and down on the bed. I did belly flops on his back. I grabbed his head and shook him. I cupped my hands into a mini megaphone and kept repeating into his ear, "Are you in there? Wake up." I inadvertently reached under his pillow and pulled out a pint bottle, half full of moonshine. It felt like a hot potato in my hand. This was the awful stuff I had heard about but had never seen. I quietly put it back under the pillow and left him in his stupor as I realized he would not be surfacing for quite some time.

One morning when Dad showed up after a night out on the town, David proceeded to question him. The Perry Mason TV show was one of David's favorites, so he decided to take on the persona of Perry. He had a tablet of paper and pencil in hand. He started following Dad around the house and interrogating him with one question after another. "Mr. Alley, where were you last night? Mr. Alley, what were you doing? Mr. Alley, who were you with?" David would then pretend to write down any comment Dad made. It was one of the few times the cat got my Dad's tongue.

Dad's binges and the fighting with Mom got progressively worse. Mom finally decided she could not live this way any longer and after a year and a half in Aunt Sister's house asked Dad for a divorce. Knowing he was on his last leg, Dad convinced a preacher to come to the house and talk Mom into giving him one more chance. Mom could bend like a willow, but eventually even a willow branch will snap. Her mind was made up.

Mom wanted David and me to go with her to the Fayette County Courthouse for the divorce proceedings as she wanted Dad to have to face us as well. Mawzy came along for moral support. It was a cold, blustery day in February 1961. He never showed up, so the divorce was final that day. I was almost seven years old and David was eight. We were too young to realize the repercussions, but knew it was a solemn day. Mom bought us each a toy to cheer us up. David got a replica of a 38 special which he proceeded to point at everyone in the courthouse. A roll of caps came with it but fortunately he didn't load the gun. I got a baby doll.

The divorce decree stated…*that the defendant, John R. Alley, Jr., is hereby required to pay to the plaintiff, Gloria C. Alley, the sum of $50.00 a month for the support and maintenance of said two infant children for as long as he is not employed. When he secures employment, he is to pay $100 a month…* No surprise that Mom did not get much help from Dad after the divorce.

Back to Mawzy's house we went. She welcomed us with open arms. She never said a bad word to us kids about our Dad, but I know it broke her heart to see her youngest daughter repeat what she had been through with her own marriage.

I thought the move back was a temporary arrangement and kept asking Mom when Dad was coming home. She tried to explain that he wasn't. We didn't see much of him after that. He moved on and before long had remarried. And not long after that was divorced again. He came to visit us once and brought a young child with him. I wonder if he was my half-brother.

On another occasion he showed up with a dog for me. It was an adorable black cocker spaniel. I named him Empy and was excited to have a new pet. He didn't last very long either. One day he disappeared, just like Dad.

The summer after the divorce, Aunt Evie and Uncle Buddy invited Mom to go with them and Norma Kaye on another vacation, this time to Buckroe Beach in Hampton, Virginia. Mawzy was happy to keep David and me. She knew Mom needed to recharge after the year she had just been through. It was a celebration for Mom as she had just finished summer school and received her master's degree from West Virginia University in August.

The neighborhood men felt sorry for David and some of them occasionally stopped by to take him places. I was never invited. I stood at the fence and watched as he got whisked away on some exciting adventure without me. I, like my Mom when she was a child, got left in the yard. I complained at one point and was told I had Mom and Mawzy to watch after me. They said David had lost his father. I didn't understand the logic as I had lost my father too.

...We have access by faith into this grace wherein we stand and rejoice in hope of the glory of God.
...But we glory in tribulations also: Knowing that tribulation worketh patience;
And patience, experience; and experience, hope:
And hope maketh not ashamed; because the love of God is shed abroad in our hearts by the Holy Ghost which is given unto us.

Romans **5: 2-5 KJV**

Mawzy's strong faith saw her through life's many trials and tribulations. Her God given name, Grace, was fitting. The *Romans* Bible verses helped her stay focused on the future, not the past.

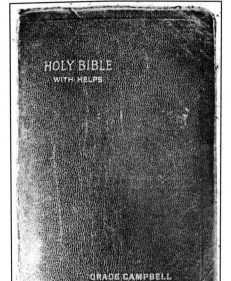

Mawzy's Bible and hymnal

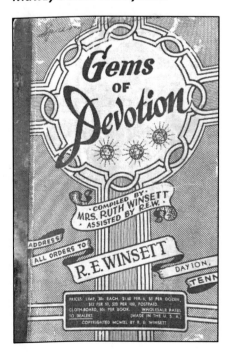

Mawzy's Favorite Hymns

Blest Be The Tie
Sweet By and By
What A Friend
The Old Time Religion
Nearer, My God, To Thee
Onward Christian Soldiers
Bringing In The Sheaves
Just As I Am
Amazing Grace
O How I Love Jesus
Holy, Holy, Holy
Rock of Ages
Blessed Assurance
He Leadeth Me
I Shall Not Be Moved
Jesus Is Calling
I'll Fly Away
Will The Circle Be Unbroken?
When The Saints Go Marching In
When The Roll Is Called Up Yonder
Leaning on The Everlasting Arms
On The Jericho Road
Christ Arose
When We All Get To Heaven
The Old Rugged Cross
Standing On The Promises
In The Garden
I Am Thine, O Lord
Love Lifted Me

Myra and Mawzy all dressed up for Easter church service, pocketbooks in hand. One of the few pictures of old garage in background.

Amazing Grace

When Mawzy moved with her three children from Poppy and Mommy Walker's place to the house in Springdale, she was excited that the Springdale Baptist Church was located next door. Since she didn't drive at that time, it made getting her kids to church on Sunday a much easier task. She reminisced about taking the kids to church in Gentry Holler. In Mom's baby book she wrote about "First Day at Sunday School" and said, *Baby was six months old the first day she went to Sunday school. Mother sat her upon the desk and she looked at everyone and wrinkled her nose up and sniffed real hard. Sunday school was held in the schoolhouse at this time because the church burned just previously.*

The Baptists' main objective was to convince people to be saved from the fiery pits of hell. There was a calling at the end of most sermons. In addition, old time revivals were held, which tended to push people a little harder for the redemption of their sins and the acceptance of Jesus as their Savior. At least once per year there was a weeklong revival, sometimes held in a large tent. Guest preachers were invited to speak. Food and fellowship were common. At the end of the evening *Just as I Am* and *Oh, Why Not Tonight?* were popular hymns sung to call

225

people forward to be saved. If response wasn't satisfactory, the song was repeated again and again.

The Baptists were strict in their beliefs of right vs wrong. Mawzy was always lamenting about the latest manifestations of the "everlastin' devil." Alcohol was often at the top of the list.

The church people were Mawzy's extended family and the church gave her a social outlet aside from teaching. For the church she was generous with her time, talents, and financial contributions. There was seldom a week go by that she didn't contribute to the church, the Sunday school, and the preacher. She served as the church treasurer for years until her mind would no longer allow her to carry on. The food she prepared for monthly church fellowships was fit for a king's banquet.

David, Myra, Stevie and Billy Boy with Easter baskets.

When I was growing up the church felt very alive. The spirit was strong. Lots of kids were involved in the Youth Fellowship group, many older than I. I looked up to them and their knowledge when we had Bible quiz competitions.

Mawzy taught the young people's Sunday school class. She encouraged Mom to teach the preschoolers so she could have David and me in her class to watch over when we were little. She agreed and was my teacher when I was pre-school age. She always gave us little prizes if we paid attention and participated. I still cherish the small, green covered New Testament she gave me. My favorite hymn was *Bringing in the Sheaves* except my rendition was "Bringing in the Sheeps."

I remember Preacher Kessler's first sermon at Springdale Baptist Church, not the contents but the fact that his son Mike, who was my age, sat on a bench behind the elevated pulpit. He was cute. He fidgeted the whole time his Dad was preaching, but I saw in him a potential friend.

Preacher was very charismatic with a hellfire and brimstone style. He got so worked up, the sweat rolled off his face and his hair became disheveled. During his prayers, with eyes shut, he tended to end many of his sentences with "Yes." Or "Yes, Lord." To keep the rhythm of the prayer going he would sometimes take a comb from his pocket and run it through his hair with each "Yes." I was misbehaving by not keeping my eyes shut as well. It was the everlastin' devil Mawzy always talked about that poked me on the shoulder and told me to take a peek.

There was a church picnic at Bass Lake every summer and Preacher Kessler got right in there with us when we played softball. I can still hear him yelling, "Here, batter, batter, batter…" over and over again. We swam in the lake to cool off after the softball game. It was an event we all looked forward to. The *Beckley Post-Herald* reported on our festivities. Attendance was often above 50.

The original Springdale church had been around a long time. Betty Lou, Mom's good friend, said it was dedicated in 1911, the year her father Bill was born.

It sat up on a barren knoll with very little grass around and was made of rough-hewn hardwood lumber, whitewashed inside and out. There had been no excavation, so the foundation was made of cut stone columns of various heights, strategically placed to offset the uneven ground. With no insulation nor flashing around

Church congregation; Myra's up front; David in Bill's arms on left.

227

the base of the building, the church was a drafty place. It was heated with coal in a pot belly stove.

The two-story steeple was a part of the vestibule and housed a large bell with a pully system. Betty Lou's dad, Bill, rang that bell for many a year - one hour before church as a clarion call to get ready and 15 minutes before to remind parishioners to get a move on, that church services would be starting shortly.

The pews were hand made of rough lumber and stained. The beauty of the church was its bay shaped, elevated alter. Three large, clear glass cathedral style windows let in an abundance of natural light and provided a peaceful, wooded backdrop.

Groundbreaking ceremony for the new church. Preacher Kessler, Uncle Chester and Oscar McKinney survey the new church site. Right, the church ladies, including Aunt Biddie second from left in the front row, enjoy the groundbreaking festivities. Below, the church gathers to celebrate. Below left, Gloria June's Easter beauty overshadows the ongoing construction of the new church.

228

Age was taking its toll on the old building and it didn't seem prudent to spend more money to keep it in repair. So, in the spring of 1962, a groundbreaking ceremony was held to begin building a new church.

We kids were sad we would be losing our under-the-church playground. It was a kid -sized space only we could walk into.

The adults were also nostalgic, but knew it was time to move forward. Many church events were already being held at the Springdale Elementary School.

One of the fund raisers solicited money for the purchase of a church window. Mawzy bought one and on the plaque she had inscribed: *In Memory of Wm. Gene "Billy" Campbell, By Mother.* She was still mourning the loss of her only son who had recently died in a car crash. The new windows were arched metal on the outside and wood framed on the

inside. The exterior of the building was "used brick" which was popular at that time. There was a full basement so fellowships could finally be held on the premises.

Many church and community members volunteered their time and talents to build the new church. Though not a church member, Phillip, one of Mawzy's neighbors, was a mason and volunteered to lay a lot of the bricks. Kids were encouraged to help. We were even given hammers to drive nails into the flooring, but bent more than we drove in.

The old church, to the west of the new, was left intact while the new building was being constructed. By the spring of 1965, Mawzy, as church treasurer, started accepting sealed bids for the purchase of the old church building. It would soon become history. Because it was built of hardwood lumber it held value and was easily salvaged.

One Sunday morning all seemed to be going well. I must confess I was not old enough to fully understand what the preacher's sermon was about. All of a sudden, a clash erupted right in the middle of the sermon. One member stood up, yelled at

Members of the congregation, including Mawzy at center, at the new church below.

the preacher, slammed his Bible on the floor and walked out of the church, never to return. There were others who joined the exodus. It was scary for me as it seemed so incongruent with what church was all about.

"Don't leave, the devil's at work here," one of the members who stayed pleaded under her breath to a couple as they walked out the door.

The passion of religion often gave way to conflicts. There's the story of one congregation in the area who had almost completed the construction of their new church when an argument arose over the door placement. One faction wanted it on the east side and the other wanted it on the west. It would seem that installing a door on each end would appease everyone, but that was not to be. The church was never finished or used. The congregation disbanded and filtered to other churches in the area. Often, the only power base a rural Appalachian community had was religion. This is likely why over 70 subdivisions of Appalachian Baptists have been identified in the area, according to *The Appalachians,* a PBS documentary. This doesn't even include other Protestants, the snake handlers or those who speak in tongues. Springdale was not immune and conflict came when the building project was in full force.

Mawzy stayed and her church became the First Springdale Baptist Church. She didn't like conflict and tended to be a diplomat when needed. Her stand won her the everlasting respect of her fellow parishioners.

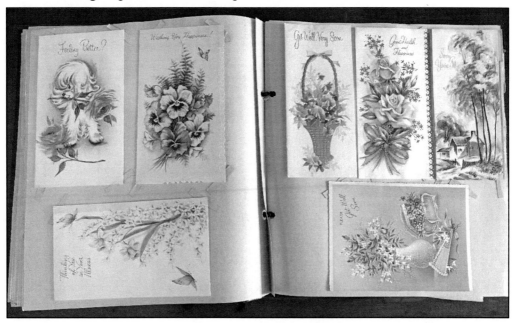

This respect is evident from the response she got when she had a lengthy hospital stay at Thomas Memorial Hospital in South Charleston not long after the church split. In her hope chest I found a scrapbook full of get-well cards. There were over 100 in all.

Hankies were included, as was the tradition. One letter came from Pauline, on behalf of the church. She wanted to give Mawzy a blow-by-blow accounting of the service she was missing; show her support for the preacher after the split and complement Mawzy's strong character.

Spring Dale Baptist Church
Feb 23, 1964, 7 p.m.
Dear Mrs. Campbell,
Herbert went to church with me tonight. First time, except Christmas, for long time. Said that he was glad that he went. Arrived early. Georgia, Bill, and Mrs. Church there...

Here comes Mr. Ernest Sims and wife. Oh, yes he has his guitar. Maybe he will sing "Where Will I Shelter My Sheep Tonight." And right behind are the Snows. All five of them. Later he led the devotional...

More arriving as it is time to start... Mrs. Pitsenbarger came with the Smiths. Did you get acquainted with her? She is modest and refined. A real lady! Rev. and

Mrs. Kessler.... Now, for the service. What do you call that kind of music? "Hill-billy" Some of that and some of the other. Mr. Sims prayed. Mrs. Pitsenbarger also. Testimonies next, but nobody has much enthusiasm tonight so few said anything. For my part, the Baptists can drop that tradition.

The sermon ... was about when disciples were with Jesus crossing water in a boat and a storm nearly wrecked them while Jesus slept. He preached like <u>his</u> <u>boat</u> was about to go down. We can't let that happen. He needs us and we need him.

Hope you are back with us soon. I have always considered you a real duchess. You always maintain your dignity and there has never been a word said about your character. You have kept your reputation spotless...

...All are praying that you will soon be well and home. Rev. Kessler says such beautiful prayers.

We love you.
Pauline

Another letter came from Frances Guyer, the parent of one of Mawzy's former school kids. She taught at Springdale school with Mawzy back in the late '30s.

March 3, 1964
Dear Mrs. Campbell,
I hope by now you are feeling much better. It is hard I know to have to be "a bed" and not be able to do for one's self. You especially, who has been so active and self-sufficient.

You may not know, but I have always <u>admired</u> you for your courage in doing alone what you have done, raising your fine family, maintaining a home, teaching school, and doing it all without a hint of gossip to mar your character. I'm sure not one woman in a thousand could have done it.

You don't deserve to be ill but you do deserve a nice long rest. Take things easy and get well soon.

Love,
Frances Guyer

I never saw or heard Mawzy ostracize or speak ill of those who left and formed the Missionary Baptist Church. She still had dealings with them at Springdale Elementary, as she taught some of their children. Just like the hymn, "I Shall Not Be Moved," she didn't let it taint her faith. I wish I could say the same for mine.

Vacation Bible School was held at the Springdale Elementary School in 1963. It was when I made Preacher Kessler aware of my desire to accept Jesus Christ as my Savior. I was nine years old and knew it was something I wanted to do but had a hard time working up the nerve to approach the preacher. There was no bolt of lightning or an epiphany that drove me. The VBS lessons resonated with me and the spirit I had felt at church grew in my heart as the week progressed. I had not discussed it with Mom or Mawzy, but I knew they would be pleased with my decision. After the last day of Bible school was over, I sought Preacher out and found him sitting at one of the tables in the school lunchroom. I shyly approached him.

"Preacher Kessler, could I talk to you?"

"Well of course you can," Preacher said as he rested his elbows on his knees. "Come on over here, have a seat and tell me what's on your mind?"

"Well, I've been thinking a lot this week about accepting Jesus Christ as my Savior."

"So, you believe Jesus died on the cross for your sins, rose three days later and ascended to heaven to be with God, his father?"

"Yes, I do."

"And you would like to be baptized as a Christian?"

"Yes, I would."

"Well, this is very good news. Bless you, Myra. I'm proud of you. We'll work out a time for your baptism later this summer," he said and gave me a hug. I was relieved I had taken the first step toward becoming a Christian.

It took me three years to get to the baptism part. There were several reasons.

I was dreadfully nervous about being led into a river or lake and being put under. I had witnessed this on many occasions and found it horrifying. I kept thinking of Herbert, in his later years, being baptized in a lake after he became unable to walk on his own. Two of the deacons pushed his wheelchair down a hill to the edge of the lake. Two others joined them to lift him out of the chair and walk him into the water. Herbert was a large man and that increased the difficulty of the task. The lake was murky so you couldn't see what laid beneath. The Preacher was already standing chest high in the water. I was glad Herbert had

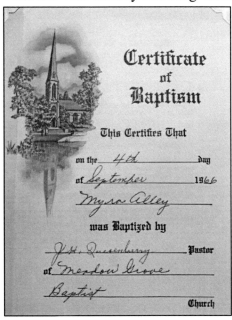

been saved in his final days but worried he wouldn't make it through the baptism. He did. There were many verses of *Shall We Gather at the River* sung that day.

Mom remarried in November 1963, about four months after my conversion. My stepfather got into a conflict with Preacher Kessler, so we moved to his former church. I never felt the spirit in that church.

Between my conversion and baptism, my stepfather was teaching me how to swim. This should have helped me feel more confident about full immersion baptism. However, on one trip to the Greenbrier River near Alderson, I decided to swim a short distance out and back from a

233

protruding rock. I pulled my inner tube off and swan out a way. As I was coming back, I started to fatigue. When I stopped swimming and put my feet down, I sank under the water. Though I'd always been instructed not to panic, I started thrashing around trying to get my head above water. Had a friend, Margaret, not been nearby in her inner tube for me to grab onto I may have drown that day. My fear of water has never gone away.

At Mom's coaxing I agreed to go to a church in Rainelle, which had a bathtub sized baptismal, and was finally baptized on September 4, 1966.

James Twohig

School Days: Spelling Bees

Oh! I wish I could spell "weirdo"!
It really bothers me.
Is it the "e" before the "i,"
or the "i" before the "e"?...
Excerpt from *Spelling Bee* by Frances King

On one of Mawzy's visits to Aunt Pansie's house, the spelling bee came up in conversation. Pansie, Mawzy's sister, was a hairdresser with a salon in her home. Her husband, Jim, was the principal of Layland School.

"Come on in Gracie. Let me clean up from my last customer and I'll get you seated. I've got a new hair rinse I'd like to try on you today. What do ya think?"

"I reckon that would be alright as long as it won't turn my hair purple," Mawzy chuckled. "When I was at Poppy's house the other day some guy came in to see him and said *I didn't know you had a blue haired daughter*."

"That's funny," Pansie said as she slapped a hand on her leg just like Mommy Walker. "Say, Jim wants to talk to you about the spelling bee. Let me see if I can find him." Pansie headed toward the den. "Jim, you back there? Gracie's here and I told 'er you wanted to visit."

"Howdy, Grace, good to see ya," Jim said as he came into Pansie's shop and extended his hand in greeting. "There's a couple of things I wanted to run by ya. I've enrolled Layland School in the *Raleigh Register* spelling bee and was wondering if you'd be our judge this year?"

"Sure, I'd be happy to help out, if I'm available."

"That's great. I know you'll do a good job. I'm the district chairman for '56 and am recruiting schools not yet involved. Have you ever thought about entering Springdale School in the bee?"

"Not really. Tell me more about it."

"Well, each participating school starts with their own spelling bee. There's a division for 5th and 6th graders, which would cover your Springdale students, and one for 7th and 8th graders. The top two winners in each division advance to the Quinnimont District Bee and compete with five other schools. This is the one I'm in charge of. The top two district winners in each division move on to the county wide bee. Then, the top two county winners per division participate in the Tri-County Bee. Prizes are awarded to winners at each level."

"That sure does give our local students a lot of opportunities, doesn't it?" Mawzy said as her head spun with the details.

"Yes, it does. All the kids who participate become better spellers, even if they don't win. It also opens the world to the students who advance in the competition. Starting next year, the winner of the 7th and 8th grade division will get an all-expense paid trip to Washington, D.C. to compete in the nationals."

"Wouldn't that be somethin'," Mawzy said as she recalled her trip to D.C. all those years ago.

"I'd be happy to reciprocate as your judge if you decide to get Springdale involved."

"I sure appreciate you thinking of me and my students and will hold you to your promise of being a judge for me. How do I proceed?"

"Just get an application from *The Raleigh Register*. The newspaper office has *Words of the Champions* booklets available for 15 cents apiece. They also print 165 words per day in the paper until all words in the booklet are provided. This way most kids have access."

Mawzy was all in. She had students participate from then on and served as judge when called upon. She also coaxed Mom into being a judge once she became a teacher.

Jim remained committed to the program. He had many students advance in the competitions. He also served as President of the Fayette County Elementary Principals Association and as chair of the Tri-County Spelling Bee.

Spelling bees have long been an American compulsion. Around the turn of the 20th century, you would as likely have read about a church women's group having an old-fashioned bee as you would any other activity.

In the '30s and '40s, when radio was king, spelling bees were a part of the local programming. Schools around Beckley had competitions on WCFC. Paul Wing's Spelling Bee on WHIS was a precursor to the modern-day game show. Paul was an author and an NBC staff director. Mawzy had the Paul Wing Spelling Bee boxed game she used with her students around that time.

"Mrs. Campbell, can we play the spelling bee game today?" was a question asked by one or more students most Friday afternoons. She often obliged.

"If all of you finish your math problems in time, we'll play a round or two," was her response one Friday.

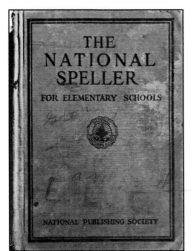

She knew that fun incentives went a long way in getting students to perform and a spelling bee was not only fun but was a learning experience as well.

"Can we play now? Can we play now?" George yelled as he was the last to turn in his math problems.

"Yes, let's do," Mawzy responded. "We need to divide into two teams. You in the first three rows go to the left side of the room and you in the last three rows go to the right."

Once lined up, each student pulled a numbered wooden coin from a bag which corresponded with the same numbered word. If the student spelled his or her word correctly, the team got a green pebble to put in their bag. It was called "honey." If the word was mis-

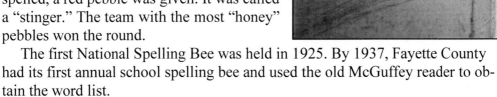

The National Speller book, list of words in book and Mawzy's instructions inside flyleaf.

spelled, a red pebble was given. It was called a "stinger." The team with the most "honey" pebbles won the round.

The first National Spelling Bee was held in 1925. By 1937, Fayette County had its first annual school spelling bee and used the old McGuffey reader to obtain the word list.

Mixed in with Mawzy's textbooks, I found a 1937 edition of *The National Speller for Elementary Schools*. On the inside cover she had handwritten her formula for success.

1. *Look at word and pronounce it.*
2. *Spell word while looking at it.*
3. *Close eyes and spell word.*
4. *Look at book and check to see if it is right.*
5. *Now write word.*
6. *Check again with book.*
7. *Now write again.*
8. *If wrong go through same process 'til you get the word right.*

Thorough would be an apt description for her process. It's the template she used for all her studies when she was in school and how she instructed me as well – read, highlight, write and repeat until comfortable the information has been retained.

Being more isolated, our end of the county wasn't affiliated with the National Spelling Bee until 1956 when *The Raleigh Register* of Beckley and the Elementary Principals Associations of Fayette, Raleigh and Wyoming Counties began sponsorship. This was huge as it gave local students a more direct track to the national competition.

Publicity was plentiful after our area became affiliated with the National Spelling Bee. Exposure was right up there with local sports coverage. *The Raleigh Register* had extensive write-ups with pictures of all the area students who had won at various levels. Even pictures of some of the prizes were featured and over time included engraved Paper-Mate pens and pen sets, a Zenith Trans-Oceanic portable radio, a set of encyclopedias, a year's supply of Britannica films for the winner's school, cameras, record players and U.S. savings bonds. Prizes sweetened the pot to entice participants. Articles about participants often reported the occupation of the parents. Many of the dads were coal miners.

Fayette Announces Spelling Bee Dates

FAYETTEVILLE (RNS) – District and county contest dates in the Tri-County Spelling Bee co-sponsored by principals and The Raleigh Register have been announced by H. F. Frazier, assistant superintendent of Fayette County schools.

The Fayetteville district contest will be held April 2: in the Mem-

Schools participating are Meadow Bridge, Ivan Cavendish and dale, Mrs. Grace Campbell principal; Bellwood, Mrs. Marie M. Griffith, principal; Layland, James R. Twalig principal; Quinnimont N, Richard Ferry, principal; Quinnimont (W), Mrs. Mabel Wichop, principal.

Williams, principal; Mulberry, W D. Sydenstricker, principal; Ingram Branch, Mrs. Carrie Turner principal; Beards Fork, Miss E. A Rowe, principal. In the sixth grade division only: Kimberly, Mrs. Vi let Henderson, principal, and Pe elton, Cecil Thompson, principal Miss Ange Rowe, Beards For School, is district chairman.

Tri-County Spelling Champions

Claiming the first Tri-County championships for their respective counties and divisions are Jerry Stewart, Wyoming speller, and Nancy Walker, Fayette.

Jerry downed five girls in the 7-8 Division Bee in Beckley Saturday to become the first boy Tri-County champion in his division. Nancy outspelled two boys

and three girls in the 5-7 Bee to claim her title.

A seventh grader, Jerry attends Pineville No. 1 School and will represent The Raleigh Register in the National Spelling Bee in Washington, D. C., the week of May 28. A sixth grader of Meadow Bridge, Nancy now has her sights on the Tri-County Bee next year when she

expense paid trip to participate in the national finals.

Jerry is the grandson of M and Mrs. C. C. Farley, 2 Teel Road, Beckley, and th son of Mr. and Mrs. Clarence Stewart, Pineville. Nancy is th 11-year-old daughter of Mr. a Mrs. Lawrence Walker, Spring dale.

(Other pictures and stories

Cousin Nancy wins big.

It got very exciting when my cousin Nancy entered the 5th and 6th grade competition. She was the daughter of Mawzy's brother, Lawrence. Though living in Springdale, she was a student at Meadow Bridge Elementary, as her mother, Lucille, taught at Meadow Bridge High. In 1959 and 1960 she won at the school level but did not advance further than the districts. In 1961 she won her school's competition and went on from there to become Fayette County's first Tri-County Spelling Bee winner.

She entered again in 1962 as a 7th grader and went all the way to win the Tri-County competition again. The family was ecstatic. She was going to the National Spelling Bee in Washington, D.C. *The Raleigh Register* reported on the details of her trip. Large spreads with Nancy's picture were printed daily for six days along with a detailed accounting of her whereabouts. She even made the front page three times.

Off To National Spelling Bee

On Monday, June 4 at 12:30 a.m. Nancy and Mrs. Kessinger, the city editor of *The Raleigh Register*, boarded the C&O passenger train in Prince and traveled through the night to D.C. She and other competitors stayed at the Mayflower Hotel. After checking in they toured Washington, visited the Smithsonian, and then headed to the FBI headquarters.

That evening at the "get acquainted" party Nancy was sitting in the front row when actor Bob Hope appeared as surprise feature of the entertainment. Nancy tried to reach him with her autograph book but to no avail. He was already headed out the door to his next engagement.

The morning of June 5 competitors toured the U.S. Capital, the Lincoln Museum, the Ford Theatre, and the Peterson House where Lincoln died. After lunch they visited the Lincoln and Jefferson Memorials, the Washington Monument and Arlington Cemetery where they witnessed the changing of the guard at the Tomb of the Unknowns.

On June 6 at 8:30 a.m., Nancy and 69 others began the spelling bee in the ballroom of the Mayflower Hotel. Nancy did well, but unfortunately, she lost out in the fourth round. That afternoon sightseeing continued with a focus on Mount Vernon followed by a steamboat ride on the Potomac River.

After the national champion was determined on June 7, touring continued with a stop at the Bureau of Printing and Engraving and the White House. A ride on a C&O canal barge put them back on the water again.

The Banquet of Champions was held on Friday, June 8. The winner received $1,000, a large trophy, a plaque for their school and $100 to spend on a weekend trip to New York City. An appearance on the Ed Sullivan show was the grand finale.

What an experience it was for Nancy. That week all of us at home were beside ourselves with excitement. I could not wait to get in from school each day to see what was in the newspaper.

Nancy represented us and West Virginia very well. One *Raleigh Register* article reported she received far more mail and telegrams than any other participant. Another article stated that many of the D.C. spelling bee escorts *have commented to Mrs. Kessinger that there must be a special quality of children in southern West Virginia for they feel every speller representing The Register in the National Bee has had the knack for making friends easily, helping make the bee an enjoyable occasion for all.*

In 1963, Mawzy encouraged David to enter the Springdale Elementary School spelling bee when he was in the sixth grade. Every evening for weeks Mawzy would summon David into the living room and begin calling out word after word for him to spell. It was boring for me, so I went off to play on my own.

David won Springdale Elementary's bee and went on to win his division in the Quinnimont District. At the Fayette County competition, he came in third. Mary Jean, the girl who beat him out went on to win the Tri-County event where she had been the runner-up the year before, so David had tough competition. She won a $25 savings bond. There was no prize for third place so Uncle Jim, the principal in charge of the county event, slipped a $5 bill from his pocket and gave it to David for his prize.

Spelling bee competitors will remember for the rest of their lives the word they misspelled. It was often reported in the

Tri-County Champ Wins Again

3 Fayette Districts Decide Best Spellers

Three Fayette County districts have announced their Spelling Bee Champions—Quinnimont, Nuttall, and Kanawha.

Nancy Suzette Walker, The Raleigh Register's Tri-County's Spelling Bee champ for 1962 is back this year as Quinnimont District Champion, after correctly spelling "banner." Runner-up of the 7-8 Grade Division is George Martin representing Layland Grade School. George is the 14-year-old son of Mr. and Mrs. George Martin, Prince.

Nancy was the 1961 Tri-County winner in the 5-6 Division. She represented her school, Meadow Bridge Grade School, as champion; runner-up in Quinnimont District; runner-up in Fayette County spelling; emerged as champion of the Tri-County Bee and is back to try again this year.

She is the 13-year-old daughter of Mr. and Mrs. Lawrence Walker, Springdale. Her father is a welder and her mother is a teacher.

David Alley, 10, son of Mrs. Gloria Alley, is the 5-6 Division champion after he spelled "mannerly", which Delia Lane, 12, daughter of Mr. and Mrs. Robert Lane, Danese, missed.

 N. Walker

 G. Martin

 D. Alley   J. Holstein

pions and two runners-up from Divide Grade School. Champion of the 7-8 Grade Division is John Bragg, 13-year-old son of Mr. and Mrs. John Bragg, Lookout.

The winning words for John was "nozzle" and "default." John spelled "nozzle" after it was

ship when she "kimona," whi shanks missed, ner-up.

Barbara is daughter of Mr. Sedlock, Hico, a daughter of Mr. Crookshanks, R Pronouncer Grenier. Judges Zickafoose and Clung, both te School.

Kanawha D Jackie Ingram o School, District 7-8 Division dur in Montgomery School, Charles Mr. Eddie Gon Heights, is runn Jackie, 13, is a Ingram, Scarbr Kingston Grade represented Dee Champion of t Dorla Gail Rich senting Powellt She is a daught Luther Richmon Runner-up is daughter of Mr. Holstein, Scarb J. D. Wicklin nouncer and ju

240

newspaper or even became a separate newspaper article unto itself. *'Cataract' Stops Top Speller* was my cousin Nancy's headline when she lost out in the 1962 national competition. David tripped up on "difficult" in his Fayette County competition.

By 1965 *The Raleigh Register* ended their sponsorship of the Tri-County Spelling Bee and it was taken over by the Beckley Elks Club. Fayette County's participation dwindled at that time. Newspaper coverage was not as predominant. The heyday was over.

I have never been a good speller. When I was in second grade, we had a spelling test for which I didn't feel adequately prepared. I don't know what got into me because I knew better, but I decided to cheat on the test. I made a small crib sheet with all the words on it. At test time I placed it on my desk and then laid my arms and head over the top of it. My desk was in the front row on the far-right side.

Every time Mawzy called out a word to spell, I had to raise my head so I could look at the crib sheet. After about three words Mawzy walked over to my desk, pulled me up by my hair, grabbed the cheat sheet and gave me a big scolding in front of the whole room. I was so embarrassed. Lesson learned. I never cheated on anything after that. After school that day, Mawzy voiced her disappointment in me and explained why.

"Spelling spills over into all other subjects," she said. "That's why it's so important as a strong base to your learning. I know you are smart enough to learn the words. Just study a little harder the next time."

She gave me a hug and sent me forth to start my homework for the next day.

The error of my ways showed up on my report card the first six weeks but improved after that.

Myra's second grade report card. The stars denote the number of books she read that year.

David, Myra, and the infamous Bellwood stairs.

You can fool all the people some of the time,
And some of the people all the time,
But you cannot fool all the people all the time.
Abraham Lincoln

David and Myra at Mawzy's house with white picket fence in background.

The Door Gets Closed

When Mom was taking courses at Concord College, A.R., an upper classman from Bellwood, befriended her. He was studying to be a history teacher. When she started taking West Virginia University graduate extension classes in 1960, it turns out he was taking graduate courses too. That spring she approached him about catching a ride to and from Morgantown to go to summer school. Her marriage was on its last leg and she knew continuing her education was paramount. A.R. picked Mom up on Sunday afternoons and dropped her off on Friday evenings. She stayed at the Women's Hall on the WVU campus during the week.

Mawzy kept David and me while Mom was at school. I found a letter Mawzy sent to Mom in the hope chest. I was listed as the sender on the envelope and on an index card she wrote, *Everything is O.K. here…The kids wanted to write you as soon as you left. Hope you made the trip O.K. We have just stayed at home all day. So long. Mother.* Mom mailed us a weekly package. It was usually a small toy or book of some sort. We started watching for the mailman on Monday afternoon as we didn't understand transit time. As soon as he pulled away from the mailbox we sprinted up the dirt road to see if it was our lucky day. The day our package finally arrived, usually toward the end of the week, we were over the top with excitement.

243

After Mom and Dad divorced, A.R. asked Mom for a date. She declined at first. Said she had too many irons in the fire. He was quite persistent. Mom eventually softened to the idea and they started dating. That he did not drink alcohol was a big plus. She wasn't going to go there again. In addition, he was educated and well respected by his students and peers. Mom's college degree and her work toward a masters compared to Dad's eighth-grade education were always a rub. "You're awfully damn dumb to be so well educated," Mom remembered Dad saying when she was trying to put together an assembly-required toy.

About six months later, Mom asked David and me if we wanted to go for a car ride. We already had our PJs on, so we thought the offer was quite a treat. David was nine years old and I was seven. We drove to Rupert and pulled into the parking lot of a drive-in restaurant. Mom just sat there. We didn't get it. Started impatiently flopping around in the back seat. Mom had been tipped off. A.R. eventually walked out of the restaurant with his arm around another woman. When he saw Mom, he came over to our car like it was no big deal. Mom told him she wanted us to witness his behavior and broke off the relationship. He worked hard to get back in her good graces. Sent flowers. Brought chocolates. Played records on Mawzy's front porch of sickeningly sweet crooner songs like *No Not Much* by The Four Lads. Mom gave in again and not long after, they became engaged.

The next rumor Mom confirmed was A.R.'s engagement to another woman, so she broke up with him again. She avoided him. He stalked her. She finally packed a bag for herself, David and me. We snuck to the house of Mawzy's sister, Evie, in Rainelle to hide from him. Evie's husband, Buddy, had recently died so she was happy for the company and to help out. A.R. kept calling Mawzy to see where Mom was, but Mawzy wouldn't have anything to do with him. He finally showed up at the house and talked Mawzy into calling Mom to leave her a message. At some point in the conversation, he got the hint he was looking for. He drove out to Evie's house to confront us. Apologized profusely. Said he had broken up with the other woman. Would never make that mistake again.

Mawzy was not happy with A.R.'s behavior and struggled with how she should address it. Should she speak up or just bite her tongue? She did not want to see Mom hurt again. Enough was enough. She finally approached Mom one Sunday after A.R. dropped her off at the house.

"Gloria, it's obvious your relationship with A.R. is growing pretty serious. Are you sure this is what you want?" Mawzy asked.

"Mother, he apologized a hundred times for the other women and promised on a stack of Bibles never to cheat on me again," Mom exclaimed.

"There's only one question I'd like you to ask yourself. If he doesn't respect you while you're dating, what makes you think he will if you're married?"

"I want to be in my own house with my children and a husband. I have concerns about David and Myra. They're becoming more difficult to handle. He's promised to help me with their discipline."

Gloria June alongside A.R.'s car while they were dating

"I don't want to tell you what to do, so all I'll say is take it slow to be sure A.R. is really the one you want to spend the rest of your life with and to serve as a father to your kids."

A.R. straightened up. Went with Mom to the Springdale Baptist Church. Became chair of the membership committee. The new church was being built so he worked on weekends to help out. Since the church was so important to Mawzy, he felt it was a way to get on her good side.

A.R. and Mom married in November 1963, without Mawzy's blessing. It was a bad year for Mawzy. She had lost her son to a car accident in January and her daughter to another bad marriage in November. And now her grandchildren were being taken away from her again.

Mawzy's intuition was correct. After the first major blow up between Mom and A.R., Mom was crying uncontrollably. She approached David and me and told us we were leaving to go to Mawzy's house. I have no idea what the fight was about but A.R. called us all into their bedroom for a conference. Mom sat in a chair by the bed, still in tears, wanting to leave and asking us kids if we wanted to go too. A.R. sat on the bed. David and I were on the bed between them. A.R. pulled a gun out of the dresser drawer, laid it beside him, looked at David and me and rhetorically asked, "Do you kids want to leave or stay?"

I don't know about David but that put the fear of God in me, so I meekly responded under my breath, "Stay." In my mind I wanted to get out of there so bad I could hardly stand it. We stayed and from that day forward Mom, David and I all knew we were under his thumb. Not appreciating Mawzy's loving guidance and all she did for us until it was gone was an understatement.

David and I quickly learned we were kids to be seen and not heard. We were not welcome in the living room when company was present. We walked on egg-shells every day because we didn't know when A. R. would explode over some-thing we had not done or had not done right. Tongue lashings were commonplace.

Initially, we moved into a house near Rainelle. When the furnace started smok-ing, A.R.'s parents offered to help remodel the second floor of their Bellwood coal company house. They were already living on the first floor. Mom made it clear she wanted a house of her own. A.R. promised the Bellwood arrangement would be temporary while they were saving to build the brick home of their dreams. So off to Bellwood we went. The house was a large rectangular two-story building with white wood siding. Outside stairs and a small porch were added so we had our own entry to the second floor, A.R.'s concession to Mom's desire for some privacy.

The outside stairs were not our friend. Mom had to contend with them for years. Having a house of her own became another promise unkept. The top section of the door to the porch was glass. When not securely shut, the wind knocked it back against the handrail. A.R. always reminded us to be sure the door was latched. One Sunday after church we came up the stairs. David and I were in the rear. The door did not get tightly closed, was caught by the wind, flew back against the handrail and the glass broke. A.R. asked who was last in. We didn't want to rat on each other so neither of us answered. Off came the belt and we were both whipped over the incident. After that we watched to see if A.R. latched the door and snickered when we found he didn't always follow his own rules.

The porch overhang created a drip which fell onto the top stairs when snow thawed during the day. At night, those stairs iced up as the temperature dropped.

One February morning as I was headed to catch the school bus I slipped on the icy stairs. That night I wrote in my diary, *Today I fell down our steps. I was on the 3rd, slipped, went down three more and fell under the banisters and on the ground.* Fortunately, I landed in a big pile of snow and was not seriously injured. A.R. said it was my own fault as it was my job to keep the stairs clean.

With earnings from mowing Mrs. Arritt's lawn, David bought a grey Phillips transistor radio which was all the craze in the 60s. He loved listening to WLS in Chicago. Cousin Rhonda stopped by one Saturday unannounced, as we were sel-dom allowed to have company. David wanted to show off his new purchase. A.R. heard the music and charged into David's bedroom. He grabbed the radio, swore as he carried it to the top of the stairs and hurled it down. The radio shattered. Mom stood up to A.R. that time and bought David a new radio.

A.R. closed the door on Mawzy as he knew she didn't like him. The line in the sand was drawn. His threats to Mom kept her silent. Mawzy was not welcome at Bellwood. I don't remember her being there very often. And when she was it was uncomfortable for us all. On a few Sundays after church, while A.R. was napping in his recliner, Mom sneaked us up to see Mawzy. We never stayed long. It was heart breaking for Mawzy. She had helped us and loved us all so much and now she was left alone, for the first time ever, void of much contact with any of us.

Mawzy schemed for ways to be with David and me. The summer following the marriage, she hired us to paint her white picket fence. I hated the work. It took forever to scrape the old paint off all four sides of each pointed paling. Mawzy supervised as she wanted to make sure the old paint was well removed. But that was only the half of it. Next, we slathered fresh paint on all four sides of each paling as well as the upper and lower cross rails. It was all worth it though because being with Mawzy again was heaven. It took us about three weeks to complete the project as she let us take lots of lemonade breaks and fed us lunch and supper. We were paid by the hour and

A Christmas photograph of Gloria June, Michael, Myra, David, and Mawzy, one of the few times Myra can remember Mawzy at Bellwood. She doesn't look happy.

were pokey slow, so it was probably the most expensive fence painting job ever completed.

When A.R. had a conflict with Preacher Kessler he pulled us out of the Springdale Baptist Church. We started going to his old church, Meadow Grove Baptist, about 10 miles further down the Springdale Road. It was yet another wedge placed between us and Mawzy.

Mawzy's Springdale church had several fellowships a year, usually on a Saturday night. Before the new church was built, fellowships were often held at the Springdale Elementary School where Mawzy was principal. Guest preachers were solicited to speak. Mawzy always invited David and me to go with her, followed by an overnight stay at her house. It was a whirlwind in Mawzy's kitchen on those Saturdays. She prepared foods like oven spaghetti, blackberry or peach cobbler and applesauce cake, to take for the covered-dish dinner that was a part of the event. We loved her cooking, but it was her company we were starved for.

Becky, Stevie, Eleanor, Jenny, Billy Boy, Mawzy, Randy, Debbie, Annie, and Danny at a family gathering.

The spring after we moved to Bellwood Mawzy got really sick. The stress in her life had finally worn her down. She called her sister, Evie, one afternoon with concern about her condition. She had pain in her pelvic area and a terrible burning sensation when she urinated. When Evie arrived, she could see Mawzy needed a doctor's attention. She called Mom to discuss the situation and they decided to take her to a hospital in Beckley. She was diagnosed with a severe case of acute nephritis and was moved from Beckley to Thomas Memorial Hospital in South Charleston. Mom, A.R. and Evie all went along. Her recovery was slow, so she did not get to come home for over two months. It was a relief that Aunt Sister lived in Charleston as she frequently checked in on Mawzy. Mom made the 85-mile trip on weekends when she could. David and I were worried about Mawzy. As children, we were not allowed to go see her in the hospital. We frequently sent cards. When she got home, Evie came to check up on her as did Mom. On one of

248

Evie's visits while she and Mawzy were sitting on the living room couch together, the conversation drifted to Mom's situation. Evie stayed with us in Bellwood for a time, as she was being stalked and feared living in her Rainelle home alone.

"When you're around A.R. and Gloria June, what is your take on their relationship?" Mawzy asked.

"Well, A.R. certainly does rule the roost. He kinda' has a Jekyll and Hyde personality," Evie replied.

"I have concerns about David and Myra. They are like Prince Albert out of the can when they come up here. They have made some rumblings about A.R.'s attitude toward them. And Gloria is always apologizing for not coming up more often. When I call her, I can tell when A.R is around 'cause her demeanor changes," Mawzy added.

"I am planning a trip to D.C. to see Thelma. What do you think of inviting Myra to go along? She could spend time with Thelma's daughter, Lola. They are about the same age," Evie offered.

"I think that's a good idea. Let me mention it to Gloria and I'll get back to you. When are you leaving?"

I got to go to D.C. with Evie or Aunt Tibbie as we always called her. It was good to get away. I remember more about the car ride up and back than anything. Aunt Tibbie brought me a *Children's Highlight* magazine to occupy my time on the road. On the way back we stopped at Natural Bridge in Virginia and I was absolutely fascinated.

After we moved to Bellwood, Mawzy bought a parakeet for company and named him Leroy. David and I got to babysit Leroy over a Christmas break when Mawzy was visiting Billy's Alabama boys. That summer, on one of our visits to see Mawzy, David brought his transistor radio and when Psychotic Reaction by the Count Five came on the air he coaxed Leroy to dance.

Leroy bobbed up and down, moved his neck forward and back and hopped from one foot to the other on his perch. What a show. Unfortunately, when he was flying around the house, someone opened the door and he flew out. Mawzy went to the front door and yelled for him on and off all day, but he never returned.

Myra, top step center, with Head Start kids at Meadow Bridge Elementary School.

Ms. Anderson,

What a wonderful start we all got! I can speak for myself, Brenda, David, and Melanie. Mrs. Campbell was our Head Start teacher and you had an excellent example---just as you have been an example to hundreds of students who have past through your classroom! We Love You, Cheryl

Written to Gloria June by one of her Meadow Bridge Elementary School students on 6/8/1996

Mawzy enriched the lives of many by bringing Head Start to the community.

Head Start Comes to the Hills

After Mom remarried and we moved to Bellwood, Mawzy continued to think of ways to remain in our lives. On an April evening in 1965 after she returned home from a county-wide principal's meeting in Fayetteville, she gave Mom a call.

"Gloria June, have you got a minute?" she asked when Mom answered the phone. "I'd like to discuss something with you."

"Sure. What's on your mind?"

"I just got home from a principal's meeting where the Head Start centers for Fayette County were announced. Have you heard much about Project Head Start?"

"No, not really."

"Well, it's a new summer program to help disadvantaged children get a jump start before they begin first grade."

"I sure do know some kids who could use something like that."

"It'll run Monday through Friday mornings and the kids get a free lunch before they go home. It's not just local. The program is being established all over the country. Meadow Bridge Elementary was selected as the site for Springdale,

251

Meadow Bridge and four other schools. I thought it would be a good project for me and you to work on together."

"It sounds interesting. And a little extra income would be nice, since we don't get paid in the summer."

"Applications are due in two weeks. I'm going to apply for the head teacher's position. I really hope it's something you'll consider. The program also needs volunteer aides. It'd be a good experience for David and Myra. They're old enough to meet the qualifications. What do you think?" Mawzy asked as she finally came up for air.

"I hear A.R. coming up the stairs, so I'd better go for now. Let me visit with him and I'll get back to you tomorrow."

Mawzy had a way of thinking through situations and presenting them like a steam engine you couldn't derail. Her knack for cutting off objections without you even being aware of it was a hidden strength.

Gloria June, center, at a Head Start conference. Mawzy's certification of training from Morehead State University.

Mom submitted her application and she, Mawzy and another teacher, Eugenia, were selected as the Meadow Bridge Head Start teachers. David and I were their first two volunteer aides - David as Mawzy's aide and I as Mom's. Eugenia's daughter, Pam, served as her aide.

Mom and Mawzy thoroughly enjoyed their time together as they traveled to training sessions. The first year they went to West Virginia State College. Mom's picture was printed in the *West Virginia School Journal* in September 1965, along with some of the other trainees. The following summer they were off to Morehead State University in Kentucky. I found Mawzy's Morehead certificate of completion in her hope chest.

One of the hired aides was Virginia Scott. Since Mom also lived in Bellwood, she gave her a ride to work every day. Mom taught some of Mrs. Scott's kids at the Bellwood School so had known her since the late '50s. Mawzy and Mrs. Scott got along famously. Mawzy appreciated her discipline with her own children and grandchildren as well as the school kids.

Ernest Roop, a student in the Meadow Bridge Headstart program, wanted the Post cameraman to take his picture, so we asked Ernest to show Diane Scott, an aide, some art work. The two were standing by the window in the Headstart classroom.

Mawzy found room for family and friends with Head Start, including Virginia Scott and her daughter, Diane, seen here. Below, the marching band was so good that they made the newspaper!

"I line 'um up and whoop 'um once a week 'cause I know they're bound to have got into something they shouldn't," Mrs. Scott said of the kids in her family. Her sense of humor was a spoon full of sugar.

"I know what you're sayin'," Mawzy responded. "I used to have my kids come clean of their horseplay once a year. Boy did I get an earful."

Mrs. Scott's daughter, Diane, was a volunteer aide later in Mawzy's Head Start tenure.

Head Start was a great experience for all of us in so many ways. David and I got to see Mawzy five days a week. We donated a lot of our outgrown toys to the program, like a plastic bowling set and my play kitchen. We helped the kids with singing, dancing, finger painting, working with model clay, recognizing numbers, and spelling their names. We even got to conduct some of the required testing of the children, which was fascinating and made us feel important.

During an art session, one of the kids, James, started making wormlike pieces from model clay and randomly placing them in his workspace. Mom came over to inspect and assist if needed.

Mrs. Campbell, teacher, is proud of her little Headstart students. Here she prepares the young ones for marching in their "toy band."

"James, what are you working on today?" she asked.

"It's an oscarpussy," he replied.

"What is that?" she asked, trying with all her might to keep from laughing.

"You know, an oscarpussy. It swims in the water."

"Oh yes, an octopus. Of course. Nice work."

Another creative activity was the marching band. Mawzy helped the kids make cone shaped paper hats, which they excitedly placed on their heads. A few instruments, like recorders and kazoos, were available. Others, such as tin pan symbols, sticks raked against a toy washboard and spoons clacked together, were improvised. A student was always appointed to carry the US flag. What a god-awful clamoring was heard as the kids marched around the rectangular classroom table. To them, it was music fit for a

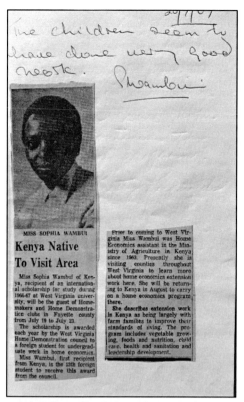

The children seem to have done very good work. Mbambui

MISS SOPHIA WAMBUI

Kenya Native To Visit Area

Miss Sophia Wambui of Kenya, recipient of an international scholarship for study during 1966-67 at West Virginia university, will be the guest of Homemakers and Home Demonstration clubs in Fayette county from July 19 to July 23.

The scholarship is awarded each year by the West Virginia Home Demonstration council to a foreign student for undergraduate work in home economics. Miss Wambui, first recipient from Kenya, is the 13th foreign student to receive this award from the council.

Prior to coming to West Virginia Miss Wambui was Home Economics assistant in the Ministry of Agriculture in Kenya since 1963. Presently she is visiting counties throughout West Virginia to learn more about home economics extension work here. She will be returning to Kenya in August to carry on a home economics program there.

She describes extension work in Kenya as being largely with farm families to improve their standards of living. The program includes vegetable growing, foods and nutrition, child care, health and sanitation and leadership development.

Sophia Wambui left with a good impression of Meadow Bridge's Head Start

king. They really knew they were hot stuff when a newspaper reporter took photos of their band and posted them in a local paper.

In 1967, Sophia Wambui, the recipient of a West Virginia University international scholarship, came to visit the Head Start kids. She was from Kenya and came to Fayette County for five days as a guest of the Homemakers and Home Demonstration clubs. Mawzy wanted her to talk to the kids about her life in Africa to expose them to a different lifestyle in a different part of the world. Sophia's undergraduate work was in home economics. She wanted to learn more about the WVU Extension Service so she could return to Kenya and emulate the program.

Mawzy was anxious for me to hear Sophia too as she had already encouraged me to major in home economics in college. She said it was a line of study that would be useful regardless of the profession I pursued. I followed her advice and subsequently worked for the Extension Service in West Virginia and Iowa for over 10 years.

Meadow Bridge Area Has Large Head Start Program was the title of a spread in one of the local newspapers in 1968. It stated that twenty-seven children were enrolled which was the largest of any of the participating schools in the area. Several pictures of the kids were displayed.

Field trips were an important part of the summer program. A school bus was used for transport. Sack lunches were packed for all. Each trip ended with a picnic, often in a state park. Since West Virginia state parks are scattered all around the area, this was an easy addition to the excursions.

The bus ride alone was a thrill for the kids. There was often a competition between those who sat on the left side vs the right side of the bus. Groundhogs could often be seen standing up on their hind legs alongside the road. As each side spotted one of the furry fellows, they would yell "whistle pig." The number of sightings was tracked until their destination was reached. A winning side would then be declared.

A whistle pig.

The kids loved the trip to the Coca-Cola Bottling Company in Beckley, which is still one of the largest Coca-Cola bottlers in the country. Beckley's Nehi Bottling plant was also an occasional stopping point. A free bottle of pop was the grand finale of the plant tours.

A visit to the Ponderosa Game Ranch on Sewell Mountain was exciting for the kids. On one trip, a group of us were observing the resident bison. Suddenly Curtis, a red headed, freckled six-year-old, yelled out. His two front teeth were missing, which exaggerated his inability to talk plain.

"Look, he "nit! Look! He 'nit."

Mawzy heard him and came over to see what all the commotion was about.

"What are you talking about, Curtis?" she asked.

"Don't you see that 'tinky pile? He "nit."

Once she caught on, Mawzy leaned over and quietly let him know that kind of talk was not appropriate.

Exposing the Head Start children to as many experiences as possible was Mawzy's mission.

Little Head Starters

Shown above is a group of children who attended Meadow Bridge grade school's Head Start Program for this summer.

Students were Beatrice Hylton, Kimberly Clay, Rita Janette Killen, Dorcus Prather, Michelle McCoin, Regina Straw, Lesa Avis, Gregory Reynolds, Robert Ennis, Alice Faye Richardson, Brenda Sue Cox, Ricky Adkins.

Jerry Ennis, Nancy Bumgarner, Ricky Lee Akers, Billy Mullens, Warren Gunter, Bryant Walkup and Carlos McGuire.

Mrs. Grace Campbell, teacher, said the children had many enjoyable experiences and seem to be ready for school.

Mrs. Thelma Heard served as social aide and Mrs. Virginia Scott was aide.

Voulenteer aides were Myra Alley, Ricky Vardall David Alley, Billy Campbell and Diana Scott. Several parents helped some in the program, especially in the trips. Myra gave more time than anyone else, Ricky was next.

Head Start field trip.

255

Students and staff pose for graduation pictures. Below, Mawzy hands a diploma to a proud graduate.

For one eight-week term the kids were also bused to the Rainelle fire house and the fish hatchery at White Sulphur Springs. In Beckley, they visited the Sunbeam Bakery, an exhibition coal mine, the airport, and the Meadow Gold dairy. Because Mawzy wanted to stress the importance of health, a trip to a dentist's office and a health center were also on the itinerary. To become more aware of each student's needs, Mawzy made home visits.

The kids had fundraising projects to enrich the program. It allowed Mawzy to teach them about teamwork. In 1970 the following funds were raised.

$ 15 collections for art smocks
$ 38 bake sale
$ 76 king and queen contest
$129

Each term concluded with a graduation ceremony. The students wore a graduation cap and received a certificate. They felt such a sense of accomplishment and pride. On occasion, the graduation celebration was held during a field trip. The graduates' group picture was usually published in the newspaper.

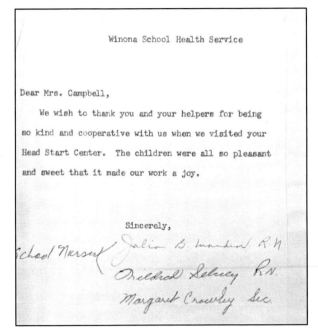

Winona School Health Service

Dear Mrs. Campbell,

We wish to thank you and your helpers for being so kind and cooperative with us when we visited your Head Start Center. The children were all so pleasant and sweet that it made our work a joy.

Sincerely,

School Nurse   Julia B. London RN

Mildred Selway RN.

Margaret Crowley Sec.

For the first three years, Mawzy made a Head Start booklet to record testimonials from visitors and to house newspaper articles. Many commented on the effectiveness of the program. Mawzy squirreled the booklets away in her hope chest. In one she made note of my volunteer work. She was proud of me.

"The children seem to have done very good work," was a comment written by Sophia from Kenya. Mawzy pasted her newspaper picture and article in the 1967 booklet.

Mom taught Head Start for three years until she became pregnant and her focus shifted. David and I weren't as involved after that as we lost our ride. In addition, David was becoming involved in football and I in band, which required summer practice.

Mawzy taught Head Start for seven years, until she retired in 1972. Her colleague, Eugenia, noted that Mawzy was quiet and tended to stay in her room even if the kids weren't present. Mawzy was shy and all business. Her focus was on

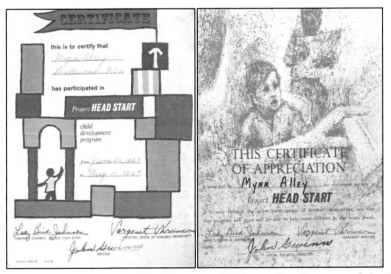

running the program to the best of her ability so she could give the kids the best head start she had to offer.

The fall of 1965 David and I each received a piece of mail from the U.S. Office of Economic Development. Inside was a thank you letter signed by Sargent Shriver, the director of the US Office of Economic Opportunity, and a certificate of appreciation signed by Lady Bird Johnson, the wife of Lyndon B. Johnson, our 36th President. Though the signatures were stamped we were still very proud of the recognition.

The trouble was not about finding acceptance.
Acceptance was available in the depths of the mind.
And among like people. The trouble was the look into the canyon
Which had come a long time earlier
And spent many years being forgotten.

Adolescence, *by Adrienne Su (first verse)*

**David and Myra at Bellwood, all grown up in their
Easter best.**

Clockwise from upper left: Becky, Eleanor, and Jenny, at Bellwood; a beaming Mawzy with the holiday turkey, Cousin Becky doing a Christmas jig, and Cousin Debbie with her Christmas doll.

Reopening the Door

Aunt Eleanor and her three daughters came to see Mawzy the Christmas of 1967 after she and Uncle Jack divorced. Being gutsy, Eleanor didn't hesitate to come to Bellwood for a visit. She insisted Mom, David and I join her family at Mawzy's house for Christmas dinner and so we did. Mawzy gave me a Polaroid "Swinger" instant camera for Christmas so I captured the joy of the occasion.

Bellwood is where David and I learned our work ethic because other than school and a few extracurricular activities that is all we did. A.R. and his mom and dad often fought over who got our services for the day. We did yard work, garden work and housework. I cooked most of the week-day evening meals and did a goodly amount of sewing for A.R.'s mom. One summer Billy Boy and

259

Stevie came by bus to visit Mawzy. We were not allowed to see them except for one afternoon because we had chores. After that Billy Boy named the Bellwood residence "the plantation."

Mom tried to intercede for us as much as she could. I ended up on the better side of it than David. She enrolled me in a book club and I savored each monthly selection as I buried myself in others' stories. I was allowed to take weekly piano lessons with Mrs. Halsley in Rainelle. They bought me an old upright piano which wasn't much to look at, but I didn't care. It played fine. Mom dropped me off for my lesson while she did the grocery shopping. I always found peace and happiness at the keyboard where I became totally absorbed in the music I was creating. The book club books and piano music were so meaningful to me, I still have them after all these years.

Track was the only girls' organized sport when I went to Meadow Bridge High. I had no interest. I was allowed to join the band and played saxophone like Mom. I also followed her footsteps to become a majorette. Music was healing for me. I loved playing the sax as much as the piano. In the beginning, I didn't own a horn, but could check one out over the weekend. Mom and A.R. bought me an old used sax after they saw I was going to stick with it. A.R. made it clear I was to practice in the well room, between the back porch and furnace room. It was the least intrusive place in the whole house. Conditions weren't ideal.

Teen dreams: Myra's book club and sheet music selections and following in Gloria June's (right) footsteps as a majorette.

260

Mawzy at Myra's high school graduation.

There was a single light bulb in the middle of the ceiling which was so dim it made reading music difficult. I used two folding chairs – one to sit on and the other to hold my sax case which propped up the music. It was cold and damp in the winter and hot and damp in the spring and summer. Regardless, it was a place that transported me to first chair sax at the Fayette County competition my senior year and receiving an All-State Band medal. Move over Mindi Abair.

David followed Mom's footsteps in another direction and signed up for 4-H where he enrolled in the entomology project, just like Uncle Billy. One day while he was doing yard work, he found a rare butterfly. He stopped his work, cautiously gathered it up and carried it in the house for mounting. A.R. saw him come in and asked what he was doing there. As David tried to explain, A.R. started ranting and told him to get the hell back to work as he kicked him down the hallway. David gave up on the 4-H project after that.

David wanted to take guitar lessons but was forbidden, as A.R. thought it was a total waste of time. Cousin Keith played the electric keyboard and envisioned he and David in a band together. David eventually bought an old used guitar and small amp with some of his summer earnings and taught himself to play by ear. The only place he was allowed to practice was the furnace room. He never took lessons, but his tenacity eventually got him a position as a bass player in a popular Charleston band called "Stubby Dill."

Mawzy was not excited about contact sports. She discouraged David from playing football. Said she didn't want to see him get his head knocked off. David had happy memories of playing football with the neighbor boys in Springdale in the field behind Mawzy's house, but he wasn't that interested until Cousin Keith went out for the team and encouraged him to do the same. Mawzy gave him her blessing when she realized it would get him out of the Bellwood house a bit longer.

David was an intellect more than an athlete, but if anyone deserved a gold medal for giving it their all, it was him. He was a year younger than his classmates due to skipping the second grade and so was smaller and not as advanced in his motor coordination.

There was no encouragement from A.R. and any comment he made was often cutting. He gave David the nickname "Bravy Screwball." One day A.R. told David he ran into the Meadow Bridge football coach at Kroger's grocery store and the coach told him David would never be good enough to play first string. It was discouraging to David, but it galvanized his resolve to prove them both wrong. David succeeded as he started for the team both his junior and senior year. He played both offensive and defensive tackle as the team was not deep enough to have a separate line up. He weighed in at 165 pounds his junior year.

Mawzy liked seeing David run track because it was not as rough nor was it a bench warming sport. At a key Meadow Bridge High track meet, David came in third place in the half mile run which pushed the school ahead just enough to win the meet.

It was against Rainelle High School where A. R. taught. As was tradition, David draped his ribbon

David played varsity football as a two-way tackle. He made his mark as a self-taught music man playing bass with Stubby Dill as a young adult.

262

around his neck as he headed to school the next morning. Could not have been prouder.

"That's the silliest God damn thing I've ever seen," A.R. sneered. "You're not wearing that to school."

David defied him and wore it anyway. All the other track team members would be wearing theirs. It was a tradition and a moment of glory for him. When David got home that night A.R. confronted him about the ribbon. When David confessed to wearing it, A.R. hauled off and hit him across the face.

Five years into the marriage, Mom became pregnant and had Michael. David and I were in high school by then. David had not only lost his number one spot from when he was at Mawzy's but was now displaced a second time. I soon discovered my status had also dropped a level. I was 14 and became Michael's little mom as I played a significant role in his childcare.

I gained weight after moving to Bellwood, mostly due to stress eating. After Mom had been to the grocery store, I remember going to the cupboard several times a night to get just one more Reese's mini peanut butter cup. As I boarded the school bus one day wearing an Ohio University sweatshirt, I heard a boy yell, "o-wide-o." That hurt. I was approaching puberty so my hormones were raging.

The three finalists of the Region 12 Junior Miss Pageant who will enter state competition January are Angela Sue Nuckols of Ansted, left, Susan Chappell of Hillsboro, center, and Myra Alley of Rainelle. They were chosen Friday night at Carnegie Hall in the first regional pageant to be held.

Myra, far right above and far left below, during her brief career in pageantry.

PAGEANT WINNER — Lynette Roper, seated, sedition girl representing Huntington, was named Miss West Virginia for 1972 at the contest Saturday in Parkersburg. She is a 21-year-old Marshall University art student. With her were, from left, Myra Alley, Miss Concord College, second runner up; Susie Young, Miss Harrison County, first runner-up; Miss West Virginia 1971 Debbie Lambert of Morgantown; Brenda Church, Miss Wood County, third runner-up, and Ann Yoho, Miss Pleasants County, Miss Congeniality.—AP Wirephoto

It was a squirrely time, a time I didn't feel I could confide in Mom. My grades slipped. The second six weeks of my fifth-grade year I made 4 Cs. Seldom did a C appear on my report cards before then. I subtly approached my teacher, Mrs. Cozort, to bargain for a better grade in science, as A.R. threatened to spank me if I brought home another C. She didn't budge. Luckily, I only received a tongue lashing.

I eventually had a growth spurt. Gained height and lost weight at the same time. As I became more confident in my own shoes, I started to explore pageantry. It was a positive outlet for my energy. Mom gave me her blessing, but I didn't solicit her help as any focus away from A.R. wasn't a good thing for any of us. The fall of my senior year in high school a fellow student and I were selected to represent Meadow Bridge High in the Oak Hill Sports Festival Beauty Contest. Neither of us placed but it was a great experience. That winter I competed in the regional Junior Miss pageant and was chosen as one of three winners who advanced to the West Virginia state pageant. As a freshman in college, I came out on top as Miss Concord College and moved on to compete in the Miss West Virginia pageant. At the week-long state pageant, flowers from sponsors and family started arriving for other contestants.

Myra with trophy and Mawzy's flowers.

Someone associated with the pageant called Mom to let her know it was tradition for participants to receive flowers. A.R. felt that was unnecessary. The moment I received flowers that week will always be engrained in my mind. They were from Mawzy.

The *Beckley Post-Herald* reported on my participation.

Pageant Contestant

Miss Myra Alley of Bellwood returned home Sunday after spending a week in Parkersburg as a Miss West Virginia Pageant participant. She was accompanied home by her stepfather and mother, ... and brother, Michael, who attended the pageant. Miss Alley won the Miss Concord College Pageant April 7 and was second runner-up in the pageant. She was awarded a trophy, arrangement of red roses, a charm bracelet, and a $300 scholarship. Her grandmother, Mrs. Grace Campbell of Springdale sent her an arrangement of purple and white mums.

The Junior Miss and Miss West Virginia pageants' focus was on the whole person, not just appearance. Grades, talent, and stage presence were taken into consideration, as was the judge's interview. Inheriting Mom's figure and her brains helped, as did Mawzy's drive. My talent was dance and baton twirling. I was told my routine was a crowd pleaser. Other than majorette camp, I had no formal training. Dad's sense of rhythm shined through in me.

I followed Mawzy's advice and majored in Home Economics at Concord College. Sewing was my passion. I made most of my clothes and wanted to become a clothing designer. Had designed and constructed my costume for the Miss West Virginia Pageant. That same summer I was hired as a seamstress for a woman in Rainelle and loved it. But I learned two things about that line of work. I made mistakes if I was in a hurry or not in the mood to sew. And to be a designer one needed artistic ability, which was not my strong suit. So, I pondered my focus.

My sophomore year at Concord College I joined the Delta Zeta sorority. I kept it from A.R. and Mom. My sisters helped cover my dues until I earned money the following summer to foot the bill.

The following summer David got a job working for the state road. One morning on his way to work it was extremely foggy. As he pulled out of our driveway, he was t-boned. In shock, he got out of the car and walked back into the house where he collapsed. Mom called an ambulance. He ended up with a broken pelvis and was bedridden for the next six weeks. Mom called A.R. to let him know of the accident.

"How's the car?" was his first question. He was very irritated that Mom had to wait on David so there was a lot of friction in the household that summer. I was away at a summer camp when the accident happened. It was eerie that out of the clear blue as I walked by a telephone booth, I decided to call home. I sensed something was wrong and was terribly upset to hear of the news. It was the turning point for David. He was 18 when he headed back to college, now legally an adult.

That fall, Dad was back in West Virginia visiting some of his family and friends. We knew his drinking had accelerated to the point his brother, Frank,

David, Michael, and Myra shortly before David left Bellwood.

265

Cousin Keith, Dad and David in Tampa.

intervened. Frank helped get him a job at General Motors in Detroit and a place to stay with the stipulation that Dad would promise to quit drinking. Dad agreed and moved out of state. When he went to visit Betty Lou and James he asked after us kids. They told him what was going on at Bellwood. He showed some remorse and went looking for David at Concord College. When he knocked on the door, David put two and two together when he saw a man standing there wearing a General Motors baseball cap. It had been years since either of us had seen Dad.

After a brief visit, Dad asked David if he would like to go to Florida to visit his Grandma Annie over the Christmas holiday. David was excited about the proposition and asked if Cousin Keith could come along. Dad said sure. They hatched a plan. Dad came to Bellwood and parked just down the road from the house on Christmas Eve. David snuck out the door that night with one suitcase in his hand,

266

walked down that flight of stairs one last time and never looked back. He was ready to get out of "Hellwood."

While on their trip, David asked if Dad would be willing to help secure him a summer job in the maintenance department of General Motors where Dad worked. Dad pulled through so David spent the next two summers working in Detroit. During the school year, Mawzy's house became his home base again. She paid for his last two years of tuition at Concord College. He covered the rest of his expenses with summer earnings.

My turning point came between my sophomore and junior year of college. I was working as a waitress in the bus station restaurant of the Terminal Drug in Rainelle. One morning as I was getting ready for work Michael came into my room and started messing with my make-up. I got upset. A.R. heard the ruckus and came to reprimand me. I responded under my breath and he heard me. He turned back toward me, grabbed me around the neck and started pounding my head against the wall. He let me go then took me to work. I was terribly upset but went about the job at hand. God came to my rescue as he brought Mawzy and Aunt Tibbie into the restaurant that day for lunch. After I served them and the crowd died down, I went over and sat in their booth. I burst into tears, told Mawzy what had happened, then asked if I could move back in with her.

"If you show up at my doorstep, I won't turn you away," she said. She didn't want to step on Mom's toes, so she left the decision up to me. I never heard Mawzy bad mouth A.R. She practiced what she taught David and me. "If you can't say something good about somebody, don't say anything at all," was her advice.

I toughed it out for the next two weeks before I returned to college. Since David was with Dad in Michigan at the time, I wrote him to explain the situation. Pleaded with him to ask Dad if he would be willing to fund my college tuition and expenses for the next two years. I knew David would sympathize with me and do all he could to garner Dad's help. Dad had abandoned us all those years ago. I felt it was the least he could do. He pulled through. From then on when I went home it was to Mawzy's house.

From the day I left Bellwood, every time I drove by that house, I got an uneasy feeling. On a recent trip home, as I drove by I noticed someone was tearing the huge house down for hardwood lumber salvage. The house of cards was finally falling. Those stairs to the second story were now gone forever.

What is a Grandmother?

She is warmth
And cheer and laughter-
Someone who does loving things
You think about long after…
Someone who gives happiness
To everyone about her,
Making all the family feel
They couldn't do without her
Someone who says the nicest things
And means them most sincerely,
Someone thought about with pride
And loved so very dearly!

An *American Greetings* card passage Myra sent to Mawzy, which she found years later tucked away in her hope chest. She wrote in the card, "*I always try to find a card that says Happy Birthday, Mawzy but never have any luck. But I liked what this one says so I got it. See you soon! Love, Myra*"

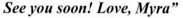

268

Mawzy at her retirement party. From the Beckley Post-Herald.

Grandmother/Granddaughter Bonding

Mawzy retired in June 1972. The local Home Demonstration Club members hosted an open house for her at the Springdale Elementary on a Friday evening the following spring. There was a big spread, including a picture, in the *Beckley Post-Herald:*

...Approximately 100 guests attended the event, giving them the opportunity to see the improvements that have been completed on the school building and to honor Mrs. Grace Campbell, recently retired from a teaching career with a span of 40 years...The students she taught at the Springdale school extended into the second generation of this community. She was also instrumental in starting the hot lunch program at this school...

Entertainment included a skit by the area kindergarten class, the reading of the "Dedication to Teachers" poem and guest singers. Refreshments followed. Mawzy saved the list of those who provided food for the event which included cakes of all kinds, deviled eggs, baked beans, cold cuts, fruit salad, cinnamon rolls, and macaroni salad.

Mawzy, Becky, Eleanor and Jenny at Busch Gardens.

Eleanor insisted Mawzy come to visit her the winter after she retired. Told her she needed to celebrate her retirement. Told her it would be good to get away from the cold winter weather for a couple of weeks. Eleanor had remarried and moved to St. Petersburg, Florida by then. Mawzy decided it would be good to spend time with her southern grand-daughters, Debbie, Jenny and Becky, so she went. She got to see a professional jai alai match and visited Busch Gardens in Tampa Bay.

The fall after I started to come to Mawzy's house on weekends from college, she was in the process of building a ranch style three-bedroom house. Now that she was retired, she had more time on her hands to work on the project. The old house had become a money pit and she was tired of hauling coal, stoking the fire, and cleaning the coal dust off everything. Enoch, the builder who completed the addition to her old house, was hired to do the work and served as general contractor. Initially, she lived in the section of the new house that was finished. A large

piece of plastic was used to partition it from the unfinished side. Mawzy had mixed emotions as they started tearing down the old house and garage. The picket fence came down too, as she was tired of trying to keep in maintained. When the last board was hauled away, all that remained was 36 years of memories.

As rooms were finished in the new house, I made curtains and drapes for the windows. Mawzy and I had a great time shopping for fabric and other accessories.

One day as Enoch was pouring the basement steps of the house, he keeled over and died of a heart attack. Mawzy was terribly upset and held a lot of guilt about being responsible for his death. She had many ties to his family. They had been janitors for the Springdale School for over 10 years. She bought eggs from them and had always counted on Enoch for any maintenance needs around her old house. His family reassured her if he hadn't been working on her house, he would have been working on another. She hired others to help finish the project, but she became the general contractor. She kept cancelled checks of all her costs. After reviewing them, it was evident when she took charge. She was no stranger to

Mawzy outside her new home.

managing projects, so it was not a problem for her. She oversaw the completion of the house and a new detached garage.

Not long after the house was finished, Mawzy kept hearing a rattling noise. When she opened the door to the basement, much to her dismay at the top of the stairs, she saw a large water snake with its body woven around several pop bottles that rattled as it slithered around them. She slammed the door and called a neighbor who brought his gun and shot the snake. Water snakes weren't that common in the area, so they decided it was likely hauled in with fill dirt for the new house.

When I came home, Mawzy always fed me well. I offered to help with cooking and cleanup.

"No, I want you to go get your lessons," was always her response. That was her priority, so I obeyed her. She reviewed her method of studying with me – read, underline, then write key learnings. Repeat until confident. It worked for me just as it had her. It was her spelling bee template. It was the method I used years later as I was studying for my Series 7 exam to become a stockbroker. It worked then too, as I passed the test first time around.

Mawzy was hooked on the *Days of Our Lives* soap opera. She took a break after school to commiserate with the characters and their woes. In the winter, she always wrapped up in a blanket to watch while the house warmed up as she always turned the heat down during the day. I watched with her when I was home. We discussed the actions of the players like they were family and friends.

Things weren't always rosy with Mawzy and me. I was in that know-it-all young adult phase. I started smoking my junior year in college. I knew Mawzy would not approve, so when I was home, I snuck a smoke whenever I could. My usual plan was to go to my bedroom in the back of the house and blow smoke out an opened window. My error was storing the ash tray in my closet. One morning while Mawzy was in the bathroom across the hall from my bedroom, I seized the opportunity. When she came out of the bathroom, I was sitting on my bed and

271

looked up to see her, still in her blue and white gingham bathrobe, and wondered why she was coming my way as she didn't say a word. She walked across the hall, went straight to the closet, stuck her head in and pulled out my butt laden ash tray. She had caught a whiff of smoke that tipped her off. She marched over to me with the ash tray in her hand. Busted. I got this prickly feeling and wondered if she would have remorse for allowing me to move back in with her and kick me out for stinking up her new house. I was speechless as I waited for the other shoe to fall like it always had at Bellwood.

"Please try not to burn down the house," was her only comment.

During one of my weekend visits home from college, the minute I got home I opened the fridge to look for a snack. I always avoided the milk, as it was usually sour. Mawzy claimed she liked sour milk. Said it wasn't a whole lot different than buttermilk and she liked to drink that too. I found some pineapple and cottage cheese. As I dished up a bowl of it and started to eat, Mawzy asked me point-blank if I was pregnant. She feared I was having a craving for something tart, as is so common with pregnant women. It was an uncomfortable question. I did not understand her fear because I had not lived her past. She cared so much about my happy ending. She knew I had my whole life ahead of me and she did not want to see it derailed. What she did not know was how determined I had become to break the cycle.

Mawzy's house was my haven. She and I became tight as I appreciated and recognized her guidance. She was my rock and I was her new hope. I valued my independence and was determined not to let any man put me through what Mawzy had gone through with Add and Mom had gone through with my Dad and A.R. I had a strong resolve to take care of myself.

When I was home I often slept in Mawzy's big fuzzy night gowns. It was like continuing to be surrounded by her love.

I didn't get my driver's license until I was in college. Driver's ed didn't fit into my high school schedule and once in college there wasn't much opportunity. At age 19, I finally got my license while still at Bellwood. Mawzy was planning a two-week trip to Alabama to see Billy's family the summer after I moved back to her house. She made me a deal. Said I could use her car while she was gone if I would look after the garden at Poppy Walker's house. I was ecstatic. I kept my end of the promise and worked the garden both weekends Mawzy was gone. I was meticulous about weeding and hoeing every plant. Even bagged and carried all the weeds off to the side of the garden. The second weekend when my task was almost complete, Poppy saw me and started walking toward the garden. I was a bit apprehensive.

"Got that garden lookin' pretty damn good," he said as he approached. "I don't see airy a weed." I knew Poppy's compliments were far and few between, so it was one of the most valued accolades I ever received.

David's V-shaped apartment with the outside stairs—shades of Bellwood! Below, David in his element as a DJ.

"Let me see 'ur hoe for a minute," he added as he seized the opportunity to give me a lesson. His demonstration was impressive. I had never seen anyone hoe that fast.

"Ya know, when I was a boy, I used ta' hoe corn from dawn to dusk for 50 cents a day," he reported. After he started getting dementia, it was one of the few stories he remembered.

That was also the summer I got a job photographing golf foursomes at The Greenbrier in White Sulphur Springs. David was out of college and working as a DJ at the radio station there, so I lived with him. He didn't charge any rent but asked that I help paint his apartment and prepare some meals for us. The apartment was on the second story of an old house and was reached by a set of stairs with an outside entry. Déjà vu.

Being an attic apartment, the ceiling was V-shaped. That limited the use of the wall space on either side. I slept on a pull-out couch in the living room at the front of the apartment. The kitchen, bathroom, and David's bedroom were small. With no air conditioning and very little insulation, it was hot up there in the summer. David thought it would be funky to paint the ceiling in a patchwork pattern, using five or six fluorescent colors to evoke a psychedelic vibe. In the beginning we worked diligently to tape the pattern, then fill each section with paint.

We bit off more than we bargained for, so the project was never completed. When I left for college in the fall, the ceiling was about half finished and none of the tape had been removed.

Mawzy was proud of David. All those spelling bees had paid off. She saw him as a celebrity and envisioned his DJ job as a steppingstone to becoming a well-known TV anchor like Walter Cronkite. Though he didn't take the TV path, he was successful. He eventually ended up in Charleston where he became the number one rated DJ for the midday show at V100, a station associated with the largest radio corporation in West Virginia.

The Greenbrier, which has always exuded opulent luxury, was first opened in 1778. Guests were enticed there to soak in natural springs for their health while

Myra's swank workplace, the Greenbrier.

surrounded by the beauty of the Allegheny Mountains. Over the years, many dignitaries have enjoyed time at the resort, including several U.S. presidents. Joseph and Rose Kennedy honeymooned there.

By the time I was hired in 1974 there were three golf courses – The Old White, The Greenbrier and The Meadows. I usually walked to work and back twice a day which was about a mile from David's apartment. My employer was Yellow Bird Photofinishing and Studio, housed in the hotel. My uniform was a canary yellow pant suit and from 10 a.m. to 2 p.m. on weekdays I drove a yellow golf cart to the first tee box of all three courses and proceeded to convince foursomes to line up for a photo op. I was trained to operate an expensive Leica 35 mm camera and a light meter. The meter was used for each shot to be assured of the camera's proper setting. Minimum wage was paid for the photo shoot, which was $1.60 an hour.

The film was then delivered to the Yellow Bird studio where it was processed into slides. In the evening, it was back to The Greenbrier to sell the photos I had taken that day. I was required to wear an evening gown as it was protocol for the female guests. I always felt a bit awkward walking the streets of White Sulphur in a gown. Straight commission was paid for sales made. Evidently, I was successful as Marshall and Niki, the photo shop owners, tried to convince me to stay on for a year before returning to college. I was happy they were pleased with my work. Mawzy's guidance with attention to detail had served me well. That summer I met so many people from so many places. The job opened my eyes to the world and made me want to go out in it.

Mawzy drove to White Sulphur, forty miles east of Springdale, a couple of times that summer to see David and me. Neither of us did a very good job of keeping the place tidy. When Mawzy was there, she never gave us grief about it, as she was more interested in how we were getting along with our lives.

On one occasion when I was sick, she came over to check up on me. We could hear her coming up the steps and were anxious to see her. She walked in, still in her Sunday best, with a batch of her peanut butter cookies that we loved so much and saw me laying on the sleeper couch.

"Myra, you look awfully peaked," she commented as she reached for my forehead. "You feel hot."

"I'm not feelin' the best," I said as I started to cough.

"I sure hope you don't have pneumonia. That cough sounds terrible," she countered as she started wringing her hands and pacing around the apartment.

"Mawzy, I'll be OK," I said as I grabbed the cough syrup and took a swig.

To get rid of some of her nervous energy, she started to tidy up the place. Even washed the dirty dishes in the sink and looked around to find something to fix for us to eat. There was her need to feed again.

Mawzy in her Sunday best.

"David, I hope you don't get what Myra's got."

"Mawzy, I feel fine. Don' worry about me," David replied.

"Well, I think we should take Myra to the hospital. There won't be any doctors' offices opened on Sunday."

"Mawzy, just let me rest today. If I don't feel better by morning, I'll go to the doctor then," I pleaded.

"Well, I reckon one more day won't matter all that much," she said, trying to convince herself all would be fine.

That summer was my first real taste of freedom. I didn't know anyone from White Sulphur, so when not working I sometimes hung out with David and his male friends. When it was time for me to head back to college, David couldn't take me back to Springdale, so three of his buddies drove me home. As we got closer to Mawzy's house I became a bit concerned about what Mawzy would think of me showing up with three guys. When we got to the house, Aunt Sister's car was parked in the driveway. That made it even worse. I started to sweat. The boys helped me unload my stuff and as we walked into the house, I was so relieved to find no one there. They had gone to see Poppy Walker. It was the Saturday of a church fellowship, so the counter was loaded down with baked goods. The boys' eyes got big as saucers and they proceeded to eat bites of the coveted blackberry cobbler, a pineapple upside down cake, peanut butter cookies and an apple pie. Now I knew I was in trouble. Fortunately, they left before Mawzy and Sister got back. I explained what had happened and expected Mawzy to be mad at me. She wasn't. She was pleased they enjoyed her efforts and told me they deserved it for bringing me back home in one piece.

David came to Concord for the first dance that fall. He sought me out as we both liked to dance and would sometimes clear the floor with our moves. It was where he met and became smitten with Chris, who had just transferred to Concord. They started dating and married the following summer. Initially, Mawzy was not excited about the relationship because Chris was a Catholic. For a while, Mawzy called her "that Catholic girl." Chris' kind and helping ways soon won Mawzy over. She grew to love and respect Chris and was happy for David. Chris and I became best of friends. Thank goodness Chris spiffed up the White Sulphur Springs apartment and replaced the patchwork ceiling with a cream color that brighten their space.

I graduated from Concord in 1975 and immediately started looking for a job. Mawzy suggested I explore the position of a Home Demonstration Agent with the West Virginia University Extension Service. Her experiences with the Service's 4-H program had been so positive. I applied for a dual position as Tyler County's 4-H and Home Demonstration Agent in Middlebourne and was called for an interview with the regional director in July. I was then contacted for a second set of interviews with four administrative staff members on the West Virginia University campus, including the Dean and Director of the Cooperative Extension Service. Mawzy loaned me her car and I headed to Morgantown on August 5.

During the interview I was informed my predecessor was let go. The agent was quite popular with some of the 4-H leaders but despised by the rest, who got her fired. I was asked my strategy to bring unity back to the program. When I got home that night, I filled Mawzy in on my day and the circumstances surrounding the job.

A week later, I walked up the dirt road to check the mail. There was a letter for me from the Extension Service. I nervously ripped it open. If interested, the job was mine. I breathed a sigh of relief as I came barreling down the road and into the house.

"Mawzy, where are you?" I yelled.

"Back here in the laundry room," she hollered back.

"Look what I got in the mail today," I exclaimed as I handed her the letter.

She read it and smiled. "I'd say it's official now. I'm proud of you, Myra. Let's talk about it over supper. I'll get these towels folded and put away while you check on the brown beans and make sure the corn bread isn't burnin'. You know I'm pretty good at that."

I had a big decision to make and was apprehensive about my ability to fix someone else's problems. The minute we were seated at the table I started firing one question after another at Mawzy.

"Do you think I should accept the offer?"

"I think you're the young, fresh start they need," Mawzy concluded.

Myra, Mawzy and David at Myra's college graduation.

"What if they don't like me? What if I'm walking into a hornet's nest?"

"I have faith in you. If you just treat everyone with respect, they'll like you. If you rise above the pettiness, you'll be able to sleep at night," was Mawzy's advice. It is advice I never forgot and that has served me well throughout my life. Mawzy practiced what she preached. The church split comes to mind, as both sides respected her diplomacy.

I took the job and the next week went shopping for a car. I settled on a new dark green Chevy Nova with a white landau top for $2,500. Mawzy cosigned for the two-year loan on the Chevy that would see me through the next seven years of my life. My payments were $118.26 per month with an interest rate of 11.13%. She also helped David with his first car, a blue used VW Beetle, by floating him a loan. She kept track of his payments in her checkbook register until the loan balance was recorded as $0.00.

I know Mawzy hated to see me move three hours away, but she was excited for me. I was a young woman about to head out on her own.

I kept the letters Mawzy wrote to me when I lived in Middlebourne. Long distance phone calls were paid for by the minute and were expensive, so letter writing was the preferred mode of communication. She worried about me. That fall she

wrote, *… I wish I was nearer so I could help you to get things straightened out…You are right about being careful of what you do because I imagine you will be watched. Do you feel afraid, living alone?"* In another letter she continued, *… It seems that if you don't freeze to death that the buggers are going to get you…I wish you could find a place to live in part of a house with other people or else get someone else to live in your trailer with you – because it is really dangerous to live in some places without someone else. I'm sending you a little gift. I hope you can use the things…* The gift was a pair of panty hose and a slip.

Mawzy made sure to send Myra a photograph of her Mother's Day flowers. Below, with Billy Boy at his wedding.

I looked forward to Mawzy's letters. She reported how many days she had recently substitute taught. Wanted me to send her my picture for a newspaper article about my job. Filled me in on how David and Chris were doing. Spoke of her communication with Mom. Encouraged me to come home for a visit. Asked how work was going. Caught me up on local news. Thanked me for her Mother's Day flowers. Reminded me to keep my car serviced. Reported on piecing a "Star of Bethlehem" quilt and canning apples from the tree out back. Talked about visits from some of her sisters as well as Uncle Earl. Earl was a bit of a nomad at that point and stayed with her sometimes if he had odd jobs lined up in the area, like bailing hay. He helped her around the house and had a knack for showing up at supper time. She felt guilty if she didn't have anything cooked when he came by. On one such occasion she wrote about fixing him a Dagwood sandwich with everything she could think of to pull out of the refrigerator. She also noted she gave him a Little Debbie cake and a glass of milk.

As Billy Boy and Donna's 1975 wedding was nearing, Mawzy wrote of her indecision about whether to attend. *I got a note from Donna. She said they especially wanted me to come to their wedding but I don't know, I may call it off. I get tired on the bus and you all just don't have time to make such a long trip so quickly. If I change my mind or you can get a day or two off I'll take my car. So*

278

Mawzy, Gloria June, and Mike with Chevy Nova in background. Below, same day with Myra in the picture.

you had better give it a lot of thought before you ask to get off so soon after you have started to work. I couldn't get off work so Mawzy took the Greyhound bus.

She always responded to my letters. In February 1978 she wrote, *I received your beautiful valentine. I have it stuck on the ref. door, the only I've received so far. I am very sorry I don't have a valentine for you. I haven't been anywhere to get one... But anyway, I am enclosing a little check. Maybe you can get a little something with it for your birthday...*

Weather was another source of concern for Mawzy. She talked about getting snowed in and wondered about my safety. *Have you been able to go out into the county in your work? You better be sure the roads are safe before you travel on them. Those old bridges are probably iced over or washed out by floods,* she wrote.

Mawzy, Mom and Mike came to visit me in Middlebourne one summer Sunday. I think it eased their mind to see the town and to be able to visualize where I was living.

Poppy Walker's health was deteriorating so Mawzy, as well as other family members, spent a goodly amount of time at his house looking after him. I sometimes went with her when I was home. On one of our visits, Mawzy also invited Mom and a newspaper reporter from the *Meadow River Post* in Rainelle. A four-generation picture was taken and printed in the August 10, 1972 edition.

Poppy's hygiene was terrible. Mawzy had a hard time getting him to change his pants so she could wash them. Before she retired, she even approached Louella, the school cook, about her dilemma. "I'm sorry but I don't know what to tell ya," was Louella's response. "My husband sleeps in his pants so I have the same problem." They both chuckled as they moved on with their day.

Poppy was not a religious man. Preacher Kessler visited him many times over the years, trying to get him to come to church. On one of the visits Preacher and Poppy were standing out in Poppy's field near the barn. "What a wonderful farm you have here, W.C.," Preacher pointed out. "Just look at what you and the Lord have done to this place."

Mawzy, Myra, Gloria June, Poppy Walker and Michael.

"Well, you should have seen it when the SOB had it by himself," was Poppy's comeback.

Poppy eventually ended up in a nursing home because of his dementia. Not long after he was admitted, he got up in the middle of the night and dumped a cold glass of water on his roommate to try to squelch his moaning.

The preacher came to see Poppy at the nursing home. Near the end of his life Poppy accepted Jesus Christ as his Savior. It pleased Mawzy. On one of Earl and Chester's visits, as they turned the corner to head into his room, they heard him praying. He ended his prayer with the comment, "And if you don't like that you can kiss my ass." Until his last breath, at age 90, he never lost his crass nature.

Billy Boy and Donna came from Alabama to visit Mawzy the summer of 1977. Much to Mawzy's excitement, Donna was pregnant with Mawzy's first great grandchild. They took a road trip. The Loops Road was a must. Billy Boy also wanted to see the recently completed New River Gorge bridge, touted as the longest single arch bridge in the Western Hemisphere, third longest in the world. Mawzy said she was afraid to go over it. Said six people had died during its construction. Billy Boy snuck across anyway and then told Mawzy. She didn't know as you couldn't see over the side to the river 876 feet below. "Boy, was she mad when I told her what we had just done," Billy Boy chuckled.

New River Gorge bridge

I came back to see Mawzy as often as I could during the three years I worked in Middlebourne. She was lonely. She didn't have school to occupy her time. Her substitute teaching helped and she was still church treasurer but was starting to get confused about the recordkeeping. On Sundays, when I was packing my bag to head back to Middlebourne, she came up with ways to keep me there a bit longer. It was often to help her with the church books or to pay bills and balance her checkbooks. I obliged and hated to leave her. At departure I always had a tear in my eye, as did she.

Mawzy outside of her church.

Live Each Day to the Fullest

*Yesterday's troubles are written
on sand,
Brushed out of existence by God's
own hand.
The things of the future our hearts
may fear,
Can all be resolved when tomorrow is here.
Out of a lifetime these hours
alone,
The hours of today are completely
our own.*

**Found in Mawzy's hope chest
with the message: *Here's a little
poem I always liked and hope
you do also. (01/04/77).* Intended
recipient unknown.**

Better than Nothin'

I purchased a calculator for Mawzy the Christmas of 1977, hoping it would help her keep her check books balanced. When she had a hard time learning to use it, I began to realize something wasn't quite right. Looking back, the progression of Mawzy's Alzheimer's disease was crystal clear, but in the moment it was cloudy. Per-

Mawzy with Billy's widow, Annie, at Christmas.

haps we all had the attitude that if we didn't acknowledge it, maybe it wasn't so.

Mawzy's missteps, like going grocery shopping and leaving the bags of food at the counter, were viewed as coincidental at first. Then there was the wreck she had when she stepped on the gas instead of the brake at a T-intersection and ran over the side of the hill. Her carrot cake did not rise the way it should because she left out some of the ingredients; and an Afghan she made contained more than a few mistakes. Then substitute teaching became more difficult to handle.

Mawzy sensed what was happening to her. This was as difficult to watch as the decline itself. How could our rock be crumbling after all these years? After Mawzy passed, I found clues in her hope chest that revealed she was aware of what was going on. There were articles about Alzheimer's disease. There were several small scraps of paper on which she had scribbled. On one she wrote "hardening of the arteries" and listed, in birth order, herself and all her siblings on the opposite side. There were two pieces with the names of Billy's four boys – Bill, Steve, Randy, Danny – written several times on both sides. She was trying so hard not to forget. On a piece of notebook paper, she had written three times "Fried Apple pies on page 212, name of cookbook Search Light". She didn't want to lose track of her beloved fried apple pie recipe. Yet another scrap of paper was dated April 6, 1983. The date was written plain as day, but the rest was chicken scratch.

The chest also contained greeting cards never sent. One was a card likely intended for one of Billy's younger boys. Below the verse, Mawzy wrote, *"and for the picture you are a sweet boy you you Mawz."* On a Christmas card she wrote,

283

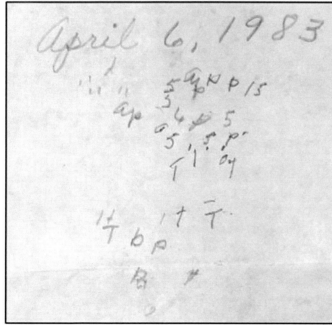

Mawzy struggled as she lost the ability to compose her writing, even when she set the record straight on the back of her retirement plaque.

"Do you still live where you always located this time last time. I needed you more than ever. About the first of Dec. Everything is pretty and white but I am... Suppose you save me a picture.

Love Grace Campbell."

When Mawzy struggled with verbal communication, she often commented, "Somebody erased my board."

On the back of Mawzy's retirement plaque she wanted to set the record straight on the number of years she taught, as the front only acknowledged her 37 years at Springdale Elementary.

Though Mom, David and I kept in touch, we were not there day by day to witness what was going on. I was still living in Middlebourne, so didn't get home that often. Mom was distracted with difficulties at Bellwood. David and his wife, Chris, had recently moved to Johnson City, Tennessee where David accepted a DJ position.

Mawzy, Mike, Chris, Myra, Gloria June, and David

One weekend a friend, Kathy, from Middlebourne came with me to Mawzy's house. David and Chris were there too. Mom and Michael came up to see us. We had a good time goofing off and decided to dig around the house for old hats to wear. After donning our hats, we asked Mawzy to name each of us. She called Chris "Indian" because her hair was in a long braid.

When it came my turn, without hesitation, Mawzy said, "You're Cuffy Arbuckle." None of us had a clue where that came from. Still don't. Mawzy decided she needed a hat too, so we found her a black cowboy hat to wear and she joined in the frivolity. Kathy took a picture of us in our hats sitting on the front porch steps.

We became concerned about Mawzy's driving. That weekend Mawzy wanted Chris to go with her for a drive. The rest of us were headed out for a hike up on the hill behind the house. Chris went and was so uncomfortable with Mawzy behind the wheel, she insisted on driving back home. Mawzy's independence was nearing its end.

Mawzy never swore a day in her life but, as is so common with the disease, she started to let a few choice words slip out every now and again. One day she was looking out the front door window as Mom headed down the sidewalk toward the detached garage. "Who is that bastard going down through there?" I heard her say. For a split second, I thought Poppy Walker was in the room.

This was around the time I started contemplating graduate school. It was a legacy I felt compelled to uphold. If Mawzy could get her master's degree while working and helping to raise Mom's and Billy's families, then surely I could do it as a single woman with no other responsibilities. And Mom earned her master's while raising David and me. Besides, I was ready to explore the world beyond West Virginia. I wanted to study consumer economics and was advised by an extension service colleague to consider The Ohio State University.

I was curious about life in the big city and Columbus wasn't that far from home. To make the big leap, I started to save every penny I possibly could to cover tuition, books and living costs. By the fall of 1978, I headed off for OSU grad school. The summer before I left for Columbus, Mom and I went shopping.

"Myra, there's something I want to talk to you about," Mom said as we were driving down the road toward the mall in Beckley. "I went for my annual checkup last week. After counseling with my doctor, he advised me to seek someone as a sounding board. I told him I didn't feel comfortable talking with friends. He asked if I had a daughter. When I said yes, he suggested I talk with you."

"What's going on Mom?" I asked, as my mind instantly ran wild with all the possibilities of what her ailment could be.

"A.R. is having an affair with one of his former students. It's been going on for a couple of years now. He's decided he wants a divorce so he can marry her. I would get out of Bellwood in a minute, but Michael doesn't want to leave his grandma and grandpa. I feel like I've been held hostage, but now we have no choice. I'm thinking of moving back in with Mother."

"Oh, Mom. This makes me so angry."

"Believe me, I know. Please don't say anything to Mother. She doesn't suspect what is going on. I feel so neglectful toward her. She's done so much for us and gets blamed by A.R. for things she doesn't deserve to. She never speaks poorly of him to me, but bad words about her are always coming from his mouth."

"Why don't you get a house of your own?" I encouraged. "It's what you've always dreamed of. I just saw a 'For Sale' sign in the yard of a nice house in Meadow Bridge. Let's go look at it."

"Mother's health is starting to decline. I really feel I need to move back there to keep an eye on her."

"I have noticed Mawzy struggling sometimes. Maybe you're right."

Mom filled Eleanor in on the circumstances. Eleanor lashed out at A.R. in a letter she wrote to him and shared with Mom. ...*We grew up with the same Mother who taught us that love is something you do – not something you say. Without a father to give us a different opinion ... we both still believe that.*

Mom's divorce was final in November 1978. She walked away from Bellwood, like David and I had, with a just few personal items in tow and moved back in with Mawzy. She too had finally descended those stairs one last time. By then I was living in Columbus, trying to wrap my head around all the adjustments and going through culture shock.

Michael and Mawzy didn't get along. She had never been around him that much. He was a 10-year-old dealing with his own issues and didn't have a clue what Mawzy was going through. It broke my heart to see Mom caught in the middle. Again.

After completing my master's degree, I was flat broke. Needed a job. I applied for and was offered a regional Consumer Economist position with Iowa State University Extension Service in Sioux City, Iowa the spring of 1980. I was torn as I was excited to move forward with my career but wondered about being so far from home. I took the job and from that point forward I only made it back to the hills twice per year - in the summer and around the Christmas holiday. Being away for longer periods of time, Mawzy's decline was more obvious to me. Yet, to the

286

end, when I went to her side, she always brightened up. I knew she still recognized me as someone important to her and I could feel her love for me. Still do.

I found letters in the hope chest from Mawzy to Aunt Sister and Aunt Tibbie written around the time I moved to Iowa. I'm not sure if they were ever mailed or if Mawzy's sisters gave them to Mom to make her aware of Mawzy's condition. Mawzy continued to write letters, but it was obvious her command of the language and her syntax were slipping.

March 20, 80
Dear Sister,

My! This is a beautiful day, but we never know what the next day will bring. I don't know if you can read this, even if I get it written or not. I am so nervous I am so . . . and dizzy. We have lost some school, due to bad weather and now some of them are striking. I don't know if it will be made up paid for or not. David and Chris spent the week end with us. They finely got moved into the new house they are buying. I am still not hearing from the home folks. It is hard to write with no letter to answer. It is a hard time for young people to start housekeeping, buy food, clothing, etc. everything is so high...

We had two or a pr. of red birds to winter with us. They have gone and two blue birds seem to be making a place to live this summer. We David Chris Mike and I went to a place near Lewisburg the other day and had supper and enjoyed it very much. I am not getting anywhere health-size. I don't do much work. G.J. runs herself to death almost. Some days I feel pretty good but other times I'm no good... I walk the floors some nights and get the nights and days mixed up. I don't care if I eat any or not. Am doing a little better but not much.

I went out by your houses the other day and everything just at a glance seemed to be O.K. David and Chris said their house looked a lot like mine. They have bought a cloths dryer and washer also. Know Chris is glad of that.

I hope you can read some of this. Bye now. Hope Mary and family are ok.

March 3/2/81
Evie,

Pains under arm not serious just come and go. Some days I am light headed others make me light-headed and falling around. As a whole believe I have improved. For a while I couldn't write anything that anyone could read. That is why I could not do any writing. I still have trouble hiding and finding things. I am what Poppy used to say weak as a cat. I am gaining too much too fast. I don't care much. Maybe when that sun you you have been talking about gets here we will we will all feel good.

Love,
Grace

Many years later, Mom made me a scrapbook of memorabilia. I was surprised to find letters Mawzy had written to me after I moved to Iowa. The letters had never been mailed.

Spring Dale
Oct. 4, 1981
Hello, how you?
We are having some bright blue weather and some other and some good and bad times and to see you Myra and how are you Everything can't all be bad. Just try to sum all the good things. Everything can't can't all be all traveling your way.

Spring Dale, W.Va
Oct 10, 1981
Dear Myra,
How are you? I have started to write to you many times <u>gave it up</u> I wish you lived near. I could have some colds time. Joe Crowder broke his arm. If you can work a work if you can do this. We heard from Debbie. I wish we could do do to cheer her. She is a sweet girl. I will her. I hope there is still

Spring Dale, 1981
Dear Myra,
You and family? I have started to write to you many times and gave and Sometimes I feel a let me down and put down the pen down and say to myself oh well what is there for for me to write for me to write about anyway anyway

I agonized over Mawzy's frustration in the letters. She wrote in pencil and had erased so many times trying to get it right, the paper had grown thin in spots. Even then, Mawzy's love of family and nature shined through. Even in her decline, she was still my cheerleader.

Not long after Mom moved back to Mawzy's house, she decided to get a dishwasher. Once installed, Mawzy watched Mom clear the table, rinse the dishes, and load the machine.

"I don't see how that saves any time," Mawzy noted. "Now you're washin' the dishes twice. Looks like to me you wasted your money."

Even then she had retained her frugal mindset. She thought paper towels were stupid too. She always guided us from the paper towel roll to a cloth hand towel whenever she caught us in the act.

Mom fed Mawzy well but she often complained. Lasagna was one of the dishes Mawzy did not like very well, so she called it "that dirty 'ole low down red dog lowjonya." Red dog was burned coal residue used to pave dirt roads back in the day. On another occasion, Mom asked, "How's your supper tonight?"

"Better than nothin," was Mawzy's response. It's an expression David and I still use to this day, always followed by a chuckle.

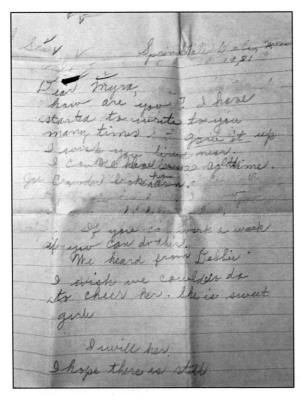

Aunt Annie, Billy's wife, was hired to come look after Mawzy during the day while Mom taught school. As Mawzy's condition worsened, a full-time caregiver, Verta, moved in to assist and Annie left to be near her boys in Alabama.

Mom took care of Mawzy for 10 years until Mawzy's death in 1988. It is truly a star in Mom's crown. Aunt Eleanor and Uncle Billy's boys signed their share of Mawzy's house over to Mom as a thank you for her dedication to Mawzy. Finally, at age 54, Mom had a house of her own. Mom's social life was non-existent when she was working and caring for Mawzy. She eventually started dating and remarried. Her third husband Dale's wife had recently passed so he and Mom decided it was time to start living again.

The fall of 1982, I met my future husband, John, on a blind date, a venture I swore I would never participate in again. It was not love at first sight, but as we spent more time together, we grew closer. Life's turning points don't always have to be in your face. For me, it was when I dozed off in his collector car as we were headed to Lincoln, Nebraska for a formal diner. My soft drink slid out of my hand and spilled. He didn't get mad at me. He was truly more concerned about my getting wet.

As we became more serious about our future together, I invited him to come home to West Virginia with me the following summer. Wanted him to meet Mom and Mawzy and to see where I grew up. When John and I walked into the house I introduced him to Mom and we found Mawzy sitting in the dining room, strapped in a wheelchair, about ready to be fed. John greeted her with a hug and a peck on the cheek.

She instantly brightened up and said, "Hands." We looked a bit puzzled, so she repeated, "Hands." In frustration, she spelled out, "H-A-N-D-S-O-M-E," just like in the spelling bees.

I am sure John's dark hair reminded her of her beau, Add, after all those years. I am also certain at that point she knew I had found my happy ending.

"Our ancestors are still actors in our lives, a source of wisdom and protection."
From *Mister Owita's Guide to Gardening* by Carol Wall

Mawzy kept two ceramic angels on the dresser in my bedroom atop doilies she crocheted.

Epilogue: Always an Angel

 I have pondered the path my life may have taken had it not been for Mawzy's guidance. The sense of order she exuded was so important to mine and David's survival in Bellwood and to our lives moving forward. I used her template for life. She was not famous yet impacted many. She was not wealthy if measured by dollars and cents. Her richness came from within. Mawzy's sister, Thelma, wrote a eulogy entitled "Always an Angel" which helps summarize the powerful reach of Mawzy's orbit. (See Appendix.)

We are a culmination of our ancestors. My best qualities I attribute to Mawzy – driven and tenacious. When I asked Mom to tell me her children's' greatest strengths, without hesitation she said: David – sensitivity (like Mom); Myra – stubbornness (like Dad, Add and Poppy Walker) and a go getter (like Mawzy); and Mike – intelligence (from both parents). It was interesting that Mom saw my stubbornness as a strength.

Mawzy's funeral was on my 34th birthday. Every time someone wished me a happy birthday, I burst into tears. There was nothing happy about that day, yet I was comforted by the nearly 200 people who came to pay their last respects. Mawzy was buried in the Wallace Memorial Cemetery where she had purchased a plot near her only true love, Add. As we left the cemetery, I had a hollow feeling. That night after I went to bed, I called out to Mawzy's spirit. The floorboards in

291

the hallway creaked. It was her, if only in my mind's eye. As I laid there I sensed our spirits being bound together forever.

Though Mawzy's been gone for over 30 years, when I'm back home her spirit is still strong. I feel it when I see the apple tree out back, the rose bush by the driveway and the huge pine trees in the front yard; when I open her old desk drawer to look for a pen; when I wrap one of her quilts around my shoulders and feel her hug me while I sit on the front porch on a crisp fall day; when I explore the house and garage and am thrilled to find yet another clue she left behind. Mawzy had an eye for history and kept good records which made finding the clues easy.

Mawzy's property is one of the most peaceful places I've ever been. On two occasions that serenity was almost destroyed – once when the land was mapped as a possible path for Interstate 64 and again when strip mining on the hill behind the house created flooding through the yard. I used to have bad dreams about getting swept up in the flood waters.

Five years after Mawzy retired, the Springdale Elementary School closed and was eventually sold. The buyer converted it to a bar and named it The Teacher's Lounge.

Mawzy's memory was fading by then so she was never aware

The site of the old Springdale Elementary School still echoes Mawzy's spirit.

of the bar, which was a good thing. We later surmised she would have turned over in her grave had she known. The bar didn't stay open long. The schoolhouse then became a private residence. I went to see the current owner not long ago. I am glad I wrote a description of the school as I remembered it before I visited as there was very little left of the days gone by – no classrooms or lunchroom, no alphabet chart on the wall, no seesaws or slicky slide, no softball field, no pile of coal in the back to heat the school and a road grown over to the point of being impassable. Yet I could still feel Mawzy's spirit there too.

When I shared portions of the book with Cousin Billy Boy, he told me some of it was troubling to him and sometimes inaccurate. I appreciated his honesty and adjusted accordingly. I have attempted to be sensitive to the feelings of the characters in this story. In some cases, names have been changed. If I got the sense I was digging too deep, I backed off.

I hope this book has brought back pleasant memories of your grandmother(s). If they are still living, have conversations with them about their past while you still can. I guarantee there is something you will learn, perhaps a lot.

I recently moved Mawzy's hope chest to Nebraska. I am the keeper of her history now. If I want to spend time with her, all I need to do is open the lid.

As I wrote Mawzy's story and her influence on my life, I often wondered if I had done her justice. Then I could hear her teasingly say with a chuckle, "Better than nothin'."

Appendix

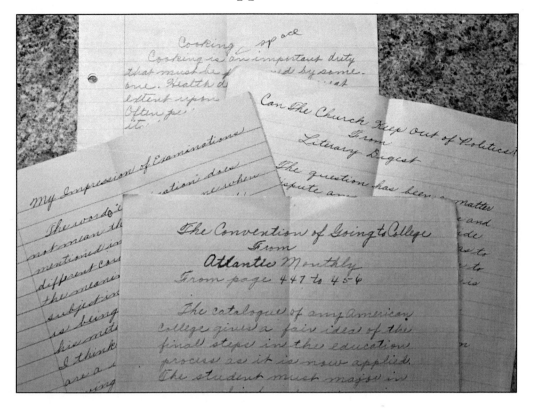

A Selection of Mawzy's College English Compositions

The Convention of Going to College

(From Atlantic Monthly) – 10/01/1929

The catalogue for any American college gives a fair idea of the final steps in the education process as it is now applied. The student must major in one subject and minor in other courses. These courses will make him profound and broad. He must undergo such exercises that will make him healthy. The social and athletic training will give him friends.

   Sometimes the very best colleges are not the right places for some people because the things which they have a talent for are given little or no time. For this reason, everyone should be given some time to decide what they wish to do. Until people are convinced that they belong in college they will never approach their college work with the purpose that brings satisfaction. Many parents seem to think that their sons and daughters must go to four years college regardless of what line of work they are going to take up later. This sometimes results as failures in college.

Probably if the ones who fail in college were in their right field of work they would make a success. It is always well to confide loyalty to those fields where they can do most good and least mischief. It should be obvious that a student's fitness for any type of school is not to be governed by the laws of heredity alone.

In seven cases out of ten the college is an enriching experience but if someone is one of the three, college may turn into a near tragedy for him. College encourages students to follow the broad cement roads to quick and apparent forms of success but it does not guide them along the side roads and by-paths which often lead to great unexpected discoveries.

Can the Church Keep Out of Politics? (From Literary Digest) - 10/09/1929

The question has been a matter of dispute among theologians on one side and laymen on the other as to whether politics be given over to the devil so far as the church is concerned? Or should the church enter the "devil's own parish", as some are apt to characterize the field of politics, and fight him on his chosen field? Dr. Stetson urged that the church should concern itself with spiritual welfare of the individual and not with political activity. The Pittsburg Christian Advocate asks why the church should not concern itself with both? He says that the church should cultivate the character of its members, but that does not make its political activity impossible or its social responsibility less heavy.

As the Pittsburg Weekly sees it, "We are in a world where public conditions affect the life of every individual. The church wants everyone to be their best and happiest, Christian, or non-Christian. The church encourages law enforcement to save and bless the individual."

Cooking - 11/08/1929

Cooking is an important duty that must be performed by someone. Health depends to a great extent upon the food one eats. Often people blame the food itself for causing indigestion or some other injury to health when the fault is not in the food at all but is due to the way in which it has been prepared to eat. Different people need a different variety of food, therefore it is necessary for one who is cooking to know about the health of the individuals for whom she is cooking. Invalids should not eat food prepared in the same form as prepared for a laboring man. Children cannot have rosy cheeks and well-formed bodies if they eat the same foods at all times that grown up people eat.

People who have always been accustomed to well prepared food and who have never study any of the consequences which occur when people eat food that has not been carefully prepared, know or think very little about this subject.

Many women of today who cannot afford a cook, think more of trying to be in society than they do about the health of their families, which could be improved through learning to prepare food in a delicious wholesome way.

(Written in class)

My Impression of Examinations – 01/31/1930

The word "examination" does not mean the same to me when mentioned in connection with different courses. The difference in the meaning depends on the subject in which the examination is being given, the teacher and his methods of teaching. While I think examinations as a whole are a waste of time, I enjoy giving my mental powers the exercise of recalling the important things learned in the past.

Examinations do not seem much of a handicap to me, providing the subject is interesting and I am acquainted with the instructor. Under these conditions I have an idea of what to expect and am not surprised at any question that he might ask. I have an impression that I am going to be asked a number of questions which will resemble a list of questions following a well-studied chapter in some familiar book.

In some courses, at the thought of an examination, I almost wish there would be none given, because I have no vision as to what sort of question might be asked or how I shall be expected to answer them. If it is my first examination under a certain instructor, I do not know to what extent he is going to measure my ability of doing the work, from this paper. This particular test may contain a number of questions which I do not understand or have forgotten for the present time, while there are other things just as important about the subject which I do know but do not have an opportunity to express myself on these points.

After considering examinations from all views, I do not think any professor should rely too much on the results of an examination for securing a knowledge of what a student is capable of doing.

Bud Harmon in photo he provided with his classes, all Mawzy's former students. Below, Harmon with students in front of school.

Memories Of A Fellow Teacher, Bud Harmon

Mrs. Campbell was very dependable as the principal of the Springdale Elementary School for some 35 years. I cannot remember her ever missing a day in my two and a half years with her. She was the first to arrive at school and the last to leave. I was confident in the fact that she would be there and capable to handle the day's activities as needed. There weren't any unresolved issues at the end of the day. We took school one day at a time and they added up to successful months and years.

Mrs. Campbell was a great listener and would calmly let the students tell their stories of the matter in question. I'm sure she would think of the young students as being her children, with the need to prevent a damaging of little spirits. Her disposition was always kind and caring. This must have come from her years of teaching, being a mother and her lifetime experiences.

Teaching isn't always an easy task; at times it can be very difficult. I felt I had Mrs. Campbell's assurances of my decisions in teaching. I didn't feel I was second guessed on what to do.

I can say that I could not have had a better person to start my teaching with than Grace Campbell. From her first call she seemed pleased that I would take the open job in a few months. Even though I had three months to graduate from Concord College, she was very happy to hold the job for me and pleased I was coming.

Springdale, being a small community, was aware of the school and its importance to the community. Mrs. Campbell lived near the school and she was very accountable for having a good, dependable school.

For about the last three years Mrs. Campbell was principal, the Bellwood school closed and its students were bused about seven miles to Springdale. These students became an asset and regular part of Springdale Elementary. They were good students and added positives to the school. Without the added number of Bellwood students and the Meadow Bridge kindergarten being moved to Springdale, our school would have surely closed a few years sooner.

Springdale School shortly before it closed.

Mrs. Campbell, as principal, had many reports to submit monthly and she said at the end of the year she had all her reports spread out on her extra bedroom bed, so as to manage them. Seems there was always a deadline and there wasn't any secretarial help, you were it.

The reports were for hot lunch, finance, enrollment, daily attendance and report cards. Report cards were time consuming, especially with two grades. Mrs. Campbell said three weekends were required to do reports. She was never in error or late in submitting any report.

Looking back at Springdale and Grace, I can say the school was well run to the benefit of the students. Bet they can't say they were ever cared for more. The days of school like Springdale Elementary will never return, that is a loss for today's youth. God had a hand on Grace and all of us and saw us through 'til the end.

Recipes from Mawzy's Kitchen

PEANUT BUTTER COOKIES
½ c soft shortening (half butter)
½ c peanut butter
½ c sugar
½ c brown sugar (packed)
1 egg
Mix thoroughly.

1 ¼ c sifted flour
½ tsp baking powder
¾ tsp soda
¼ tsp salt
Sift together and stir in.
Chill dough. Roll into balls size of large walnuts. Place 3" apart on lightly greased baking sheet. Flatten with fork dipped in flour. Crisscross. Bake until set, but not hard.
Temp 375 degrees.
Time 10 – 12 mins.
Amt about 3 doz 2 ½" cookies

UNBAKED COOKIES
2 c sugar
1 stick oleo
¼ c cocoa
½ c milk
Boil together 1 min after it starts to boil hard.
Mix in quickly:
½ c peanut butter
3 c quick oats
1 tsp vanilla
Drop on cookie sheet from teaspoon.

PEANUT BUTTER WHIRLS

½ c mashed potatoes
1 lb conf sugar
½ c peanut butter

Cream together the warm mashed potatoes (do not add milk) and conf. sugar. The mix should resemble fondant. Press into a rectangular shape ¼ to ½ in. thick. Spread with peanut butter and roll as a jelly roll. Refrigerate until firm and slice.

Mawzy's notation: This is good candy when the sugar and potatoes are boiled together for a few minutes, then taken off and peanut butter stirred in. It will not get thick when the potatoes and sugar are mixed as recipe says. The mixture must be stirred continuously while it is cooking.

MRS. BARRON'S APPLESAUCE CAKE

½ c butter
2 eggs
¼ tsp nutmeg
2 tsp baking powder
1 c black walnuts (broken)
1 c maraschino cherries (drained)
½ t vanilla
1 c brown sugar (firmly packed)
½ tsp cinnamon
1/8 tsp cloves
1½ tsp baking soda
2 c sifted flour
1 c chopped dates
1½ c apple sauce
1 c raisins

Cream together the butter and sugar until light and fluffy. Add one egg at a time beating well after each addition. Add vanilla and mix. Sift together all dry ingredients. Reserve ½ c of the dry ingredients to mix with the fruit and nuts. Add dry ingredients to the butter sugar mixture, alternating with the applesauce. Start and end with the dry mixture. Beat just enough to mix. Do not over beat. Add fruit mixture. Stir. Pour in lined, well-greased and floured tube cake pan. Bake at 325 degrees for 50 or 60 min.

Author's Note: William Wallace "Wally" Barron was West Virginia's governor from 1961 to 1965. This is his wife's recipe. "Wally" was a charismatic governor, but corruption tainted his legacy and he later served a prison term.

BLACKBERRY JAM CAKE

6 eggs
2 c sugar
1 c buttermilk
½ c butter or shortening
2 scants tsp soda
1 c blackberry jam
1 tsp cinnamon
1 tsp cloves
1 tsp allspice
1 tsp nutmeg

Cream shortening and sugar. Add eggs one at a time and beat well. Add dry ingredients and buttermilk. Stir in jam. Bake in tube pan at 325 degrees for about an hour or layer pans at 350 degrees for 30 min.

Author's Note: Made with Mawzy's homemade blackberry jam with blackberries picked near home.

SPICED PRUNE CAKE

½ c shortening
1 c sugar
2 eggs, well beaten
1 ¼ c finely chopped cooked prunes
2 c sifted flour
1 ½ tsp soda
1 tsp cinnamon
¾ tsp cloves
¾ tsp salt
½ c sour milk

Cream shortening and add sugar. Cream until fluffy. Add eggs and beat well. Blend in prunes.
Sift together flour, soda, spices and salt. Add to creamed mixture in three portions alternatingly with the sour milk in two portions.
Turn into greased shallow pan about 12 x 8 inches.
Bake at 350 degrees – 35 to 40 minutes

Mawzy's Notation: Good with coconut and brown sugar icing browned in oven. Cake is even better after being baked two or three days or more.

AUNT BIDDIE'S CHOCOLATE CAKE

2 c sugar
1 c shortening
4 eggs
¼ tsp salt
2 c flour
1 tsp vanilla
6 T cocoa
2/3 c buttermilk
1 tsp soda dissolved in 1 c boiling water

Cream shortening and sugar. Add eggs and beat well. Add salt, flour and cocoa alternating with buttermilk. Dissolve soda in boiling water and add mixing only until blended. Add vanilla. Bake at 350 degrees – 45 min or until toothpick comes out dry.

Frosting
¼ lb butter
2/3 box conf sugar
1 T milk
1 T water
2 T flour
3 T cocoa

Melt butter. Add other ingredients – alternating with water/milk over low heat and beating. Cook until shiny. If too stiff, add water. If too thin, add conf. sugar.

WV APPLE CUSTARD PIE

3 eggs
1 ¼ c sugar or 1 ½ c
2 c apple chips
½ tsp nutmeg
1 tsp cinnamon
¼ c butter

Beat eggs then add sugar and spices. Add melted butter and apples to the egg mixture. Pour in unbaked pie shell and bake at 400 degrees for 15 min. Reduce heat to 350 degrees and bake 45 min.

__Author's Note__: I found a lot of apple recipes in Mawzy's recipe box. She had apple trees in her yard, so it made for less expensive goodies.

FRIED APPLE PIES

Roll plain doughnut dough in sheet ¼ inch thick. Cut in 6-inch rounds. Place 1-2 tablespoons thick, well-flavored apple sauce on each round. Moisten edges. Fold over. Press edges firmly together. Slip pies into deep fat (365 degrees F). Fry until puffed and browned. Drain on crumpled absorbent paper. Serve with cheese and hot coffee. Florence Taft Eaton, Concord, Mass. (From *Searchlight Recipe Book)*

<u>Doughnut Dough</u>

1 c sugar

2 T melted shortening

2 eggs, slightly beaten

1 c milk

½ tsp vanilla flavoring

1 tsp salt

3 tsps baking powder

½ tsp cinnamon

½ tsp nutmeg

1/8 tsp ginger

4 ¾ c flour

½ tsp lemon flavoring

Combine eggs and sugar, blend carefully. Sift flour, measure and sift with salt, baking powder, and spices. Add alternately with combined milk, shortening, and flavorings to first mixture. Chill dough. (From *Searchlight Recipe Book*)

ORANGE EASTER CAKE

½ c butter

1 ¼ c sugar

1 ¼ tsp soda

1 ¼ tsp baking powder

¼ tsp salt

2 ½ c flour

1 ¼ c buttermilk or sour cream

3 eggs

1 tsp vanilla

1/8 c concentrated orange juice

Cream sugar and butter. Sift together dry ingredients. Beat eggs and stir in buttermilk, vanilla and concentrated orange juice. Add egg mixture to the creamed sugar and butter, alternating with flour. Blend well. Pour batter into greased baking pans. Bake at 350 degrees for 20 or 30 mins. Remove from oven. Punch holes in warm cake. Pour topping over cake while warm.

<u>Topping</u>

½ c concentrated orange juice

1 c sugar

OVEN SPAGHETTI

1 lb ground beef
1 T butter
½ c chopped onion
3 c tomato juice
¼ tsp mace
¼ tsp allspice
½ tsp mustard
½ tsp salt
¼ tsp pepper
2 ½ c broken spaghetti

Melt butter in baking pan. Add ground beef and chopped onion. Cook until brown. Stir in seasoning and add tomato juice. Sprinkle broken spaghetti over tomato mixture. Press into juice. Bake at 350 degrees for 30 mins.

CHEESE QUICK

1 T dry mustard
¼ tsp salt
¼ tsp cayenne
1 T Worcestershire sauce
2 lbs cheese, cut or grated
2 c water

In top part of boiler, mix mustard and cayenne. Add Worcestershire sauce and water and cheese. Place pan over boiling water. Cover and keep over simmering water until cheese melts. Stir several times during the heating process. Beat until smooth. (Mixture will be thin.) Cool slightly to thicken. To store, pour into a refrigerator container, cover and refrigerate. Use either cold or reheated. Makes 5 3/4 cups.

Mawzy's Notation: It Spreads – It Melts – It Keeps – It's Cheap
Suggestions for Using Cheese Quick: use as a sandwich spread; use in a toasted or grilled sandwich; pour over a frankfurter in a bun; serve on a hamburger patty; used over cooked macaroni; use as a topping for baked potato

Author's Note: Being in abundant supply, commodity cheese from Springdale Elementary School precipitated the use of this recipe.

PUMPKIN PIE

1 ½ cups cooked pumpkin, fresh or canned
  1 c rich milk
  1 c sugar
  ¼ teaspoon salt
  ¼ teaspoon nutmeg
  ¼ teaspoon cinnamon
  2 eggs, slightly beaten
  1 tablespoon butter or butter substitute

Combine ingredients. Mix thoroughly. Pour into pastry-lined pie pan. Bake in hot oven (425 degrees F), or until an inserted knife comes out clean. Serve with whipped cream. If desired, ½ cup raisins may be added to pumpkin filling. Virginia Cooper, New Orleans, La. (From *Searchlight Recipe Book*)

Mawzy's Notation: Good. (She wrote page number of recipe in front of cookbook.)

UNCOOKED LYE SOAP

6 c warm water
1 can lye
1 c borax
9 c grease
½ c ammonia

Using large flat porcelain pan, mix together water, lye and borax; let stand one hour. Add grease and ammonia; stir constantly for 10 minutes. Let set until hard; cut into bars.

Author's Note: This recipe came from a newspaper column called "Tell Dottie" by Dorothy Evelyn Comer, homemaking writer.

HOG'S HEAD CHEESE

1 Hog's Head
1 Hog's Tongue
Sage and Chili Powder
Salt and Pepper

Clean and scrape hog's head. Wash thoroughly. Wash and trim tongue. Cover tongue and head with slightly salted water. Simmer until meat falls from bone. Drain meat. Shred. Season to taste. Mix thoroughly. Pack tightly in bowl. Cover and weight down. Let stand three days. Slice. (From *Searchlight Recipe Book).*

Author's Note: This is an example of Mawzy's "Waste not, want not" mentality. My thoughts? – nasty looking and tasting.

APPALACHIAN SQUIRREL STEW

2-3 squirrels
2 c water
4 T bacon fat
2-3 onions, sliced thin
1 ½ tsp salt
1 T Worcestershire sauce
1 tsp pepper
1 tsp rosemary
1 tsp thyme
1 bay leaf
¾ c tomatoes peeled, seeded, and chopped
1 c pinto beans
1 c corn

Place whole squirrels in a Dutch oven with 2 cups water. Braise the squirrel meat, covered for about 30 minutes until tender.

Remove squirrels and stock to a different container to cool. Debone squirrels when cool enough to handle and add meat back into the stock. Reserve it all for adding back into the Dutch oven later.

Add 4 tablespoons of bacon drippings to the empty Dutch oven and fry the onions until browned.

Pour the stock and squirrel meat into the hot Dutch oven.

Add in all the remaining ingredients including spices and vegetables. Cover and simmer for about 30 minutes.

16 Hours

Some people say a teacher's head is made out of wood.
The best one's made of things that are good.
Patience and love, skill and sense
And knowledge acquired at a great expense.

Your work 16 hours and whatta you get?
Another night's worry cause you ain't done yet.
St. Peter don't you call me cause sure as fate,
I'll be doin' extra duty at the Golden Gate.
.

I was born one morning according to rule,
Picked up my papers and I walked to school.
I worked 16 hours the very first day
Educating the youth without much pay
.

You work 16 hours far into the night
Planning out ways to do your job right.
St Peter don't you call me cause I can't stop.
I've got to be running to the teacher's workshop.

I was born one morning with a book in my hand.
Teaching the youth in this fair land.
Working with parents, supervisors and staff,
Worked 16 hours no time and a half.

You work 16 hours and whatta you get?
Another dirty note as you worry and fret.
St. Peter don't call me for without fail,
You'll have to call a postman to bring my mail.

If you see me comin' better step aside.
I'll have to be walkin' too poor to ride.
My clothes are cheap my pockets bare.
The taxpayers love it, so you shouldn't care.

You work 16 hours and whatta you get?
You clean dirty noses and pamper and pet.
St. Peter, don't you call me cause sure as fate,
I'll be cleaning their noses at the Pearly Gate.

If you see me comin' don't you step aside.
As the Legislature did when the school bill died.
Just greet me as usual with a "Howdy You fool."
If you had any gumption you wouldn't teach school.

You work 16 hours and whatta you get?
More criticism, but there's no raise yet.
St. Peter don't you call me, for I won't heed.
I'd be kicked out of heaven cause Jonny can't read.

(Author Unknown – Two copies found in Mawzy's hope chest)

The song *16 Tons*, originally written by Merle Travis in 1947 and made popular by Tennessee Ernie Ford in 1955, portrayed the coal miner's plight of hard work and low pay. *16 Hours* mimics this theme for schoolteachers.

The teacher's poem was probably written in the 1950s as a manual typewriter was used and it was a time when schools and teachers were getting squeezed by the baby boomers. An October 3, 1952, article in *The Beckley Post-Herald* reported,

> *"The war and post war boom in babies gave the schools more children than they knew what to do with – as most parents know. There were not enough school buildings. Qualified teachers were scarce and got scarcer as some of them went into war work or sought other occupations because teacher pay lagged. Sometimes there were not enough textbooks. School agencies have been scrambling for funds to remedy deficits but they work under a handicap. Every year they are asked to take care of more and more children. The lack of elementary school teachers was particularly acute…"*

Battles in the West Virginia state legislature for school appropriations and teacher raises were in the news quite often. It was around this time Poppy Walker wrote a letter to the editor of a local newspaper to complain about the higher taxes levied to cover an increase in teacher's pay.

It was very upsetting to Mawzy that he would voice his displeasure, especially in public, when his daughter had given her heart and soul to teaching the children. Poppy never had trouble voicing his opinion about anything. And so, when the West Virginia legislature was debating tax increases to support teachers' salaries he let his feelings be known. In a letter to the editor on March 9, 1957, he threw Mawzy, Aunt Lucille, Uncle Jim, Aunt Eleanor and Mom under the bus. He was almost 71 years old at the time.

Reader Hits Legislature On Tax Hikes

I notice the Legislature is still making a big fight to raise taxes on land and real estate. They have run about all the young generation off the farms now, I suppose they want to chase the remaining ones away. As it is the farmer pays double taxes, they assess the land, then the stock and everything he produces. A few years back I had a team of horses assessed at $250 and cows at $50 each, and soon thereafter I lost one of the horses and two cows; whereas I had to pay taxes on $225 of stock that was dead. This happens to others every year.

The salary of the office holders has raised two or three thousand dollars on the year. Why don't they assess their pay check same as they do the farmers stock?

Who is it that is putting up all this big howl about raising the school teacher's salary? I have five school teachers in my family; a daughter, daughter-in-law, son-in-law and two granddaughters, and I have the first time yet to hear any one of them say they

are not satisfied with their salary. These hill-billys on these small farms don't average buying a suit of clothes once in ten years. Most office holders and school teachers get a new suit for every season of the year. A farmer can be spotted when seen in town; never see one with a top coat on, they never get enough ahead to buy one; but the salaried class will have a silk scarf tied around their neck and a top coat on with the collar turned up at the back of their neck if they only have a half block to walk to church or the grocery store.

I raised a family of ten children, and they have all gone either to teaching or other work and I am left by myself. I am not able to work my farm anymore and I offered to give it to any one of them, with what stock and farm implements I have and I got the same answer from everyone of them. "Oh, no, Dad, I know what you went through; work from 18 to 20 hours a day, in rain, mud, snow, etc. Didn't get any rest from it when Sunday came; have to be out

at least half a day feeding, and we only work from 30 to 40 hours per week and make more in one hour than you made in a week. I wouldn't want to go back to that kind of life unless I am compelled to. We have from 16 to 18 hours pleasure time and you didn't have any."

A few days ago I was on my way to the post office. Four small boys ranging from 8 to 12 years in age, came out of one of these muddy hollows going to school. The snow was about three inches deep and only one out of the four had on overshoes; the others feet and legs were wet to the knees. I said "Boys, aren't your feet cold?" They answered, "Yes, they are cold." "But," one of the boys said, "it takes money to buy overshoes, and that is something we don't have."

If anyone doubts this come out and stay with me a week and I will show you around and you will see more than I have told you here.

W. C. Walker
Springdale, W. Va.

Poppy's Rant

Voice of the People - Reader Hits Legislature on Tax Hikes

I notice the Legislature is still making a big fight to raise taxes on land and real estate. They have run about all the young generation off the farms now. I suppose they want to chase the remaining ones away. As it is the farmer pays double taxes, they assess the land, then the stock and everything he produces. A few years back I had a team of horses assessed at $250 and cows at $50 each, and soon thereafter I lost one of the horses and two cows; whereas I had to pay taxes on $225 of stock that was dead. This happens to others every year.

The salary of the office holders has raised two or three thousand dollars on the year. Why don't they assess their pay check same as they do the farmers stock?

Who is it that is putting up all this big howl about raising the school teacher's salary? I have five school teachers in my family; a daughter, daughter-in-law, son-in-law and two granddaughters, and I have the first time yet to hear any one of them say they are not satisfied with their salary.

These hill-billys on these small farms don't average buying a suit of clothes once in ten years. Most office holders and school teachers get a new

309

suit for every season of the year. A farmer can be spotted when seen in town; never see one with a top coat on; they never get enough ahead to buy one; but the salaried class will have a silk scarf tied around their neck and a top coat on with the collar turned up at the back of their neck if they only have a half block to walk to church or the grocery store.

I raised a family of ten children, and they have all gone either to teaching or other work and I am left by myself. I am not able to work my farm anymore and I offered to give it to any one of them, with what stock and farm implements I have and I got the same answer from everyone of them. "Oh, no, Dad, I know what you went through; work from 18 to 20 hours a day, in rain, mud, snow, etc. Didn't get any rest from it when Sunday came; have to be out at least half a day feeding and we only work from 30 to 40 hours per week and make more in one hour then you made in a week. I wouldn't want to go back to that kind of life unless I am compelled to. We had from 16 to 18 hours of pleasure time and you didn't have any."

A few days ago I was on my way to the post office. Four small boys ranging from 8 to 12 years in age came out of one of these muddy hollows going to school. The snow was about three inches deep and only one out of the four had on overshoes; the others feet and legs were wet to the knees.

I said "Boys, aren't your feet cold?" They answered, "Yes, they are cold."

"But," one of the boys said, "It takes money to buy overshoes and that is something we don't have."

If anyone doubts this come out and stay with me a week and I will show you around and you will see more than I have told you here.

W.C. Walker, Springdale, W.Va.

Remembering an Angel

Sister Thelma's Eulogy

On November 5, 1907 an angel was born to a young couple in Layland, West Virginia. Instantly, there was a daughter, a father, and a mother, as well as two grandfathers, two grandmothers, and of course, endless great grandparents in the background.

The angel became a cousin, a niece, and a granddaughter. Shortly, she became a sister, a playmate, and a friend to many sisters and brothers. She was like a second mother to her younger brothers and sisters while she was growing into adulthood.

As a young lady, she became a teacher and some of her younger brothers and sister became her students. Among her friends she found a sweetheart and she was married. Now she was a wife, an aunt, an in-law, and a teacher, too. Soon she became a mother and her angels grew up, matured, and married and were blessed with children. She enjoyed working in the church, which was an outlet from her heavy schedule. Great grandchildren were born, making her then a great grandmother.

Truly, she was an angel in disguise, giving of herself to others. She grew old and tired. The Savior tapped her on her shoulder and called her Home.

Now her life cycle is complete and she is an angel again. Yes, she has earned her reward in Heaven. Now she is smiling down on her big family and will welcome them Home when they, too, grow old and tired, or when their names are called. Be aware that she is with her loved ones who have gone on before.

We all love you, Gracie, and deeply miss you, but you still live in our hearts. You are an inspiration and the world could use more like you.

Love, Your devoted Sister, Thelma

Sissy's letter

Dear Gloria June,

How are you doing? I hope everything is fine. I know you miss Mawzy. We miss her very much. Is there anything we can do for you? Mawzy was so special to me. I did not have the privilege of knowing her long but the influence she had on Steve will always be precious to me. I believe she had a big part in shaping the sweet husband that I have... Sissy

Acknowledgements

I would like to give a heartfelt thanks to my husband, John, who read and offered suggestions for many of the chapters in this book. He endured my ups and downs as I spent many hours, weeks, months and years preoccupied with the research and writing of this book. He can attest to my stubborn nature!

Much love goes out to my Mom, Gloria June. I know she did the best she could, given her circumstances. The greatest example she set for me was her dedicated, loving care of Mawzy during Mawzy's Alzheimer years. At the time of this writing, Mom has Alzheimer's and is in a memory care assisted living facility near me. I am managing her affairs. After Mawzy died, she approached me to apply for long term care insurance. She said she did not want me to go through what she had just endured. I was a financial advisor by then and fulfilled her wishes. Though I'm not sure she knows me, my time with her is precious. Just like Mawzy, I feel she sees me as someone important to her.

I would also like to thank my father and mother in-law, Fran and Vernice, as they, like Mawzy, have been such a positive influence on my life. Fran has always been the perfect father figure for me – one of the few I've ever had. Vernice has been supportive of my endeavors. She was excited about this book and hoped she would still be alive by the time it was published. She has macular degeneration, so John and I provided her with chapters in large print as I finished them. She enjoyed getting to know more about me and my family. She has spent many hours compiling her and Fran's family history for her own children. I pray I will be able to hand Fran and Vernice the final version of this book. At the time of this writing, Fran is 99 years old and Vernice is 98.

I would never have completed this book had it not been for James Abraham, my editor and publisher, who guided me through the process of completing *Mawzy's Hope Chest*. I know my perfectionism and stubbornness tested him on many occasions. He has the patience of Job and an essential sense of humor. I appreciate his wisdom and insights so much more now than I did at the beginning of this journey.

I am forever grateful to my good friend, Heather Craig-Oldsen, who provided a tremendous amount of support. I know I wore her out talking about "the book". We formed a writer's group and critiqued each other's drafts. I am thankful of her sharp eye for clarity, punctuation and flow.

I cherished my visits with Aunt Biddie, Mawzy's brother Chester's wife, on her front porch and in her kitchen and living room. She told me so many stories about the Walker family's past I filled up a whole notepad. She helped bring Mawzy's early years of life more into focus for me. We laughed through most of our time together. Her son, Gary, and daughter, Rhonda, kicked in with their stories if they happened to be visiting when I was there. Some are featured in the book. I love the layers of color they added.

I also spent a lot of time up on the hill quizzing my Mom's best friend, Betty Lou Puckett, and relished her thoughts and remembrances of the Springdale School in the early years, of Mawzy and the church, of she and Mom in their youth, as young mothers and in later years and of my brother, David, and me when she was our babysitter. She still reminds me of my "bull fits".

I give credit to my Mom's third husband, Dale, who provided a ton of insight into what life was like in Gentry Holler and growing up in the same era as Mom. He also remembered stories Mom told him about her childhood before Alzheimer's took her memory away. Dale gets a star in his crown for caring for Mom until it became too difficult and we had to move her to a memory care facility.

Cousin Becky, Aunt Eleanor's daughter, gladly shared many stories about her mom's shenanigans growing up. Her sister, Deborah, also helped fill gaps for some of the stories. When Aunt Eleanor was still living, we had many a conversation at her kitchen table about what her life was like growing up in the hills and her errant behavior.

Cousin Bill, Uncle Billy's oldest son, and I reminisced about Mawzy's influence on our lives. I'm grateful for his help with filling in some of the blanks about life in Alabama. Sadly he recently passed away before having a chance to read the book.

Aunt Lucille, Mawzy's brother Lawrence's wife, and I had a wonderful visit as she told of her early years at Springdale School and her life as a young woman getting her college education. She has since passed.

Bud Harmon was invaluable in clarifying and expanding the Springdale School stories, which are in the School Days sections of the book and the appendix. Most of the school pictures in this book were provided by Bud.

Mike Arritt posted pictures on Facebook of the Meadow Bridge High School *Montrados*, the school newspaper. They helped to paint a clearer picture of my Mom, Aunt Eleanor and Uncle Billy in junior high and high school. Serendipitously, they came through just as I was working on that era in the "A Stiff Upper Lip" and "Mawzy's Brood" chapters. Thanks, Mike, for the perfect timing. Mike is the son of Celeste and Frank Arritt who were prominent influences as teachers, a coach and principal at MBHS.

I am grateful to Louella Patterson who welcomed me into her home to talk about the Springdale School hot lunch program and her experiences at the school. What an enlightening visit it was. Louella has since passed.

Shelia Fitzgerald Withrow, who works at the Fayette County Board of Education, helped with my Springdale School research. For this, I'm much obliged. She was a next-door neighbor friend I played with as a child.

Patty Burwell was a great and appreciated resource for information on Springdale's history.

I value the input of Eugenia Thomas and daughter, Pam, who provided insights about the Head Start Program in Meadow Bridge.

Joy Cox and his brother, Wayne, shared their memories of helping their dad, Enoch, remodel Mawzy's old house and later build her new one and of being janitors for the Springdale School. Conversations with them were fascinating and invaluable.

A thanks goes out to Lana Montague and Andy Pendleton for help with WOW women who worked at the Meadow River Lumber Company in Rainelle, WV during World War II.

To my friends Bonnie, Kathie and Laura who encouraged me along the way. They and friend Heather are strong women who have also had a positive influence on my life. I love you guys!

Hats off again to my brother David who was my cheerleader throughout the whole process. We sure had some fun times reminiscing.

For those who helped, but aren't mentioned, my apologies for the oversight. Just know any assistance you provided was appreciated.

Bibliography

"A Christmas Story House & Museum", https://achristmasstoryhouse.com/filming-locations/higbees/

Beckley Post-Herald and *The Raleigh Register,* Beckley Newspapers Corporation, Beckley, WV, 1915 to 1977

Bersch, Maxine J. and Elgin, Josephine Johnson, *A Voice in the Wilderness*, BookSurge, LLC, Charleston, SC, 2003

Bersch, Maxine J., *Under the Gooseberry Bush*, CreateSpace Independent Publishing Platform, Columbia, SC, 2013

Bogan, Dallas, "Buffalo Trails Led the Way for Pioneers", https://www.tngenweb.org/campbell/hist-bogan/BuffaloTrails.html

Bourque, Dan, "Appalachian Railroad Modeling – C&O NC Nicholas Fayette & Greenbrier Railroad, WV Track Plan N, *Basement-sized, C&O Track Plans, N scale, NYC Track Plans, Track Plans*", 2017

Bowden, Mary Deborah, *Little Lestoil Ladies,* The Harp Tree Publishing, London, UK, 2016

Bragg, Melody, *Window to the Past*, Gem Publications, Glen Jean, WV, 1990

Browning, Joan C., Pendleton, Andrea J. and Shelton, Autumn G., *Images of America – Rainelle*, Arcadia Publishing, Charleston, SC, 2014

Capper, Arthur, *Searchlight Recipe Book*, Capper Publications, Inc., *The Household Magazine*, Topeka, KS, compiled and edited by Migliario, Ida, Titus, Zorada Z., Allard, Harriet W., and Nunemaker, Irene, 1945

Clarkson, Roy B., *Tumult on the Mountains*, McClain Publishing Company, Parsons, WV, 1964

Coleman, Rhonda Janney, "Coal Miners and Their Communities in Southern Appalachia, 1925-1941, Part One", *West Virginia Historical Society Quarterly,* West Virginia Department of Arts, Culture and History, Charleston, WV, Volume XV, No. 2, April 2001

Colman, Penny, *Rosie the Riveter - Women Working on the Home Front in World War II*, Yearling, a division of Random House, LLC, New York, NY, 1995

"Company Towns in the U.S.: 1880s to 1935", https://socialwelfare.library.vcu.edu/programs/housing/company-towns-1890s-to-1935/

"Company Scrip", https://en.wikipedia.org/wiki/Company_scrip

Crislip, Don, "Project Head Start", *West Virginia School Journal*, State Department of Education, Charleston, WV, September 1965

Crookshanks, Ben, "Nothing but Hardwood - The Meadow River Lumber Company", *Goldenseal*, Mountain Arts Foundation in behalf of the Division of Culture and History, Charleston, WV, Winter 1991

Day, Peggy Ann Houchins, *My Hometown - History of Meadow Bridge and Beelick Knob, West Virginia,* P.A.H. Day (self-published), Beelick Knob, WV 1986

"Doodlebug (rail car)", https://en.wikipedia.org/wiki/Doodlebug_(rail_car)

Ganzel, Bill, "Duck and Cover Drills Bring the Cold War Home", https://livinghistoryfarm.org/farminginthe50s/life_04.html

General Mills staff, *Betty Crocker's Picture Cook Book,* John Wiley and Sons, Hoboken, NJ, 1950

Greene, Janet W., "Strategies for Survival: Women's Work in the Southern West Virginia Coal Camps", *West Virginia History*, Volume 49, 1990

Hanna, Isaac, "The Company Store", *United Mine Worker's Journal,* Englewood, FL, May 23, 1895

Hepler, Linda, *The Characteristics of Rural One-Room Schools in Barbour County, West Virginia, that Represent Characteristics of Rural One-Room Schools in General,* A Thesis Presented to The Faculty of the Master of Arts Degree Program, Salem-Teikyo University, Salem, WV, 1998

Klaus, Fran, *Images of America – Beckley*, Arcadia Publishing, Charleston, SC, 2012

Korson, George, *Coal Dust on the Fiddle*, Folklore Associates, Inc., Hatboro, Pennsylvania, 1965

Larson, Lilly, "1920s Marriage", https://prezi.com/2ghbadiq51gm/1920s-marriage

Lutz, Paul F., "One Room was Enough", *Goldenseal*, Mountain Arts Foundation in behalf of the Division of Culture and History, Charleston, WV, Fall, 1996

Meador, Michael M., "The Influenza Epidemic of 1918", *e-WV: The West Virginia Encyclopedia*, 2017

Meadow River Post, Bob Holliday, editor, East Rainelle, WV, 1967-1972

Miller, Jeff, "History of Woodrow Wilson High School", https://jeff560.tripod.com/wwhs.html

Mountjoy, Eileen, "A Woman's Day: Work and Anxiety", https://www.iup.edu/library/department/archives/coal/people-lives-stories/a-womans-day-work-and-anxiety/

New River Coal Field, *West Virginia (WV) Cycloedia,*http://www.wvexp.com/index.php?title=New_River_Coal_Field_&oldid=33495", 2015

O'Brian, Robert J., "Persecution and Acceptance: The Strange History of Discrimination Against Married Women Teachers in West Virginia", *West Virginia History*, Volume 56, 1997

Peregoy, C.G., "High Schools in Beckley", *Beckley USA*, Published and Copyrighted by Harlow Warren, Beckley, WV, 1955

Rakes, Paul H., "Coal Mechanization", https://*wvencyclopedia.org/print/Article*/1364

Richlak, Sr., Jerry L, *Glide to Glory*, Cedar House, Madison Heights, VA, 2002

"Root Hog or Die", https://en.m.wikipedia.org/wiki/Root_hog_or_die

Samuk, Mehmet, "The American Lyceums", https://stmuhistorymedia.org/the-american-lyceums

Shaw, Ruth, "Going to School in the 1930s", https://ruthlace.blogspot.com

Snapp, Charlotte, "School Days in the 1920s and 1930s", *The Mountain Laurel*, North Greenville University, Tigerville, SC, 1992

The Appalachians – America's First and Last Frontier, Companion to the Public Television Series, edited by Evans, Mari-Lynn, Santelli, Robert and George-Warren, Holly, West Virginia University Press, Morgantown, WV, 2013

The Montrado, edited and published by the journalism students at Meadow Bridge High School, Meadow Bridge, WV, 1942 to 1951

The Echo, Woodrow Wilson High School yearbook, Beckley, WV, 1929

The Monte Meade, Meadow Bridge High School yearbook, Meadow Bridge, WV, 1951

"The Real McCoys Quotes", https://www.quotes.net/movies/the_real_mccoys_107713

Thomas, Jerry Bruce, "New Deal", https://*wvencyclopedia.org/print/Article/2265*

Thomas, Jerry Bruce, "The Great Depression", https://*wvencyclopedia.org/print/Article/2155*

True Story magazine, https://en.wikipedia.org/wiki/True_Story_(magazine)

Truth be Told – Perspectives on the Great West Virginia Mine War 1890-Present, compiled and edited by Harris, Wess, Appalachian Community Services, Gay, WV, 2015

Walden, Harley, *Miners and Mentors: Memory and Experiences in Coal Camp School in Appalachia,* Research Paper submitted for the Appalachian Studies Conference, Marshall University, South Charleston, WV, 2015

West Virginia University Institute of Technology, https://en.wikipedia.org/wiki/West_Virginia_University_Institute_of_Technology, 2019

"1930s Flour Sacks Featured Colorful Patterns for Women to Make Dresses", https://littlethings.com/family-and-parenting/flour-sack-dresses